CHINESE PHILOSOPHERS IN COMICS

The Silence of
the Wise

The Sayings of
Lao Zi

Edited and illustrated by
Tsai Chih Chung

Translated by
Koh Kok Kiang
Wong Lit Khiong

ASIAPAC • SINGAPORE

Publisher
ASIAPAC BOOKS & EDUCATIONAL AIDS (S) PTE LTD
2 Leng Kee Road
#02-08 Thye Hong Centre
Singapore 0315
Tel: 4751777, 4751773
Fax: 4796366

First published 1989

© Asiapac Books, 1989

ISBN 9971-985-42-X

Cover Design Soffian

Typeset by Superskill Graphics Pte Ltd.

Printed in Singapore by Loi Printing Pte Ltd.

Publisher's Note

As a publisher dedicated to the promotion of Chinese culture and literary works, we are pleased to present you the **Chinese Philosophers in Comics** series by famous cartoonist Tsai Chih Chung to enable you to understand the schools of thoughts of the great ancient Chinese sages, such as Zhuang Zi, Confucius and Lao Zi.

Lao Zi was the founder of Taoism, one of the most influential philosophical thoughts in Chinese civilization, besides Confucianism. Featuring the selected sayings from Tao De Jing, the book written most probably in the sixth century B.C. by Lao Zi, 'The Sayings of Lao Zi' provides the readers with a fast and easy way to understand Lao Zi's thoughts.

'The Sayings of Lao Zi' is the third book we have published under the **Chinese Philosophers in Comics** Series, but it was the second attempt by Tsai Chih Chung in visualising Chinese philosophy by way of comics.

We feel honoured to have Tsai Chih Chung's permission to the translation rights to his bestselling comics series and would also like to thank the translators for putting in their best efforts in the translation of this series.

Other Titles in the Chinese Philosophers in Comics Series:

☐ The Sayings of Confucius
☐ The Sayings of Zhuang Zi

About the Translators

Koh Kok Kiang

Koh Kok Kiang is a journalist by vocation and a quietist by inclination. He has been a sub-editor with The Straits Times for eight years. His interest in cultural topics and things of the mind started in his schooling years. It was his wish to discover the wisdom of the East that has kindled his interest in Eastern philosophy.

Wong Lit Khiong

Raised in a middle-class family and in an environment where the vast majority of his neighbours were not educated, Wong Lit Khiong realised the extreme importance of education at a very young age. He therefore made up his mind to become a teacher. He embarked on his teaching career in 1950 and it remained his only profession until his retirement 36 years later. He had been attached to Catholic High School for 34 years.

"**Knowledge leads to success.**" This is the philosophy of life which Wong Lit Khiong never fails to impart onto his charges.

Translator's Note

by Koh Kok Kiang

I first read the Tao Teaching (Tao De Jing) in English translation during my teen years. Being English-educated, it did not
occur to me that I should read it in the original classical
Chinese script. At that time, the inadequate English translations had the effect of causing me, in my youthful folly, to
dismiss the Tao De Jing as something abstract (**"The Tao is an
empty vessel; it is used, but never filled"**), illogical (**"Give
up learning, and put an end to your troubles"**) and, in short,
irrelevant to my daily life. Still, some fairly competent English
translations did leave seeds of Taoist wisdom in my young
mind.

A hectic life in a fast-paced and demanding society later
made me 'return to the source,' so to speak. And those seeds
were showing signs of life! I remembered statements such as
**"The sage works without effort, accomplishes without striv-
ing"**, **"Without stepping out of the house, one may know
the ways of the world. Without looking through the window, one may understand the Universe"** and **"My words are
easy to understand and easy to follow, yet no man under
heaven knows them or practises them."** These statements
made me wonder if there was something in the Tao De Jing
that I had failed to perceive.

By chance, I met a scholar of Taoism who told me: **"The
only way to understand the Tao is by quiet contemplation.
The more you read, the more you get stuck with empty
words."** This was precisely the message in the opening statement of the Tao De Jing: **"The Tao that can be told is not the
eternal Tao."**

So what is special about the **Tao**? Tao is simply the Way (of
Life). It is just living — naturally, effortlessly, spontaneously
and correctly. The term *Wu Wei* (action without striving, that
is, life without struggle) then made sense to me. So, too, did
De, usually translated as virtue or morality. As one Western
translator said, "It is the moral force or strength that comes
with a wholesome life. The Chinese character for *De* (德) is

made of three parts: To go (彳) straight (直) to the heart (心). There is nothing mysterious about this **De**: If you eat properly, you are well-nourished, if you exercise, you get strong. If you abide by the Tao, you obtain Virtue.

Though Tsai Chih Chung has not included some of the most profound chapters in the Tao De Jing, all the same he has given readers unfamiliar with Taoism a good appetizer. There is much to chew on and digest.

About the Editor/Illustrator

Tsai Chih Chung was born in 1948 in the Chang Hwa County of Taiwan. He began drawing cartoon strips at the age of 17 and worked as Art Director for Kuang Chi Programme Service in 1971. He founded the Far East Animation Production Company and the Dragon Cartoon Production Company in 1976, where he produced two cartoon films entitled 'Old Master Q' and 'Shao Lin Temple'.

Tsai Chih Chung first got his four-box comics published in newspapers and magazines in 1983. His funny comic characters such as the Drunken Swordsman, Fat Dragon, One-eyed Marshal and Bold Supersleuth have been serialised in newspapers in Singapore, Malaysia, Taiwan, Hong Kong, Japan, Europe and the United States. He was voted one of the Ten Outstanding Young People of Taiwan in 1985 and was acclaimed by the media and the academic circle in Taiwan.

The comics book of 'The Sayings of Zhuang Zi' was published in 1986 and marked a milestone in Tsai's career. Within two years, 'Zhuang Zi' went into more than 70 reprints in Taiwan and 15 in Hong Kong and has to-date sold over 175,000 copies. There is also a Japanese translation of the book.

In 1987, Tsai Chih Chung published 'The Sayings of Lao Zi', 'The Sayings of Confucius' and a few books based on Zen and mythology. Since then, he has published 26 titles, out of which 10 are about ancient thinkers and the rest are based on historical and literary classics. All these books topped the bestsellers' list at one time or another.

Tsai Chih Chung can be said to be the pioneer in the art of visualising Chinese literature and philosophy by way of comics.

Preface

I consider myself fortunate to be a Chinese and to be a Chinese cartoonist as well.

The reasons are simple: Firstly, being a Chinese cartoonist, I have a big following of readers and the widest media for my works; secondly, the long history of China with its cultural and literary heritage, passed down from the ancients, have become the inexhaustible source of inspiration for my cartoons.

The book 'The Sayings of Zhuang Zi' is a result of much mental and physical endeavours.

A lot of people have heard of Zhuang Zi, but they do not know who he was or what the good points in his writings are. I drew him to express what I know of him so that the reader, like me, would not only be able to hear of Zhuang Zi's name, but also be able to appreciate his writings.

After working on 'The Sayings of Zhuang Zi', 'The Sayings of Lao Zi' naturally becomes the choice of my next project. And I will tirelessly gather materials for the production of 'The Sayings of Confucius', 'The Sayings of Buddha', 'The Book on Zen' and perhaps even a book on 'Nonsensical Talks'.

'The Sayings of Lao Zi' is my second step in my endeavour. I hope you will enjoy reading it and kindly share your comments with me.

Tsai Chih Chung
Taipei 1986

Foreword

Cartoon is an art form that allows the artist to express himself freely. An environment conducive to the development of cartoons must possess the following conditions:

Freedom — Only in a free society can we fully utilise our imaginative power and creativity; and express our thoughts by means of art, without any political or social restrictions.

Democracy — A democratic way of life respects the people's rights and does not advocate that what one does is always right. It accepts unconditionally ideas that are different from ours. It tolerates policies that may not necessarily be beneficial to us. Cartoon drawing is the materialisation of the desire for social progress through satirical means.

Love and Concern — Cartoon is an art form that is down-to-earth. It can be used to eliminate inequalities in life, to help the weak and unfortunate; to condemn violence, rape, greed, corruption and other inhuman deeds. Behind the face of sarcasm lies a deep concern for mankind.

Calm — When natural resources are inadequate and limited, people compete to satisfy their needs, resulting in a life of insecurity and anxiety, pressures coming to them from all sides. In such situations, cartoon serves as a cooling medicine that can provide some comfort to relieve the tension.

Cartoonists are artists who truly understand worldly affairs. They not only possess a knack for details, but also, through their discreet observation of what is going on in society, are able to see the hidden truths. Innocently, their challenge to the authorities, their fury, dissatisfaction, hopes and requests are manifested through the strokes of their drawing pens. A successful cartoonist must not only be able to express profoundly with his artistic ability, he must also be able to observe accurately, be filled with a sense of justice in his mission, comprehend the sufferings and aspirations of his countrymen; and have trust and respect for others.

Most people recognise a fact when discussing about Chinese culture: that it concerns the people's lives, is involved in the people's lives and is a reflection of the people's lives. The works of past intellectuals also revolve around this topic, yet we know very little about our cultural heritage which is thousands of years old. Alas, its stern surface and profound contents frighten us and we distance ourselves from it, resulting in our being unable to gain wisdom and instructions from it.

As Tsai Chih Chung began to realise the strength of cartoons in arousing readers' interest, he published 'The Sayings of Zhuang Zi' and, through his skill in cartoon drawing, guided readers into having a look at Zhuang Zi's thoughtful and mysterious realm. This publication was a great success. Now he has published another book entitled 'The Sayings of Lao Zi' to open the door of the ancient classic to the reader so that he can enter and ponder Tao with the wise sage. This is indeed an exciting undertaking.

Lao Zi was truly a wise man who not only taught people to have a gentle and meek presentation, but also to be motiveless, selfless, pliant, yielding, pure-minded and natural... It is difficult for people to accept his thoughts because generally people only notice the surface of things but Lao Zi could comprehend the essence. The normal person notices only the obverse side of things but Lao Zi could see the reverse. Lao Zi's thoughts have widened the scope of our culture and increased its profoundness. In this scientifically advanced and materialistic world of today, instead of feeling a sense of satisfaction, people suffer from spiritual emptiness. To carry on the pursuit of a luxurious life would cause stiff competition and bring about damage to the environment; so much so that eventually the earth, which is ultimately the only place we can depend on for survival, might be unsuitable for human habitation. Lao Zi opposes the relentless pursuit of satisfaction of materialistic wants. He advocates the advancement of spiritual pursuits. He opposes doing things with human artifice, advocating the natural way. This is the best solution for today's crisis.

With the strokes of his flourishing pen and his concern for mankind, Tsai Chih Chung has produced the thoughts of Lao Zi in a light-hearted, entertaining manner without shedding its original message, which is just like an oasis in the desert: It nourishes the soul and gives unlimited delight to the readers.

Cai Songlin

11

Contents

The Life
of
Lao Zi

The Great Wisdom Of Life

1. For ages, the general belief has been: Man must show that he is strong and not pliant; smart and not dull.

2. But there appears in Chinese history a man named Lao Zi who is different from the rest.

3. Man must show that he is pliant and not tough. Man must appear guileness and not shrewd. Man must have no motives, be selfless, have no desires, be self-effacing, pure-minded and natural...

4. Generally people believe that it is good to be tough.

   That which is hard is brittle, it breaks easily. That which is pliant endures.

He's the champion in chess!

I know very little about it. I've only a superficial knowledge of everything.

A person must not pretend to be wise in all things and to be successful in all undertakings. Superficial knowledge ends in failure in all undertakings.

18

19

Lao Zi believes that to be pliant is to be humble and uncompetitive; to be wise and know the essence of life. A simple mind can avoid vanity. Everything is in accordance with nature.

Generally an ordinary person can only see the superficial side of something but Lao Zi can see the essence.

21

Generally people can see only one side of something but Lao Zi can see the other side of it.

It's sharp.

But it's blunt on this side.

20

22

Lao Zi's philosophy is all-embracing, extensive and eternal. It endures in either favourable or unfavourable circumstances. In meeting obstacles, it will not falter but moves around them and proceeds on.

23

Lao Zi is against materialism and advocates a spiritual life...He opposes human artifice and advocates a life of natural goodness.

24

19

Lao Zi is just like a Dragon

Over 2 700 years ago, several ancient civilizations manifested the most brilliant cultures, producing some eminent scholars and thinkers. In Greece there were the great philosophers, Socrates and Pluto.

1

2

In India there was the founder of Buddhism, Sakyamuni.

In China, during the Spring and Autumn Period, towards the end of the Eastern Zhou Dynasty, there was an abundance of talent, contending to be heard.

Artisans Logician Semanticist Legalist Agriculturists
Mohist Taoist Yin yang Confucianist

3

Among all, Confucianism, Taoism, Mohism and Legalism had the greatest influence and the founder of Taoism was Lao Zi.

4

Confucius stayed at Luoyang for a few days. He discussed many things with Lao Zi.

10

Thank you for your teachings which have benefited me a great deal. Goodbye!

Let me say two things as a parting gift.

11

12

Most of the things that you have studied were uttered by the ancients. But these people are already dead, even their bones have decayed, so you must not take what they have said too seriously.

People of supreme virtue are all down-to-earth. It would be well to banish arrogance and vanity and to end illusion. It will stand you in good stead.

Confucius left Luoyang with a heart full of gratitude to Lao Zi. When he returned to the state of Lu, he always praised Lao Zi.

I know that birds can fly,

13

Fish can swim,

14

Animals can run,

15

But the dragon, soaring in the clouds and in the sky, is inscrutable and beyond our reach. Li Er is just like a dragon!

16

In the twenty-third year of King Zhao's reign, Lao Zi perceived that the kingdom was disintegrating, so he left Luoyand and went west through the Han Gu Pass.

17

18

I'm Lin YiXi, a keeper of the pass. I'm very interested in Taoism.

19

Master, since you're about to go into seclusion, could you please write something to give me guidance?

So Lao Zi wrote a book made up of two parts, consisting of about 5 000 characters.

20

Upon completing the book, Lao Zi left. Nobody knew his whereabouts ever since.

21

Tao De Jing

On the Absolute Tao

28

That's impossible to say.

What's this doctrine that encompasses all things?

4

It's impossible to give it a name...

Because if you call it A, then it's not B; if you say it's white, then it's not black.

5

To comprehend Tao, one must not approach it through language, words or any definition.

One must comprehend it with one's heart and soul, otherwise one would go astray.

6

With this understanding, we can talk about the beginning of things in the universe.

Great! Please tell us quickly!

7

8

In the beginning there were no objects or images in the universe. This state of life can be called 'Nothingness'.

'Nothingness' is the essence of Tao and the origin of the universe.

When Tao acquires the power of production, all things in the universe begin to come into existence spontaneously.

This state of affairs can be called 'manifestation,' which is the result of Tao.

So when you realise that the origin of the universe is 'nothingness', you will understand how mysterious Tao is.

'Nothingness.'

When you realise that the origin of all things is the manifestation of Tao, you will understand that the usefulness of Tao is limitless.

'Manifestation'

'Nothingness' and 'manifestation.' One is the essence of Tao and the other, its productive aspect. Both have their origin in Tao, only they are named differently.

12

They are a mystery. Mystery upon mystery.

13

Tao
is the
source of all things
in the universe.

14

The original condition of the universe is 'nothingness.' From 'nothingness', there emerged heaven and earth which produced all the things that constitute this colourful and complicated world.

The Rise
of
Relative Opposites

The difference between 'long' and 'short' is noticed only when comparison is made.

Long

Short

8

'High' and 'low' exist only when they are compared.

High

Low

9

Two sounds become harmonised only when they are put together.

Back

Front

The order of 'front' and 'back' come about when they are compared.

10

So the sage manages worldly affairs without motives and self-interest and teaches without using words.

11

When things develop, you must not interrupt; when things grow, you must not claim possession of them; when things turn out successfully, you must not allege that it is solely due to your ability. When successful, do not claim credit.

Because the sage abides by selflessness, his good work endures.

All values and concepts are conceived by people, and all value judgements arise upon comparison. The relationship between the opposite objects is always changing whereas the definition of value judgement is ever static.

Therefore, be calm about the difference between beauty and ugliness, 'have' and 'have not', difficult and easy, long and short, high and low, front and back. It is foolish to think that all these values will last forever.

12

13

The Role of the Government

Do not treasure things that are hard to obtain and people will not have the desire to steal.

By not giving importance to wealth, people will not become avaricious.

Status

9

8

So the wise man in government will purify the people's minds, provide them with food and livelihood, reduce their ambition and strengthen their physical and spiritual health.

A good government will always help people to discard hypocrisy and cunning. It will deter those with a pretence of wisdom from acting arrogantly.

10

11

12

With such a selfless way of governing and acting according to what is naturally right, a country will be well-administered.

Honour leads to contention and wealth leads to covetousness. People become scheming to fulfil their desires. Such avarice is the root cause of the myriad problems in our society.

The Essence of Tao

The essence of Tao is nothingness, yet its usefulness is limitless.

1

2

I have no idea from where it originated. Probably it came into being even before the existence of a Creator.

The immensity of Tao creates all things and is the source of all things. It is invisible and shapeless, it seems insubstantial and yet it exists.

Tao is fathomless, insubstantial and yet it is all-pervading and limitless. Its use is inexhaustible and it gives rise to all things.

3

The Impartiality of the Universe

1

The universe is impartial and without self. It treats all things equally. It treats all things like sacrificial straw dogs, showing neither love nor hatred for them.

A sage is also impartial and without self, treating all the subjects like straw dogs to whom he shows neither love nor hatred. All are equal in his eyes.

2

The universe is like a furnace. The interior is hollow, and because of its hollowness, it enables all things to be produced.

3

From here we can see that the more one tries to be smart and productive, the more errors one is bound to make, resulting in failure.

4

5

It is better to live a simple life, to observe silence and live effortlessly.

Tao creates all things according to the law of nature, without favouritism or self-interest. A monarch must rule his country with this spirit, living amicably with his subjects. In this way, the society will naturally become peaceful.

Living a Selfless Life

1

The universe can last long because whatever it does is not out of self-interest; therefore it endures.

2

Being humble and non-contentious, the sage earns the love and respect of other people.

One who is not calculative about gains and losses when handling matters will reap benefits.

3

4

Because the sage does not contend and is selfless, he knows fulfilment.

Modesty earns one the love and respect of others. Think of the welfare of others and your own wishes will be fulfilled.

The Characteristics of Water

1 A virtuous person is just like water.

2 Water has three special characteristics:

3 Firstly, it has the ability to nourish all things;

4 Secondly, being soft, it does not fight against odds but lets things take their natural course;

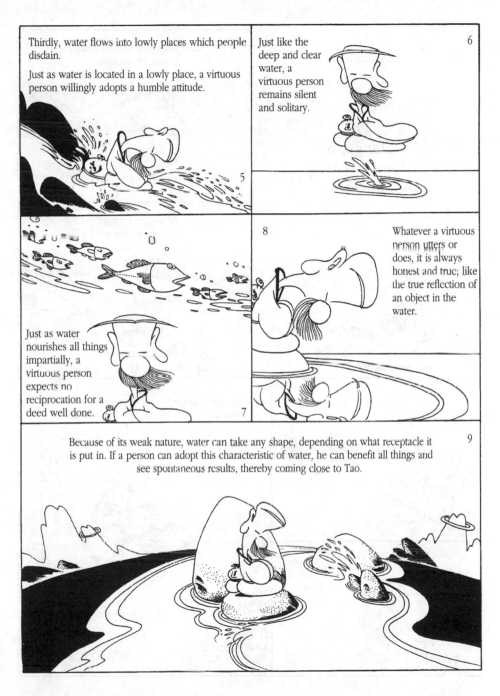

Thirdly, water flows into lowly places which people disdain.

Just as water is located in a lowly place, a virtuous person willingly adopts a humble attitude.

5

Just like the deep and clear water, a virtuous person remains silent and solitary.

6

Just as water nourishes all things impartially, a virtuous person expects no reciprocation for a deed well done.

7

8

Whatever a virtuous person utters or does, it is always honest and true; like the true reflection of an object in the water.

Because of its weak nature, water can take any shape, depending on what receptacle it is put in. If a person can adopt this characteristic of water, he can benefit all things and see spontaneous results, thereby coming close to Tao.

9

The Danger of Overweening Success

1. Water will overflow if poured until it reaches the brim.

2. Enough, enough! Three-quarter full is enough!

3. As long as a knife is sharp enough, do not sharpen it any more.

4. If it is too sharp, it will break easily.

5. A person who has too many valuables arouses envy and attracts the attention of criminals.

This abundance of wealth will cause him to lead a dissolute life; until at last all his wealth is squandered away.

6

Gone! All my riches have been squandered!

7

8

So after a person has become successful in life, he must resolve to be upright. This fits into the law of nature.

9

It's just like creation, in which you find all the living things. Creation is without selfish motives; it is wholesome and quietly accomplished.

Embracing the Tao

1. If you keep Tao uppermost in your mind, can your thought and body be one, never to be separated?

2. Can the mind be naturally quiet like that of a new-born babe?

3. Can the mind be totally free of delusions?

4. In ruling a country, can one love the country and rule the subjects effortlessly and without self-interest?

5. In perceiving the outside world with one's senses, can one be calm and alert?

6. Since perception is limited, one needs to work extra hard.

Life should be a harmony of mind and body. Living in accordance with Tao brings this about.

The Utility
of
Not-Being

Panel 1: In this world, people know only the usefulness of what is there, but they do not know the advantage of what is not there.

In fact the usefulness of what is not there is greater than that of what is there.

Panel 2: The wheel of a carriage has thirty spokes fixed into the hub. Because the hub is hollow, the carriage can move.

Hollow

Panel 3: Take this cup.

Panel 4: This cup can hold things because it is hollow on the inside.

Hollow

Substance

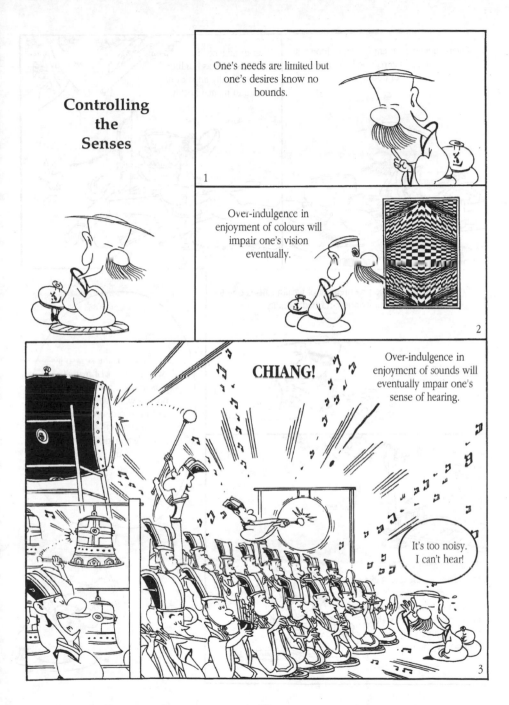

Controlling the Senses

1 One's needs are limited but one's desires know no bounds.

2 Over-indulgence in enjoyment of colours will impair one's vision eventually.

3 Over-indulgence in enjoyment of sounds will eventually impair one's sense of hearing.

CHIANG!

It's too noisy. I can't hear!

Over-indulgence in enjoyment of food will eventually impair one's sense of taste.

Over-indulgence in activities such as hunting will eventually impair one's mind and mental health.

Over-indulgence in the procurement of wealth causes one to suffer insecurity and tarnished morality.

Fathomless is the sea, so it's with the ways of man. To pursue one's ambitions and not knowing when to stop, alas! Instead of contentment and comfort, it brings endless anxieties and disasters upon oneself.

Thus one anchored in Tao lives a simple life. He seeks only to fill the stomach, not to gratify the tastes. He prefers a life of plainness and solitude to that of luxury and pomposity.

48

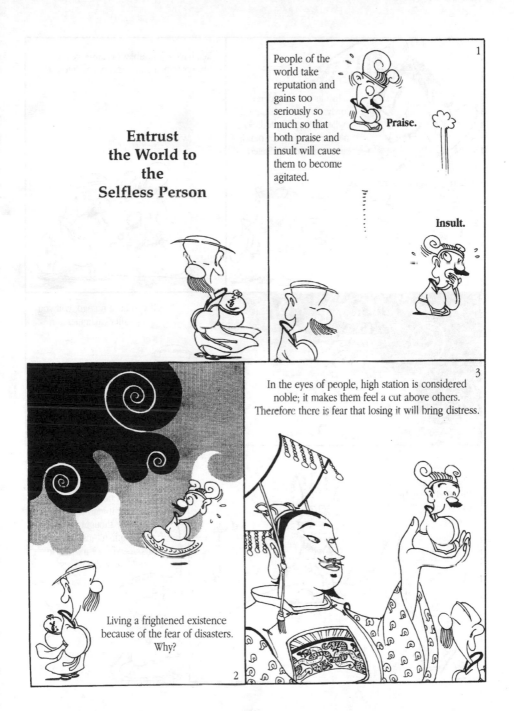

Entrust the World to the Selfless Person

People of the world take reputation and gains too seriously so much so that both praise and insult will cause them to become agitated.

Praise.

Insult.

Living a frightened existence because of the fear of disasters. Why?

In the eyes of people, high station is considered noble; it makes them feel a cut above others. Therefore there is fear that losing it will bring distress.

Knowing the Eternal Law

1. Man's mind is originally clear, quiet and peaceful

2. But it is often clouded by harmful desires.

Jade!

3. Consequently, it is led to perceive matters in an improper manner and it acts improperly.

4. Thus we must try our best to bring our mind back to its clear and quiescent state. Then we can see clearly the cycle of existence and all things flourishing.

All things will return to their source. This source is called 'stillness'; it is also called 'constant'. To understand the 'constant' is called 'insight'. Not to understand the 'constant', acting rashly, is to court disaster.

5

6

Those who understand the 'Eternal Tao' can perform many different things. They can be frank, upright, unprejudiced and can comply with nature and can thus act in accordance with Tao.

Living in accordance with the Great Tao is to know the eternal. And you will encounter no danger for the whole of your life.

One who is adept at attaining 'simplicity of mind' and 'quietude' will be all-comprehending, able to know the regulation of changes in all things. He will be able to penetrate the mysteries of existence and be one with the Tao.

7

Four Classes of Rulers

There are four classes of monarchs who rule their countries by different methods. The top-class ruler applies silent instructions, leaving his subjects to do what they like and to lead their own lives.

> I only know we've a monarch but I don't know what he's done for us.

The second-class monarch uses moral principles to influence his subjects and to rule his subjects with benevolence and rewards.

> Our ruler is wonderful! He's done a lot of things for us.

3 The third-class monarch controls his subjects with political power and threatens them with punishment.

Our ruler controls us sternly. He's fierce and frightening.

4 The fourth-class monarch makes a show of force and deceives his subjects with stratagems.

Our ruler bullies us beyond the limit. We must unite and rise against him!

The best way of administration is 'to rule effortlessly without striving'. Let the populace do what they like and lead the way of life they wish, thereby bringing about the greatest benefit so much so that the populace do not realise their government's achievement, alleging it comes about spontaneously.

Oh, such peace and prosperity is as it should be.

5

Good government can be likened to the lungs in our body. The best lungs work so effortlessly that you do not feel your own breathing. If you can feel your lungs doing the breathing, then there must be something wrong with your lungs.

The Decline of Tao

In the most ancient times, the people were simple and honest without pretensions.

Using my wits, I can prevent tax evasion!

By the time of the early kingdoms, the people's minds have improved. The rulers therefore thought of a system to control their subjects. And so cheating and trickery came into existence.

I can evade tax with my cleverness!

Members of the family could live together harmoniously, giving way to each other. Filial piety or kindness need not be mentioned.

Only when there are squabbles and disharmony in the family do the terms 'filial piety' and 'kindness' arise.

You must live harmoniously! You must be filial! You must be obedient!

When a country is peaceful, government officials perform their duties properly, according to their stations. The term 'loyalty' does not exist.

They are all my officials!

5

When the country is in turmoil, government officials cannot perform their duties properly. In this situation, the term 'loyal officials' come into being.

6

7

Benevolence, intellect, filial piety and loyalty come into play only because Tao is not adhered to. The fact that they are necessary proves that Tao is forgotten and human goodness is in decline. This is retrogression, not progress.

He is the only official who is loyal to me.

The World and I

Knowledge is the root cause of worries. Discarding intellect and knowledge will rid one of anxieties.

1

People tend to seek honour and shun humiliation; to seek kindness and disdain cruelty. But how great is the difference between honour and disgrace? And how great is the difference between nobility and humility?

Is there any difference between kindness and cruelty?

2

. But I mustn't act differently from others, showing my invincibility. It is a fact that one feels compelled to fear what others fear.

3

But as Tao is so immense and limitless, it is far different from the ways of the world.

4

57

The multitude seems to be indescribably happy and excited; seeming to be relishing a pompous feast, enjoying the view from a terrace during the spring festival.

I'm the exception. I'm like an innocent and unsmiling baby unmoved by these activities. Weary of worldly ways, I'm like a homeless drifter.

5

People have more than enough, except me. I seem to suffer from insufficiency. I appear to be like a fool.

6

People of the world are showing off their learning, except me. I seem to be muddle-headed.

7

People of the world are shrewd and quick-witted, except me. I seem to be artless.

8

9

道

TAO

Everyone seems to be very capable, except me. I'm stupid and clumsy. I'm different from the people in general, as I take seriously living a life of Tao.

Wealth, debauchery, good, evil, right, wrong, beauty and ugliness. These are all concepts of the mind. There is no absolute truth in these value judgements. They make sense only as opposites, and are subject to changing times and circumstances. People generally pursue pleasure and honour, when in fact life should be simple and plain, so that one's energy is not dissipated, and our spiritual life can be upgraded.

**The Futility
of
Contention**

To yield is to be preserved.

To bend is to advance.

A low-lying pool gets filled.

To get something new, the old
must be discarded.

5 Having little at first enables you to gain more in the end.

Reasonable!

You deserve it!

6 Over-abundance causes perplexity.

7 So the sage observes Tao, making it the basis for all actions in the world.

8 Do not show off your ability and it will be more noticeable.
Do not think that you are always right and you will be more popular.
Do not boast and what you do will be more effective.
Do not be arrogant and your actions will endure.

9 Because a man does not compete with others, nobody in the world will compete with him. There are ancient sayings like: "To yield is to be preserved."
Surely these are not mere nonsensical utterances.

The common man has the tendency to pursue material gains, seeking greater and greater gains, thereby giving rise to innumerable competitions and contentions. Man must be meek and amiable, modest and not assertive in order to reach a state of 'non-contention'.

Weapons are objects of ill omen which gentlemen do not use. When it is unavoidable to deploy soldiers, do so with great restraint. In victory, do not feel elated. If you rejoice in victory, it shows you delight in killing and so you cannot be successful in ruling the world.

Kill! Kill! Kill!

5

Happy occasions: On a happy occasion, the left side is considered more respectful.

Sad occasions: On a sad occasion, the right side is considered more respectable.

Left!

Right!

In war, the top commander-in-chief stays on the right side while the general stays on the left. This arrangement means that war is treated like a funeral.

6

7

喪

Funeral

Having killed a multitude of people, one must mourn their deaths with heart-felt sorrow. Even after a battle is won, the victory must be observed like a funeral.

War brings catastrophes. If deploying soldiers is unavoidable, one must not act too harshly and stop when one has achieved one's purpose.

8

The Virtue of Self-knowing

1. The ability to understand the good and bad of others merely shows your mind is sharp.

2. Whereas the ability to know your true self shows real insight.

3. The ability to defeat others physically shows merely that you have strength.

4. Whereas to be master of yourself shows your resolution.

I'm finished! I can't quit drinking!

Wine

5. To be contented with your lot and to treat worldly possessions lightly is deemed to be wealthy.

I'm very satisfied with my present life.

63

To be able to diligently abide by the Tao is to have determination.

Tao!

6

To abide by the Tao always and not move away from it is to live in the eternal.

7

Even though the body dies, the spirit of truth perpetuates; that can be considered as the immortal.

Tao! Tao! Tao! Tao! Tao! Tao! Tao! Tao! Tao! Tao! Tao!

8

Everybody has his self-interest and desires. To rid yourself of desires, examine yourself and then clear yourself of all hypocrisies. If you have reached the stage of knowing yourself and being your own master, as well as being contented and resolute, you can be considered as having attained Tao.

The Peace of Tao

He who abides by the Great Tao attracts people who are keen to learn the Way.

In an atmosphere of goodness, people do not harm each other and they live peacefully and amicably.

Good food and music can attract passers-by.

Tao is plain, tasteless, invisible and inaudible but it is inexhaustible.

Like music and delicious food, moral principles can only satisfy people's mundane needs whereas Tao gives spiritual sustenance.

The Rythm of Life

1

He who is to be made to dwindle in power must first be caused to expand.

He who is to be weakened must first be made strong.

He who is to be laid low must first be exalted to power.

He who is to be taken away from must first be given.

2

The meek will overcome the tough. This is the natural law.

3

Fish can never leave water; once they are out of the water, they would die.

To be meek is the basis of ruling a country. By not applying this method, a country would be doomed.

5

The situation will change for the worse when it reaches its extremity. The powerful becoming weak is an unalterable fact since time immemorial.

The rule of force and punishments are deadly things which must not be imposed on the populace.

4

66

On the Supreme Virtue

Panel 5: A courteous person whose politeness is not reciprocated...

Rite!

Panel 6: Will force others to be polite to him.

Hmmmph! What an impolite fellow!

Panel 7: So the sequence goes as follows: When Tao is lost, there arises morality; When morality is lost, there arises benevolence; When benevolence is lost, there arises righteousness; When righteousness is lost, there arises propriety.

Tao!

Morality!

Benevolence!

Righteousness!

Propriety!

Panel 8: When a society needs 'propriety' or rules of conduct for relationships, hypocrisies and deceit will emerge. This leads to social turmoil.

Panel 9: A person who thinks he is wise tries to be perfect, using his wits. This is the cause of stupidity.

Panel 10: Therefore the truly great men of Tao dwell in what is fundamental and shun what is trivial. They abide by what is real, and discard what is ornamental.

So we must adhere to the plain and honest Tao and not hypocritical intellect. We must abandon vain luxury and make use of the rules of Tao.

Cultivation of the Way emcompasses Tao, Virtue, Goodness, Justice, Rectitude and Wisdom. To have a society that is in accord with the Tao, every step taken must follow the law of nature. When a society needs intellect and rules of conduct to carry on, hypocrisies and deceit will emerge. The situation here has reached a lamentable stage.

**The Cycle
of
Existence**

The movement of Tao which is cyclical and unending produces perpetual life.

1

To be yielding and pliant is the function of Tao.

2

All things in the world arises from the state of 'Being.'

3

'Being'

'Being' arises from 'Nothingness'.

4

'Nothingness'

'Nothingness' is the essence of Tao and 'Being' is the manifestation of Tao. One has to be without motives, trouble-free, unintellectual, devoid of knowledge, without desires, and selfless in order to reach the acme of Tao.

The Origin of Things

Tao is that from which all things in the world are created. The process by which all things are created is produced by a kind of qi* that originated from Tao.

Tao.

1

This qi is divided into two types: yin and yang.

2

When yin and yang are mixed, a state of harmony emerges.

3

All things are produced in this state.

4

All things have yang on one side and yin on the other. When yin and yang blend together, they produce a new harmonious body.

5

Tao creates all things, after which things have to function in accordance with the spirit of Tao. Be pliant, and follow the natural law.

* qi : life force

71

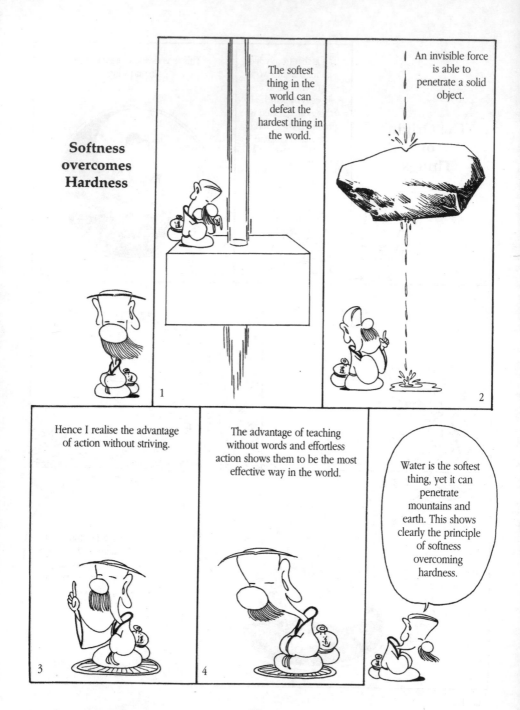

Softness overcomes Hardness

1. The softest thing in the world can defeat the hardest thing in the world.

2. An invisible force is able to penetrate a solid object.

3. Hence I realise the advantage of action without striving.

4. The advantage of teaching without words and effortless action shows them to be the most effective way in the world.

Water is the softest thing, yet it can penetrate mountains and earth. This shows clearly the principle of softness overcoming hardness.

The Virtue of Contentment

1. Which is more precious, honour or life?

Honour / Life

2. Which is more valuable, possessions or life?

Possessions / Life

3. Which is worse — to have reputation and wealth or loss of life?

Honour and Gains

4. Prize / Famous person / Champion

So to crave too much for reputation, you would have to pay a high price.

5. To hoard too much wealth would be to incur serious loss.

6. To be contented with what you have, you would not suffer humiliation.
To be able to stop at the right time, no danger would befall you.

We must cherish our bodies and lives and must not pursue reputation and gains too excessively. To gain fame and wealth at the expense of your life is not worthwhile.

Discontentment leads to Social Disorder

1

When Tao prevails in the world, the people are contented and all countries co-exist in peace.

2

When there is no war, horses reared for the battlefield are instead used for ploughing the field.

3

When Tao does not prevail in the world, people tend to fight for reputation and gains.

4

And there is constant warfare between one country and another. All horses have to be deployed to fight in the battlefield. Even the mares have to give birth in the battlefield.

My state's territory is too small; that in the neighbouring state is vast.

It's big enough! Don't be greedy!

No! No! It's too small!

Invade the neighbouring country and seize its territory.

No disaster in the world is greater than discontentment. No sin in the world is greater than greed.

Therefore only contentment can give you permanent satisfaction. If everyone knows what contentment is, the world would be a peaceful place.

Knowing the Universe

The theory of everything is not found in a faraway place; it is right in our mind.

1

If you can look within and have self-awareness, end desires and give up self-interest, you will understand the ways of the world even if you have not stepped out of your house. You can understand the law of nature even if you have not looked out of the window.

2

3

The farther you go, the less you know.

4

So a sage does not go far away, yet he is able to understand the things of the world.

5

Without interference, things can grow spontaneously.

The depths of our mind are as translucent as a mirror. One must end self-interest and desire and remove mental obstacles so as to know the world.

The Impartiality of the Sage

The sage has no prejudices. He accepts without mental barriers the views of all the populace.

1

I treat good people with goodness; I also treat bad people with goodness. In this way, people can be taught to return to goodness.

Goodness!

2

I treat trustworthy people with kindness; I also treat untrustworthy people with kindness. In this way, everybody will be trustworthy.

Trustworthy!

3

When the sage is on the throne, he ends his self-interest, making his subject simple and thrifty. They listen to the sage's speeches with full attention. The sage treats them lovingly as if they are infants.

4

An ideal monarch ends his self-interest. He does not set the standard of good and evil with his subjective values. He treats all the people with kindness and sincerity.

The Preservation
of
Life

It is said that a person who knows how to safeguard his life would never be attacked by rhinoceroses and tigers while walking in the deep jungle.

4

In a war, he would not be wounded by weapons.

5

6

A rhinoceros may be fierce, but it is unable to use its horns on him.

7

A tiger may be fierce and strong, but it cannot put its claws on him.

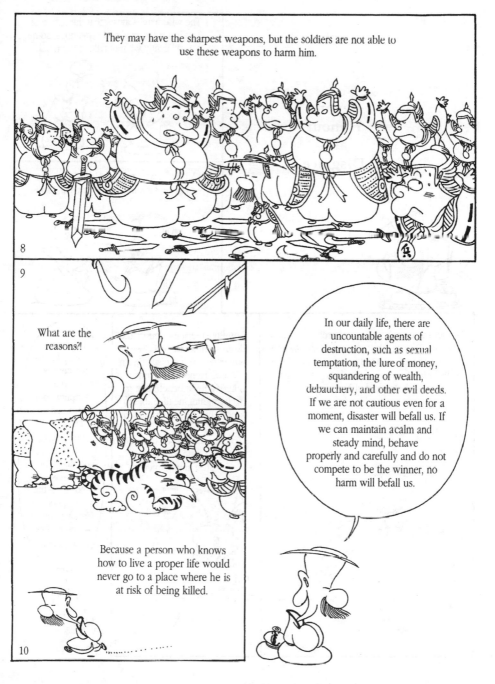

Beyond Honour and Disgrace

The wise man is aware that the nature of Tao is insubstantial and mysterious, so he acts diligently without talking too much.

1

A person who prattles all the time does not have the faintest idea of what Tao is.

2

Do not show one's ability and problems can be avoided. Do not show off one's brilliance and live in harmony with the ordinary people. This is the state of mystic unity which is the highest standard of Tao.

Simplify your mind, purify the desire, neither be too close to others nor be too distant from them. Honour or shame, neither able to benefit him nor to harm him, neither able to honour him nor to shame him.

To cultivate oneself to reach such a state is to be the greatest among men.

Sagehood is the ability to temper your sharpness, simplify your problems, mask your brightness, behave normally like the masses and reach the state of mystic unity — the highest state of man.

3 4

82

The Art of Government

1

To rule a country with pure and quiet methods,

To apply stratagems in warfare,

2

3

To administer the world with the policy of non-interference towards the populace.

How do I know the above-mentioned facts? The following incidents will provide the answers.

4

5

Forbidden! Forbidden!

The more you forbid, the poorer the populace will become.

6

Send troops to attack the neighbouring country!

Yes, Your Highness!

The greater the power of the government, the more turmoil there will be in the nation. The more the ruler's strategies, the more often evil deeds will occur.

7

The harsher the laws, the rifer is the banditry.

8

So the sage says, "I abide by inaction and the people do things on their own initiative; I esteem quietude and the people follow the proper path spontaneously; I don't interfere and the people prosper by themselves; I have no desires and the people naturally return to the good and simple life.

The ruler always thinks that he is a special figure in society and, according to his whims and fancies, enacts diverse rules and regulations and enforces them by brute power. If the person vested with power can be artless, have a quiet mind and have no desires, peace will become a reality in the world.

84

Ruling a Big Country

1
Ruling a big country is similar to frying a small fish, one must not keep turning it over.

2
If it is turned over too often, the small fish will fall into pieces.

If a world is ruled with pure, silent and motiveless methods, spirits, human beings and ghosts will stay in their respective places. So the ghosts do not harm or charm people.

3

Neither will the spirits.

4

Nor will the sage.

5

6
If the monarch on the top and the populace at the bottom do not harm each other, there will be peace in the world.

The ruler must have a quiet and unruffled mind. If he can be quiet and motiveless, people can do what they wish to earn a living and there will be peace among them.

The Function of Keeping Low

1 The sea can become the king of a hundred streams, making them flow into it because it manages to stay in a lower position.

2 So if the sage wants to be the leader of the people, he must be most humble towards them. To set a good example, he must put the welfare of others above self-interest.

3 So when the sage occupies the top position, people do not feel his weight; when he stays in front, people do not feel threatened. So people are glad to support him wholeheartedly.

4 Because he does not compete with others, nobody in the world can compete with him.

If a ruler misuses his power and acts wrongly and uncontrollably, the people will suffer tremendously. Therefore he must avoid bringing burdens and harm to his subjects.

The Virtue
of
Non-Contending

A good commander does not show off his prowess and bravery. A good fighter does not lose his temper.

1

A general who can defeat his enemics need not confront them.

No, it's not necessary. They'll definitely be defeated. They'll undoubtedly lose!

General, we'll fight them with all our might!

2

A person who is good at employing people is modest before them.

3

By not taking part in a fight or getting angry, it means you have the virtue of not wanting to compete with others.

4

To be able to accomplish all these is to comply with the law of nature.

5

Fighting and anger are acts of aggression. Not fighting, not feeling provoked, not showing your strength and being not tyrannical — these attributes are in accordance with the laws of nature.

Wisdom of Realising Your Own Ignorance

Panel 1: To be able to realise your own ignorance is to be wise.

Sorry! I am ignorant of the subject.

Panel 2: To think that you understand what you really do not know is a major fault.

I know a lot, and I am good at poetry, literature and art.

In fact, all you know is just a smattering of everything.

Panel 3: The sage does not have this fault because he steers clear of such a fault.

Ha! Ha!

Some people understand only the superficial aspect of things. By understanding a little bit, they think they've understood the whole thing fully well.
To be able to realise your own ignorance is wisdom.
To be unable to realise your own stupidity, that's real foolishness!

The Bravery
of
the Soft
enables
Survival

To daringly display toughness is to court death.

Whereas to display softness enables you to survive.

Both these instances show bravery.
The bravery of the soft is beneficial whereas the daring of the tough brings harm.

Death!

Survival!

It is the rule of nature to succeed without competing; to get response without uttering anything; to have things come spontaneously without demand. It is magnanimous yet its policies are excellent.

Why does Heaven abhor daring to be brave? Does anybody know the reason?

The rule of nature is to be pliant and yielding and not to contend. Man's conduct should follow the rule of nature, and to end the desire to be strong and tough and war-like.

Nature's expanse is vast and infinite, just like a huge net which covers everything and everywhere on earth. Though full of meshes, it lets nothing slip through.

90

Between
Stiffness and Softness

When a person is alive, his body is soft and supple. When he dies, it becomes stiff.

When trees and grass are growing, they are supple and soft.

When they die, they become dried up.

Stiffness is the characteristic of the dead.

Softness is the characteristic of the living.

6 Invading others to show your prowess...

7 Results in deaths and annihilation.

8 When the tree is big and hardy,

9 It will be felled.

10 Those who are strong and big occupy the lower position whereas those who are gentle and soft occupy the top position.

When the hurricane comes, big trees are, more often than not, struck down; while the grass, due to its pliancy, can withstand the gust, swaying with the force of the cyclone. It is thus obvious that gentleness and pliancy can defeat strength and toughness.

The Strength of Water

There is nothing in the world that is softer and weaker than water.

1

But water possesses the ability to penetrate hard objects.

2

Everyone in the world knows that weakness overcomes strength and gentleness overcomes toughness but nobody practises this.

3

So the sage says, "He who takes upon himself the humiliation of the people is fit to rule them. He who takes upon himself the country's disasters deserves to be their monarch."

4

Though water is gentle and weak, it can destroy hard objects and overcome strong obstacles. Gentleness and weakness contain hard and indestructible characteristics to overcome toughness and strength.

The Virtue of the Giver

Even if a serious animosity has been reconciled, there still remains in one's mind a residue of hatred. How can you say that this is the best solution?

You're in the wrong!

Don't argue any more!

You're wrong!

So the sage retains the bill. He only gives money to others but never asks for repayment.

A virtuous person is like the person who holds the receipt. He only gives money to others but never demands repayment.

Bill

A person without virtue is akin to a tax-collector who only demands payment but never gives money to others.

Tax

The law of Heaven is unselfish and unprejudiced. It always favours good people.

A ruler must not blame the populace. He must not extort taxes from them. He must not control them with punishment. Ideal politics applies 'virtue' to educate the people and to assist them. The authorities would always give judiciously and never demand and must not disturb the populace.

The Way
of
Truth

1
Truths may not be pleasing to the ear.

2
What is pleasing to the ear may not be the truth.

3
A good person does not argue.

4
A person who argues is not good.

5
A person who really knows is aware that Tao of the universe is right in his mind and he does not seek it elsewhere.

95

A learned person may not really know Tao.

6

A sage has no desire to possess and does not accumulate possessions. The more he gives, the greater his abundance.

7

In giving, you become richer. Heaven is unselfish; it benefits all things and causes no harm to them.

8

9

The sage follows the Tao of Heaven. He gives without reservations and does not fight for anything.

The sage follows the principle of benefiting without causing harm and thus he acts but does not compete. He thus cultivates the spirit of not fighting for anything in the world because to him, the giver is more fortunate than the receiver. This spirit of not competing for honour and reputation is great virtue.

Remarks
on
Tao

The
Nature
of
Tao

Wisdom of the Ruler

1. Yang Zhu paid a visit to Lao Zi.

If a man is shrewd, sharp and strong, is he considered a good ruler?

2. Once a person like him possesses ability, he will be in the service of others. He will be tied down and burdened by his own skills, thereby vainly exerting himself and drifting farther and farther away from Tao.

3. Tigers and leopards are hunted for their beautiful fur. Monkeys are caught because of their agility as pets. Do you think they are really wise?

4. So what's a good monarch?

An intelligent monarch does not claim credit in ruling his country. His rule benefits all strata of life and yet his subjects do not realise it. This inscrutable monarch is considered a good one!

In an ideal age, people do not realise the existence of the ruler. As there is no pressure from the administration, people lead a carefree and peaceful life.

101

102

Empty Display is not Wisdom

A sage paid Lie Zi a visit.

1

He noticed a lot of shoes outside Lie Zi's house.

2

Sir, someone is looking for you!

3

Sir, since you've already come, why don't you come in and instruct me?

4

A good person is tactful, retiring and does not show off. Yet Lie Zi displayed his glory, thereby attracting many people. This is a petty show of cleverness and not wisdom.

Forget it! I've told you before that you must conceal your brilliance and not make a display of it.

Now you've let people submit to you and yet you're unable to make them not submit to you. This is where you inadvertently expose your unique character.

5

Chaos in the World

1 — When there are many methods of shooting at birds, the flight of the birds becomes haphazard.

2 — Because of the diverse methods of catching fish, the fish no longer swim smoothly.

3 — Because of the varied ways of trapping animals, the beasts of the forest have to run wildly for their lives.

4 — The cleverer a man is, the more he becomes deceitful, cunning, argumentative and the more he uses unscrupulous methods.

5 — When man is fond of using his ingenuity, the world plunges into turmoil.

The more restrictions there are, the poorer the people become. The greater the government's power, the more chaotic the nation would become. The more the ruler imposes laws and prohibitions on his people, the more frequently evil deeds would occur.

The Strength of A Good Fighter

There was a man who reared a fighting cock for Emperor Xian of the state of Zhou.

Have you completed preparing the fighting cock? Is it ready to fight?

No, not yet, because this cock's morale is high and its fighting spirit is strong.

1

Ten days later.

No, not yet. That cock becomes highly agitated upon seeing the shadow of another cock.

2

Another ten days went by.

Still not yet. That cock always looks all around in a wrathful manner, feeling that it's invincible.

3

4

It's almost ready. When it hears other cocks crowing, it has no response, behaving like a wooden cock. Its mind cannot be moved by the happenings around it.

Another ten days elapsed.

That's great!

5

Emperor Xian took that cock to the arena. When the other cocks noticed that it was motionless, they were so frightened that they did not have the courage to fight with it.

A cock which has no intention to fight would not be attacked. But its prowess and strength would emerge instantaneously the moment it is provoked.

107

Forthcoming Titles
by Tsai Chih Chung

- [ ] Fun with Animals
- [ ] Records of the Historian or Shiji
- [ ] Strange Tales of Liaozhai
- [ ] Analects by Confucius
- [ ] The book on Zen
- [ ] The Sayings of Han Fei Zi

Other Asiapac Titles

Asia Pacific Heritage Series

☐ 100 Similes from Traditional China

☐ An Anthology of Chinese Humour

☐ Fascinating Tales of Old Beijing

☐ Folk Tales of the West Lake

☐ Ghosts Stories of Old China

☐ The Golden Ox and Other Chinese Comic Tales

☐ Liaozhai Stories by Fox-fairies, Ghosts and Other Marvels

☐ Myths of Ancient China

Astrology and Geomacy

☐ Cast Your Chinese Horoscope (a series of the 12 zodiacal animals)

☐ Feng Shui *Perfect Placing for your Happiness & Prosperity*

☐ Ming Shu *The Art & Practice of Chinese Astrology*

Chinese Classical Novels

☐ A Dream of Red Mansions

☐ Outlaws of the Marsh

☐ Strange Tales of Liaozhai

Asia Pacific Creative Writing

- ☐ Chess King
- ☐ Heroin Trail
- ☐ Shades of Grey
- ☐ A Posthumous Son and other Stories
- ☐ The God of Television
- ☐ The God with the Laughing Face
- ☐ The Dark Secret and Other Strange Tales

《漫画中国哲学家系列》

智者的低语

老子说

编著：蔡志忠
翻译：许国强
　　　黄力强

亚太图书(新)有限公司出版

Series Preface

One of the great privileges of being a pastor is that people seek out your presence in some of life's most jarring transitions. They want to give thanks. Or cry out for help. They seek wisdom and think you may know where to find some. Above all, they long for God, even if they wouldn't know to put it that way. I remember phone calls that came in a rush of excitement, terror, and hope. "We had our baby!" "It looks like she is going to die." "I think I'm going to retire." "He's turning sixteen!" "We got our diagnosis." Sometimes the caller didn't know why they were calling their pastor. They just knew it was a good thing to do. They were right. I will always treasure the privilege of being in the room for some of life's most intense moments.

And, of course, we don't pastor only during intense times. No one can live at that decibel level all the time. We pastor in the ordinary, the mundane, the beautiful (or depressing!) day-by-day most of the time. Yet it is striking how often during those everyday moments our talk turns to the transitions of birth, death, illness, and the beginning and end of vocation. Pastors sometimes joke, or lament, that we are only ever called when people want to be "hatched, matched, or dispatched"—born or baptized, married, or eulogized. But those are moments we share with all humanity, and they are good moments in which to do gospel work. As an American, it feels perfectly natural to ask a couple how they met. But a South African friend told me he feels this is exceedingly intrusive! What I am really asking is how

someone met God as they met the person to whom they have made lifelong promises. I am asking about transition and encounter—the tender places where the God of cross and resurrection meets us. And I am thinking about how to bear witness amid the transitions that are our lives. Pastors are the ones who get phone calls at these moments and have the joy, burden, or just plain old workaday job of showing up with oil for anointing, with prayers, to be a sign of the Holy Spirit's overshadowing goodness in all of our lives.

I am so proud of this series of books. The authors are remarkable, the scholarship first-rate, the prose readable—even elegant—the claims made ambitious and then well defended. I am especially pleased because so often in the church we play small ball. We argue with one another over intramural matters while the world around us struggles, burns, ignores, or otherwise proceeds on its way. The problem is that the gospel of Jesus Christ isn't just for the renewal of the church. It's for the renewal of the cosmos—everything God bothered to create in the first place. God's gifts are not *for* God's people. They are *through* God's people, *for* everybody else. These authors write with wisdom, precision, insight, grace, and good humor. I so love the books that have resulted. May God use them to bring glory to God's name, grace to God's children, renewal to the church, and blessings to the world that God so loves and is dying to save.

Jason Byassee

Introduction

One of my favorite photos of my namesake, Will, is of the two of us, he in his second summer of life on his first trip to the South Carolina coast. I'm leading into the surf at sunset one who only recently had learned to walk. I expected him to be afraid at his first meeting of the sea. He is no fear and all joy. He holds my hand. In the photo, you can see only our backs, an old man stooping toward the child, the child eagerly pushing forward. You can't see, but I'll never forget, the smile on his face, Will's delight as he eagerly entered the waves at my encouraging, "Jump!"

I love that photo's depiction of one of the great joys of aging—leading a little one toward the grand adventure of the wide world, gripping his hand reassuringly, egging him on to face into the wind and to leap the waves.

But yesterday, when I looked at that picture of the two of us—the little boy and the old man, the growing child and the aging adult—it occurred to me that I had misread that moment. I, who presumed to be leading the child, saw that I was being led. Here at sunset, the sea, the vast eternity of time that was rushing toward him with promise, was ebbing away from me, taking from me all that I loved, including the little boy named for me.

He was all future; I was now mostly past. Most of his life was ahead of him; most of my life was behind me. In truth, the little one, still fresh in the world, had me by the hand, encouraging me

1

to make my way into the deep, departing. He begins life by eagerly jumping forward. I clutch his tiny hand tightly, my last grasp of the future, at the end of day as I stagger uncertainly, unwillingly toward the engulfing, eternal sea. Not long from now, much sooner than I'd like, he'll have to let go and venture on without me. His grip is not tight enough to rescue me from the encroaching dark, the inundating deep.

When all is said and done (which will occur before long for this septuagenarian), there's no cure for that but God.[1] Just about everybody wants a long life; nobody wants to be old. Well, I'm growing old. So are you. Whether that's good news or bad depends not only on our physical and mental health, our financial situation, and our friends and family but also on the God who created us to be tethered to temporality and is our sole hope for resurrection.

"I grow old. . . . I shall wear the bottoms of my trousers rolled," I read at nineteen and snickered.[2] Aging is diminishment, finding yourself on the short end of life, with more yesterdays and fewer tomorrows, too small for your britches. Poet Dylan Thomas famously urged his aged father, "Do not go gentle into that good night. . . . Rage against dying of the light."[3] Is there somewhere to stand between stoic acquiescence and impotent wrath to the diminishment of aging before the gathering dark?

The day I began research on this book a colleague asked menacingly, "Ought not you to be thinking of . . . retirement?" I replied that I felt I was making a solid contribution to the school, my classes were well filled, and I expected to be teaching for a few more years. "But don't you think there's a time to back away?" she asked. Was the Lord behind this colleague's efforts to point this septuagenarian to the door? Maybe. All I know for sure is that the humbling conversation filled me with new enthusiasm for writing this book.

I write not only as a pastor, bishop, author, and theological educator but also as someone with personal experience of elderhood. I'm an aging Baby Boomer Christian. A widespread generational desire of us Boomers is to pioneer fresh ways of aging. A study of us Boomers approaching retirement by Princeton Survey Research Associates International found that we have "a vision of the post-midlife years that is inimical to the notion of decline, whether that be . . . pulling

back gradually but steadily, or phasing out."⁴ This book is proof that we Boomers plan to age differently.

Ralph Waldo Emerson wrote his essay "Old-Age" at age fifty-seven. Simone D. Beauvoir wrote her rather depressing *The Coming of Age* at sixty. Cicero wrote his classic *De Senectute* at sixty-two. While I am not as smart as these earlier commentators on aging, I have one thing on them—I am actually old!

As a doctor looks at a sick man on his deathbed, shakes his head, and says, "He won't get over this," one could look into our crib, said Augustine in a sermon, and say on the first day of life, "He won't get out of this alive."⁵ Aging is a natural, predictable life process that imperceptibly begins at birth, accelerates in a few decades, eventually becomes undeniable, ends in death, and is the dominant factor in the last third of most people's lives. Natural and predictable though aging may be, let's be honest: one of the reasons aging requires courage is the looming, encroaching specter of death. Though mortality may have resided somewhere in our consciousness—as something unpleasant that happens to others—after sixty-five, most of us become more aware of what's next.

All of us are either participants or observers in a longevity revolution. Old age isn't as short as it used to be. If people retire at fifty, they can expect to spend nearly half their lives doing something other than their job. Just this week I read another book on the predicted doom of pension plans in North America (the crash comes in 2050). The reason for the coming pension crisis? People like me are refusing to die according to actuarial expectations. Genesis 6:3 defines maximum human longevity as "one hundred twenty years" (which is now the official maximum life span for humans). Psalm 90:10 more realistically says,

> The days of our life are seventy years,
>   or perhaps eighty, if we are strong. (NRSV)

Defying biblical marks for longevity, most of us will live thirty-four years longer than our great-grandparents.

During his earthly ministry, Jesus probably met few people my age. The average life span for men in the Roman Empire was twenty-five,

probably less for women, and, as everyone knows, Jesus and many of his disciples were denied the opportunity to grow old.[6] Many of our quandaries about aging were unknown in biblical times or in the early church. However, that does not mean that Scripture, Christian theology, and local church life have nothing to contribute to our reflection on aging. As we think about aging *as Christians*, we should expect fresh insights and a fundamental reframing of what the world considers to be "the problem of aging."

Though any interest in math was killed in me by the time I hit junior high, even I can't talk about aging without first doing the numbers: In the United States the average life span is eighty, double that of two hundred years ago. Seventy million people will be over sixty-five by 2030, double today's numbers. Because women have a longer life span than men, American women beyond age seventy-five outnumber men three to one. The very old—those over eighty-six—are one of the fastest-growing age groups. This group numbered four million in 2000 and are projected to grow to nearly nine million by 2030 and to sixteen million by 2050. Centenarians increased from fifteen thousand in 1982 to well over one hundred thousand today. The aged segment of the population will grow from 12 percent to 21 percent, compared with 1900, when those sixty-five and over were only 4 percent of the population.[7] By 2058 the number of people sixty and older worldwide will triple to two billion, with aging persons comprising one-fifth of the world's population. Most will be living in rural poverty.

Dramatic changes in life spans have shifted our views of aging and our expectations for how adults function in the last quarter of life. The challenges of caring for the aged and the sheer size of the exploding aging population have made aging not only a major public policy dilemma and a disruption in millions of families but also an opportunity for Christians to rediscover the unique consolations and challenges that our faith has to offer in the last quarter of life.

Churches in North America are graying even faster than the general American population. Though there are few explicit resources in Scripture for aging, the Christian faith has the capacity to find fresh meaning in the last decades of our life cycle. After interviews and visits in dozens of congregations for whom ministry with the

aging is a major part of their mission, I believe that Christians can prepare for the predictable crises of aging and that congregational leaders can be key to that preparation.

The Christian is commissioned to give testimony throughout the entire life cycle—including retirement, aging, sickness, and death—that God is faithful all the days of our lives. We can retire from our careers but not from discipleship; the church has a responsibility to equip us for discipleship in the last years of our lives. Even though growing old usually includes some painful events, the Christian faith can enable us to live through both the joys and the anguish of aging with confidence and hope.

Those who care for, work with, preach to, and counsel the exploding aging population need help to understand the aging process and its predictable crises as well as theological resources for speaking to aging persons and helping them to conceive of and negotiate the crises of growing old. This book hopes to help people answer the question, "Where is God leading me in this time of life?"

Some of us in my generation of aging Americans are the first to have the extraordinary financial resources that enabled us to retire earlier than ever imaginable for previous generations. For others, unaffordable health care, poverty, housing insecurity, and painful dislocation fill their last years with anxiety and fear. Many find that they are unprepared intellectually, emotionally, and spiritually for those years. Personal resolve and positive attitudes cannot rescue the aging from systemic injustices that make their last years of life anything but golden. This book is written to help Christians—the young who care for the aging and who are themselves preparing to age as well as those entering into and living through aging—think like Christians about elderhood and to see their congregations as ideal locations for ministry with and for the aging.

The median age of my own denomination is now sixty-two. "If you plan to be a Methodist preacher," I recently told a group of seminarians, "learn to love ministry with the elderly." Caring for and caring about, working with and understanding better, and offering compassionate support for the elderly and their caregivers have become a major mission opportunity. This book intends to offer biblical and theological reflection in conversation with some of the latest

research on aging to provide specific, practical steps for congregations to engage in elder ministry. I hope that you will read this book
as my joyful testimony that though working for and with Jesus can
be daunting at any time of life, his light is our life and in his service
is our joy, particularly toward the end of our lives.

Thanks to Carsten Bryant, who helped with the research and edit-
ing, and to Jason Byassee, who asked me for the book. My goal? To
assist Christians to love God by honoring their elders and to help
us prepare for aging like Christians so that we can die holy deaths.

ONE

Aging with Scripture

The most expensive advertisements on the nightly news tout drugs for the aging. Some drugs promise relief for the aches, pains, and illnesses of aging; other drugs swear they can stem the effects of growing old. In these ads, older adults appear peddling bicycles, bungee jumping, or gleefully splashing about in the pool with their grandkids. "Grow old along with me! / The best is yet to be."[1] We wish the exaggerated claims of these advertisements were true because when people are asked what comes to mind when they hear the term *growing old*, the majority respond not with words about golden years but with talk of loss, loneliness, dependency, grief, sadness, abandonment, dementia, and regret.

Somewhere between bungee jumping and despondent loneliness lies the truth of old age.

As Christians, we gather weekly in order to bend our lives toward an ancient text, a collection of writings that we believe to be strong evidence that God has graciously condescended toward us. Yet when we search the Scriptures, we find that the Bible's verdict on human aging is ambiguous.

Aging in the Old Testament

Well into his retirement, Billy Graham wrote a little book, *Nearing Home: Life, Faith, and Finishing Well*, in which he assembled his

favorite Scripture passages related to aging.[2] While he found 175
references to elders in the Bible, even one so adept with the Bible
as Graham had a tough time finding explicit biblical material that
helps us think about elderhood—people didn't live very long in Bible
times. There's also a theological reason for Scripture's relative lack
of interest in aging: Israel and the church didn't place much stress
on different ages and stages of life. Aging and dying were considered to be natural, expected, even providential processes that were
ordained and guided by God rather than discrete chronological stages
of human development.

It's possible that our negative and unrealistic attitudes about aging—as displayed in those pharmaceutical ads—are evidence of the
North American church's cultural captivity, of Christians' capitula-
tion to the mores and values of a culture that's not Christian. In a
death-denial society, we the aging tell the young a tough truth even
without intending to do so: we are everyone's future, whether they
want to face it or not.

Graham notes that some Scripture passages look at longevity as
God's reward for a life well lived. Proverbs 16:31 calls gray hair "a
crown of glory" that "is found on the path of righteousness." The
young have a duty to esteem their long-lived elders: "Honor your
father and your mother so that your life will be long on the fertile
land that the LORD your God is giving you" (Exod. 20:12).

Yet there is another side to old age. Graham calls Ecclesiastes
12:1–8 "one of the most poetic (and yet candid) descriptions in all
literature of old-age."[3] I less charitably characterize this passage as
beautiful but brutal.

> Remember your creator in the days of your youth, before the days
> of trouble come, and the years draw near when you will say, "I have
> no pleasure in them"; before the sun and the light and the moon and
> the stars are darkened and the clouds return with the rain; in the day
> when the guards of the house tremble, and the strong men are bent,
> and the women who grind cease working because they are few, and
> those who look through the windows see dimly; when the doors on
> the street are shut, and the sound of the grinding is low, and one rises
> up at the sound of a bird, and all the daughters of song are brought
> low; when one is afraid of heights, and terrors are in the road; the

almond tree blossoms, the grasshopper drags itself along and desire fails; because all must go to their eternal home, and the mourners will go about the streets; before the silver cord is snapped, and the golden bowl is broken, and the pitcher is broken at the fountain, and the wheel broken at the cistern, and the dust returns to the earth as it was, and the breath returns to God who gave it. Vanity of vanities, says the Teacher; all is vanity. (NRSV)

"Remember your creator in the days of your youth" sounds like the advice of the old to the young. Attend the church youth group, study Scripture every day, and obey God's statutes when you are young because your youthful commitments are determinative of your later faith. But then Ecclesiastes puts forth a more somber reason to be with God in youth: "Before the days of trouble come, and the years draw near when you will say, 'I have no pleasure in them'; before the sun and the light and the moon and the stars are darkened and the clouds return with the rain" (12:1–2 NRSV).

Though Graham doesn't even note these verses, Ecclesiastes is not the cheeriest view of old age by a long shot. Ecclesiastes characterizes the supposedly golden years as "days of trouble" in which, when the sky turns dark and the light is dim, we are likely to look on the joys of earlier days and say, "I have no pleasure in them." Kids, remember your creator when you are young because when you are old, you will despise God. What a thought to lay on the young!

Ecclesiastes also waxes grimly poetic in describing the aging body: "the guards of the house tremble" (that is, your hands palsy), "the strong men are bent" (your weak legs get crooked), "the women who grind cease working because they are few" (your teeth fall out), "those who look through the windows see dimly" (you are blind), "the doors on the street are shut" (you are lonely), "the sound of the grinding is low, and one rises up at the sound of a bird" (you never get a good night's rest), "all the daughters of song are brought low" (your voice is weak and trembling), "one is afraid of heights, and terrors are in the road" (you are timid and fearful), "the almond tree blossoms" (your hair is white), "the grasshopper drags itself along" (you creak and stumble around), "desire fails" (need I spell this one out?), "and the dust returns to the earth as it was, and the breath

returns to God who gave it. Vanity of vanities, says the Teacher, all is vanity."

I'm grateful that the canon kept the wisdom of Ecclesiastes, refusing to sugarcoat some of the realities of aging. Heap honor and gratitude on aging all you want, but you haven't told the truth about aging until you have done business with Ecclesiastes 12 and the Teacher's characterization of the troubled days.

Better think about God and the blessings of life when you are young because when the "days of trouble come" you may not want to be around God. These melancholy words from Ecclesiastes imply that more preparation is required for the rigors of aging than the accumulation of a hefty 401(k).

Aging in the New Testament

This negative side to the ambiguity of aging in the Old Testament seems less pronounced in the New Testament. While older adults are few in the Gospels or the letters of Paul, the elderly are major actors in the opening of Luke's Gospel. Luke believes that we can't get to the babe of Bethlehem without being led there by old people such as the priest Zechariah and his wife, Elizabeth, a childless older couple who are "very old" (Luke 1:7). The angel Gabriel appears to Zechariah and promises that Elizabeth will bear a son named John, bumping her from the geriatric ward to the maternity ward. Even in her old age, God calls this woman into faithful service. Zechariah finds this promise incredible due to their advanced age, but— wonder of wonders—embarrassed Elizabeth gives birth. Even though Elizabeth is old, she is the very first character in Luke's story to be "filled with the Holy Spirit" (v. 41). Elders become God's inspired instruments, commissioned interpreters to the Virgin Mary.

Next Luke introduces us to old Simeon and Anna, who welcome Jesus to the temple (2:25–38). Simeon hopes for the deliverance of Israel from oppression and, upon seeing the infant Jesus, proclaims Jesus as the chosen one who is the Deliverer. Throughout Luke, people have difficulty understanding who Jesus is and what he is up to. Is Simeon's astute perception of Jesus and Jesus's identity a function

of the wisdom he has accrued over the years? Does Simeon see the child as God's rebuke to those who have given up hope for deliverance? Are older folks the first to get the astounding news of Jesus's birth because after many decades of living they are now unsurprised by the stunts of God?

Both Zechariah and Elizabeth and Simeon and Anna embody wisdom and insight—some gained through past experience, some as gift of the Holy Spirit. They are presented by Luke as prophets who point younger folks toward the future with expectation and hope. By the grace of God, they publicly, hopefully testify about tomorrow. Might Luke be suggesting that rather than being stuck in the past and unable to adjust to change, older adults who have been well-formed in the faith have a radical openness to the future and wise discernment of the times?

While many of us elders value continuity, tradition, and stability, it is striking that Luke connects older people to the possibility of unanticipated divine intervention. They have many years on them, but they point toward God's radical new future, as in, "Your young men shall see visions, and your old men shall dream dreams" (Acts 2:17 NRSV). In the outpouring of the Holy Spirit, the elderly are called to be dreamers. The Holy Spirit is a gift that keeps pointing the elderly toward visions of tomorrow rather than leaving them to wallow in memories of yesterday.

The Pastoral Epistles depict the early church as a place of respect for and honor of elders. First Timothy 5:1 says, "Do not rebuke an older man but exhort him as you would a father" (RSV). There are also specific directives to the community to provide assistance to widows. While the church owes elders honor and respect, it is noteworthy that responsible discipleship is expected from the elders. Older men like me, when necessary, can be exhorted. Widows are directed to devote themselves to prayer, hospitality, and service of the afflicted (vv. 3–16)—not only to be served but also to serve. Elders are called to be paradigms of faith and role models (Titus 2:2–5), teaching, counseling, and offering what guidance they can. Clearly, the New Testament authors consider elders to be worthy of special care yet still under Christ's vocational mandate to follow him as responsible agents.

After looking over the New Testament material on aging, Duke's Richard and Judith Hays note what is *not* said about older people in the New Testament: "Nowhere in the biblical canon are they pitied, patronized, or treated with condescension. Nowhere is growing old itself described as a problem. Nowhere are the eldest described as pitiable, irrelevant, or behind the curve, as inactive or unproductive. Nowhere are they, as in so many Western dramas and narratives, lampooned as comic figures."[4]

Even more remarkable, the New Testament, while calling death "the last enemy" (1 Cor. 15:26), does not consider death the worst thing that can happen to old people. The Hayses say that Jesus's death at an early age (he was no more than thirty-six) stands as a permanent reminder that fidelity is more important than longevity and that there is something worse than not living to a ripe old age.[5] Infidelity is a sin; mortality is not.

While long years are a blessing (Prov. 16:31; 20:29), a long life is not an inherent right, nor can it be the supreme goal of life. God, the giver of life, may call us to surrender our lives. The way of discipleship in the name of Jesus may not lead to a fruitful retirement but to the cross (Mark 8:34–38; Luke 14:25–27). I know a pastor who, on the verge of retirement, has been appointed to serve the most divided, difficult congregation of his entire ministry. Though his plan was to retire next year, he has committed to the bishop to stay at his post (in his words) "until this church gets healed of its craziness or I drop dead." I have many friends who, having enjoyed good health for most of their lives, are straining to offer a positive witness to the world even while under the burden of pain and sickness at the end of their lives. Discipleship, the way of the cross, is not for the faint of heart of any age.

Aging as Vocation

Researchers into successful aging stress the importance of seeing our last third of life as a time of continuing change and development. Some of these developments are necessitated by changing bodies and economic circumstances; others are precipitated by shifting social and familial relationships. Yet it's important for Christians to note

that some of the change and development that's required in our last years is instigated by a living God who keeps calling us to witness, to testify, and to continue to walk the narrow way of discipleship. In John 3, we meet a man named Nicodemus who comes to Jesus by night. Though John doesn't tell us Nicodemus's specific age, when Nicodemus questions how a man can be born when he is old, Jesus responds that the Holy Spirit is able to provide new birth even among the aging. One is never too old to be rebirthed, made young again, sent on outrageous errands, or discombobulated by the Holy Spirit.

Because God isn't "the God of the dead but of the living" (Mark 12:27), our lives are subject not only to chronology and the possibility of mental and physical incapacity but also to a God who thinks nothing of constantly calling ordinary people—of any age—to follow him. A key question for each Christian is, "What is God doing in my life now?" Or more to the point of vocation, "What does God expect from me and to what tasks am I now being assigned?"

The God of the Bible who called people late in life—Elizabeth and Zechariah, Abraham and Sarah—keeps calling. Simeon blesses the young holy family and yet speaks a hard truth to Mary concerning the future of her son (Luke 2:34–35). Simeon and Anna show a boldness that characterizes some older people who, after a lifetime of responsible caution—keeping a job, being an example to their children—are now free to use their remaining precious time telling the truth—that is, being God's prophets. Though Anna is a person of great age, she is a truth-telling prophet in her last years. Perhaps this is the blessed, fruitful old age promised by the psalmist: "In old age they still produce fruit" (Ps. 92:14 NRSV).

Stuck in jail, Paul calls himself an old man, but still he expressed hope that he would be released for the express purpose of continuing his missionary vocation (Phil. 1:19, 22). This lifetime quality of divine vocation may explain why the only explicit reference to retirement in the Bible concerns the members of the tribe of Levi, who assisted in Israel's worship and began their work at age twenty, "and from the age of fifty years they shall retire from the duty of the service and serve no more" (Num. 8:25 NRSV). Though my colleagues can encourage me to retire from active teaching, no one can excuse me from my vocation except the one who called me.

The psalmist prays not for long life but for life long enough to tell future generations the truth about God:

> So even to old age and gray hairs,
>   O God, do not forsake me,
> until I proclaim your might
>   to all the generations to come. (Ps. 71:18 NRSV)

Billy Graham pointed me to an elder I'd never heard of: old Barzillai, who, at great risk to himself, provided food and shelter for King David and his men (2 Sam. 17:27–29). In gratitude for Barzillai's hospitality, David invited the old man to spend the rest of his days in the king's palace. Barzillai refused the king's hospitality, pleading, "How many years do I have left that I should go up with the king to Jerusalem? I am now 80 years old. Do I know what is good or bad anymore? Can your servant taste what I eat or drink? Can I even hear the voices of men or women singers? Why should your servant be a burden to my master and king?" (19:34–35). Barzillai was old enough to provide help to the king but too old (and too wise in his old age) to find much enjoyment in the king's palatial comforts.

Scripture is honest about the dependency that usually comes with old age, but I'm unsure if that dependency is viewed negatively or positively. As Jesus said to Peter, "Truly, truly, I say to you, when you were young, you girded yourself and walked where you would; but when you are old, you will stretch out your hands, and another will gird you and carry you where you do not wish to go" (John 21:18 RSV). This is probably a prophecy of martyrdom for Peter as an old man, but it can more generally apply to the rest of us. Aging requires a person to "stretch out your hands" and ask for help from others as well as to submit to be carried "where you do not wish to go." Dependency on the kindness of others is a curse only in a world that worships self-sufficiency.

Martha Nussbaum, one of our greatest living philosophers, says that in a culture that adulates youth, bodily perfection, potency, and independence, is it a wonder that the aged are the subject of "widespread, indeed, virtually universal, social stigma"?[6] *The Cambridge Handbook of Age and Ageing* criticizes our culture's bleak stereotypes of aging as a mere social construction "reflecting negative

beliefs and attitudes about old age rather than any valid objective evidence concerning the quality of life of older people or their ability to make a positive contribution to society. . . . Ageism, then, refers to a process of collective stereotyping which emphasizes the negative features of ageing which are ultimately traced back to biomedical 'decline,' rather than backed up by empirical research."[7]

A negative view of elderhood does not come from Christian Scripture but is among the many cultural accommodations that the North American church has made to American culture. Ageism, like sexism or racism, is not only a social construction; it's a sin to be confessed.

John Calvin famously spoke of Scripture as the lens through which Christians look at ourselves and the world.[8] The ambiguity, the truthfulness, and the peculiarity of biblical views on aging speak to us of the distinctiveness of the church's witness on elderhood. The church ought to articulate and underscore the disparity between how Christians talk about the last years of life and how the world characterizes aging. We must demonstrate, in our congregational life, the difference that Christ makes in the way we age and in how we relate to and engage in ministry to and with the aging.

I have an acquaintance, a distinguished biologist who retired after a lifetime of teaching and research. I was surprised when he called me and said, "I need a suggestion of a good, readable biblical commentary. I was quite an enthusiastic young Christian, active in campus religious groups during college. But then there was graduate school, followed by my first teaching position. My wife never cared much for church. I drifted away, became focused on other matters. Now that I'm retired, I've got time to think more deeply about things. I want to read systematically through the Bible, paying closer attention and spending more time with some parts of it. Can you suggest a commentary that would help me?"

It's wrong to focus too much on the losses of aging without also noting the gains, such as the gift of "time to think more deeply about things." When we Christians go to Scripture, it's not usually to find answers to specific questions like, "How can I endure the last decades of my life?" Rather, we live with Scripture, regularly spending time with the stories of God with us, not primarily as a rule book or a set of answers but rather as an old friend, a companion on life's journey.

As with any old friend, we are patient with the friend's retelling of stories they have told us before. Sometimes there is joy in hearing familiar words that are beloved all the more for their familiarity. We delight to find passages that spoke to us during one stage of our lives speak differently now. Or we are surprised by biblical characters we failed to notice in previous trips through Scripture. (Have you noted either Simeon's or Anna's age on your previous encounters with the story of the nativity?)

We speak of a biblical "passage." Through Scripture, we travel from one place to another, guided, enticed, and urged on by the text. As we make our passage into and through elderhood, the Bible, once spoken of quaintly as "the Book of the Ages," can be a trustworthy guide and companion.

TWO

The Storm of Aging

When speaking of America's exploding aging population, we reach for meteorological metaphors. Health care providers face a "tidal wave" of needy elderly. An "avalanche" of increased longevity will sweep away pension programs and Social Security. An aging population is a "death tsunami" in which so many Americans will be dying that all institutions (especially mainline Protestant churches) will be drained of membership and financial support. Expect a "demographic earthquake" when younger generations will be overwhelmed by the burden of caring for the elderly.

For the aging themselves, the financial, psychological, mental, sociological, and spiritual challenges of aging can make it feel as if moving into the last decades of life is like being cast into a storm. A storm's a-coming. The unprepared will be swept away. Batten down the hatches!

To be sure, Scripture suggests that a Christian view of aging begins with gratitude that we've been given an undeserved gift that someone in the first century would find inconceivable. And yet a peculiarly Christian view of aging cannot end in gratitude but must move toward an honest admission that this last act of our lives is ambiguous both in its meaning and in our individual experiences, a time of both fruition and decay, fulfillment and loss, freedom and dependence. These qualitative challenges are now aggravated by a quantitative crisis: so many of us are aged.

Most want to live longer; few want to grow old. Like the Teacher of Ecclesiastes, many have regarded elderhood not as an unambiguous

gift but rather as a morose, burdensome, meaningless finale. Ecclesiastes's gloomy heir was William Shakespeare, who famously characterized aging as the sad sixth and seventh acts in life's tragic drama
that ends somberly with the loss of everything.

> All the world's a stage,
> And all the men and women merely players;
> They have their exits and their entrances,
> And one man in his time plays many parts,
> His acts being seven ages. At first the infant,
> Mewling and puking in the nurse's arms;
> And then the whining schoolboy, with his satchel
> And shining morning face, creeping like snail
> Unwillingly to school. And then the lover,
> Sighing like furnace, with a woeful ballad
> Made to his mistress' eyebrow. Then a soldier,
> Full of strange oaths, and bearded like the pard,
> Jealous in honor, sudden and quick in quarrel,
> Seeking the bubble reputation
> Even in the cannon's mouth. And then the justice,
> In fair round belly with good capon lined,
> With eyes severe and beard of formal cut,
> Full of wise saws and modern instances;
> And so he plays his part. The sixth age shifts
> Into the lean and slippered pantaloon,
> With spectacles on nose and pouch on side;
> His youthful hose, well saved, a world too wide
> For his shrunk shank; and his big manly voice,
> Turning again toward childish treble, pipes
> And whistles in his sound. Last scene of all,
> That ends this strange eventful history,
> Is second childishness and mere oblivion,
> Sans teeth, sans eyes, sans taste, sans everything.[1]

King Lear's Retirement

The bard who characterized old age as "second childishness and mere
oblivion, sans teeth, sans eyes, sans taste, sans everything" wrote the
most famous (and tragic) drama of aging, *King Lear*. After read-

ing *Lear*, poet David Wright wrote a poem that sees the play as a
warning.

> You can't trust the sweetnesses your friends will
> offer, when they really want your office.[2]

Lear's eventual fatal train of disintegration of self, family, and
friends is set in motion by his realization that he is getting old and
ought to retire. Lear resolves to divide his realm among his three
daughters but only after demanding that each of them outdo the
others in publicly proclaiming her love for him, boasting that he
will offer the largest share of his estate to the daughter who loves
him most. Goneril and her sister Regan take turns fawning over the
old man. Cordelia modestly refuses to say anything in response to
Lear's outrageous proposition. Lear fumes, "Nothing shall come of
nothing"[3] and promptly disinherits daughter Cordelia, taking her
share and dividing it among her sisters. When Goneril and Regan talk
together alone, they admit that their declarations of love were bogus.
Their real estimate of their father is that he is a foolish old man.

Initially, Lear looked forward to relinquishing the burdens of ruling, "to shake all cares and business off our state, confirming them
on younger years."[4] Yet he makes a mess of his retirement by fatally
rejecting Cordelia's love as well as the loyalty of his dear friend Kent.
When Kent protests Lear's treatment of Cordelia, petulant Lear banishes him. Observing the old man's appalling behavior makes us
wonder, "Is the king becoming senile, or is he plain crazy?"

In the climactic act 2, after relations between Lear and Goneril and
Regan have thoroughly deteriorated, Lear yields completely to his
rage, cursing his ungrateful daughters. Accompanied by his mocking fool (now his sole companion), Lear rushes out of the familial
storm in the palace into a violent storm on the heath, where he rants
against his daughters and descends into raving madness, blaspheming
the gods who have failed him, loathing his own children, welcoming
death, and contemptuously dismissing life as an unbearably meaningless tragedy.

Nothing that I (or the author of Ecclesiastes) could say about the
melancholy of aging is as candid or as bleak as *King Lear*. Though

I am uncertain in what fashion Shakespeare was a Christian, and though the Christian faith appears to play no role in the lives of the characters in this epic drama, *Lear* is a helpful, if morose, conversation partner for Christian reflection on aging.

For many interpreters, *Lear* is little more than a nihilistic, dark depiction of the horrors of growing old. Old age is a pathless wasteland, a storm of unspeakable loss in which blind rage is an understandable, though impotent, response. Some point out that while Lear is childish, petulant, and resentful, mostly Lear is old. *Old* is the chief excuse given for the king's behavior by those few who manage still to love him: his friends Kent, Gloucester, and most especially the wise fool. *Old* is the charge made against Lear by his two elder disgusted daughters. "You see how full of changes his age is," Goneril says to Regan, citing Lear's "poor judgment" in banishing Cordelia. "'Tis the infirmity of his age," Regan replies, charitably.[5]

Old becomes Lear's excuse for why his life has careened out of control. Before growing old, Lear ruled; now he is ruled over, subject to mental and physical deterioration, humiliatingly aware that his end draws near. "Pray, do not mock me: I am a very foolish fond old man," Lear says in his final reunion scene with Cordelia, blaming the sad course of events on the curse of being old.[6]

Lear cherishes his family. He hopes that his daughters love him enough to care for him in his last days and is deeply hurt by his (foolish) belief that daughter Cordelia does not love him and (later) his conclusion that daughters Goneril and Regan don't either. After his bumbling and ranting, Lear goes out into the rain and the cold, though the weather is not the tempest that has driven him to this end. Lear is bested by the "storm" of aging, forced to acknowledge his impotency and loneliness and to spend his last days confronting the results of his own weaknesses.

True, few children go so far as to have their parent's eyes gouged out, but the manner in which Goneril and Regan abuse their father continues in the crime of elder abuse in our day. After Lear cruelly banishes Cordelia, responsibility for him falls to the two elder sisters, who are none too pleased. "If our father carry authority with such disposition as he bears, this last surrender of his will but offend us," Goneril says. "We must do something, and i'th'heat."[7] They instruct

their servants to ignore their father's peevish and (to Goneril's mind) pointless demands. Regan shuts up her house when she hears that the old man is on his way for a visit. The daughters complain about what is (in their estimation) their father's excessive demand for servants, but one feels that they would complain about him and lock him out even without his one hundred knights. Finally, they close their gates to Lear, leaving him at the mercy of the storm. Good riddance to an unbearable burden.

Bastard son Edmund, in his sham letter to his brother Edgar, sees Lear's decline and divestment as an opportunity for his personal aggrandizement. "The younger rises when the old doth fall," says Edmund as he busily betrays his father to the Duke of Cornwall.[8] The old man's decline is an opportunity for his children to make their move on Lear's inheritance.

The play ends (depending on which version is used) with Edgar pronouncing, "The oldest have borne most. We that are young shall never see so much, nor live so long."[9] The young can't conceive of the horrible burdens of being old: sans teeth, sans eyes, sans children, sans everything.

This masterwork of Shakespeare leaves me with a question: What in Lear's aging leads to this tragedy? Philosopher Martha Nussbaum notes that many recent productions of *King Lear* portray Lear as an older adult who suffers from dementia. Nussbaum objects. That we must have the king afflicted with dementia may say more about our culture than about Lear.[10] There is nothing in Shakespeare's play to suggest that dementia is Lear's problem.

Lear's mistake is that he retires by *shedding responsibility but continuing to control*. Lear strides into aging as a proud, powerful, willful regent, obsessed with controlling his kingdom and its future. He ages as he lived—vainly attempting to exercise omnipotent command. The play is set in motion when Lear makes the equivalent of a living will. Before I die, Lear says, I will dictate the distribution of my world. I determine that my loved ones respond to me as I demand. I will "retire," but I will do so without relinquishing my determination of them.

Nussbaum notes that the powerlessness of aging is particularly devastating to a person like Lear, who has "been totally hooked on his

own power and fantasized invulnerability."[11] As Lear's fool candidly says to him, Lear has foolishly made "thy daughters thy mothers,"[12] reducing Lear to a needy child of his own children. Because control has been the purpose of his life, Lear rages, not so much against the perils of old age but against the powerlessness that he experiences in old age. He is not living demented, without memory or in another reality; he is raging against his painful new reality, which has occurred not because he is old but because he is a control freak who has mismanaged his retirement. His "madness" is not really dementia; it is rage against his loss of control and his impotency to defend himself against his daughters' attempts to do him in.

Aging as a Test of Character

Still, it's not quite right to see Lear's troubles as stemming from his botched retirement. He is brought to grief by his character. Lear moves from being an omnipotent king to being an ordinary man, a father, a friend and equal, changes for which Lear is ill-equipped. He foolishly thinks he can give away all that he has and yet retain lordship over it, dramatically divest the burdens of responsibility and divide his estate while still exercising control over the life he previously so proudly enjoyed.

Was Lear prone to anger when he was younger? Lear is certainly a very angry old man, but much of his anger stems from his anguished frustration, not at being old but at finding himself dependent and vulnerable.

Retirement goes poorly for Lear, not because his retirement led to dementia or to the dissolution of his family and friends but because in old age Lear's flaws caught up with him. Full of pride, puffed up by an inflated ego, Lear divides his estate, but only after demanding that his children flatter him. When his best friend questions his actions, Lear curses him. Lear insists not only that his family look after him in his old age but also that they maintain him as if he were still king, parading with a retinue of a hundred knights before he finally storms out into lonely oblivion.

Dementia or mistakes in retirement planning are not Lear's problem; Lear is Lear's problem. While aging may not bring out the best

or the worst in us, aging often magnifies tendencies that were present in our characters throughout our lives.[13] Sometimes it's only in our later years that our chickens come home to roost. Lear's pompousness and pride, his petulance and peevishness are made worse in a man who values power and control. If your major needs are control, independence, and power over your circumstances (I confess I'm guilty on all counts!), retirement and aging can be tough. With the predictable physical, social, financial, and emotional changes that occur in aging, control-hoarding people (like me!) are in trouble once they're members of the AARP.

Lear's aging could have gone differently. He could have made different decisions, could have listened to the advice of his friends, could have been more sensitive to the points of view of his children, or could have been more honest with himself about his retirement as the ending of one way of life and more hopeful about the beginning of another phase of existence.

On the heath—alone except for his faithful fool, stripped of everything he loves, and at his life's end—Lear is forced into brutal self-awareness. He repents of some of his earlier impetuousness, but his honest self-assessment comes too late.

Too late for Lear, but perhaps not too late for us. Was Shakespeare's intent in writing *Lear* to show, through this worst-case scenario, what aging need not be? We can see aging and retirement as "mere oblivion," "sans everything," or we can view this stage of life as a call for self-reflection, for life-course correction, and for the embrace of a new direction in relating to others and to the world in a different but not altogether unhappy way.

For Christians, aging can be a call for increased attentiveness to and engagement with God. We believe that in Christ we are not destined to end alienated from those we love, raging and impotent, cursing our fate, at the mercy of a violent storm that sweeps all away. The One who loved us into life loves us to the end. God is with us as we go into life's last age, transforming our fate into our destiny.

More than one Shakespearean actor has quipped that by the time one is old enough to have had enough experience to play King Lear, one is too old for the demanding role. Perhaps we, by the grace of God, can prove these actors wrong. By the time we attain Lear's age,

can we arrive with the conviction that God is there to welcome us? We are not alone in the storm. There's a way to age well, *and* we don't have to do it alone.

"Have you prepared for your retirement?" the TV ads ask as they hawk financial planning services. What if Lear had begun to experience, perhaps even to enjoy, moments of being less in control? What if a friend of Lear's had been able to tell him, in a way he could hear, "You are kidding yourself if you think you can distribute your goods to your daughters and still have sovereignty over them"? What if Lear had asked for help in acquiring the new skills he needed to turn the disaster of his retirement into an opportunity to be a better person?

What if Lear had been part of a church that felt responsibility for helping him prepare for his retirement by candidly confronting him with the challenges of aging and then helping him practice some of the spiritual disciplines needed to negotiate this tricky time of life?

Furthermore, if Lear's downfall is due to flaws in character, those of us in the church—the people whom Stanley Hauerwas calls the "community of character"[14]—ought to take note. Changing when we are old is tough, but with a living, constantly intrusive, transforming God and a caring, truthful church of God, it's never too late to be born again and again. Some of the most important work the church does in us is preparatory: preparing us for loss and teaching us how to grieve, how to confess, and how to receive forgiveness, thus "equipping the saints for the work of ministry" (Eph. 4:12–16) so that we may walk into life's tempests with confident faith.

When I offered a former parishioner comfort after the death of his wife of forty-six years, he said, "Preacher, I've been preparing for this for a month of Sundays. All the sermons I've heard, all the Sunday school classes I've sat through—homework for the big exam. Now we're gonna find out just how well I've listened." Or as jazz artist Eubie Blake is commonly quoted as saying, "If I'd known I was going to live this long, I'd have taken better care of myself."

THREE

Retiring with God

Chronology is not very helpful in defining late adulthood, with many people maintaining high physical and intellectual functioning into their eighties. The age of sixty-five remains a powerful cultural marker since that's when Americans are eligible for Social Security benefits. While sixty-five is the conventional door into late life through retirement, it can be too late to think about the challenges of retirement.

"There are at least two major tasks to human life," says Franciscan priest Richard Rohr, thinking developmentally rather than chronologically. "The first task is to build a strong 'container' or identity; the second is to find the contents that the container was meant to hold."[1] Rohr emphasizes the importance of completing the first task well in order to engage the second: "You need a very strong container to hold the contents and contradictions that arrive later in life. You ironically need a very strong ego structure to let go of your ego. You need to struggle with the rules more than a bit before you throw them out. You only internalize values by butting up against external values for a while."[2]

Rohr characterizes the first half of life as a time of building purpose and direction in life and fulfilling commitments. The first half is "largely concerned about *surviving successfully* . . . establishing an identity, a home, relationships, friends, community, security, and building a proper platform for our life."[3] In the first half, one is a

25

"soldier" who is "very loyal to strict meritocracy, to his own entitlement, to obedience and loyalty."[4]

The second half of life is "falling"—a form of suffering, a failure,
a loss, or a stumbling. We must thoughtfully "fall into" this rather
than simply fall backward. This falling is usually something that happens to us rather than something we choose. The crucial thing, says
Rohr, is to use this time to clarify and to refine in order to see "the
task within the task" and to "recognize the intentions and motives
for what one needs to do."[5] What we call retirement is not so much
losing a job as taking on a new job.

Oliver O'Donovan sounds much like Rohr when he says that the
task of aging is moving from "realizing unexplored potential to making sense of accumulated experience."[6] Rohr teaches that we live out
our true selves in the second half of life when we attempt to live in a
way that integrates our first half of life by discerning what we need
to keep and what we need to let go. Rohr puts it this way: "How can I
honor the legitimate needs of the first half of life while creating space,
vision, time, and grace for the second? *The holding of this tension*
is the very shape of wisdom." Rohr famously says that "the way up
is the way down, or if you prefer, the way down is the way up."[7]

The Challenges of Retirement

I fear that Rohr risks putting too positive a face on the losses of
aging. The bleakest cinematic depiction of retirement as a way down,
down, down is the first scene of *About Schmidt*. The 2002 film opens
with Jack Nicholson sitting in a stripped-down office, surrounded
by empty shelves and packed boxes, impassively watching an office
clock tick off the minutes until five on his last hour of his last day
at his last job. When the clock strikes five, Nicholson sighs, gathers
his few belongings, and silently walks out on life as he has known it.

After seeing *About Schmidt*, a friend called to say, "The movie
begins with the saddest scene imaginable, then tells the saddest story
about a sad retirement. Everybody on the way to retirement should
be required to see it. But be warned: there's a nude scene with Jack
Nicholson and Kathy Bates in a hot tub. Though you'll try not to,
you'll be unable to keep yourself from looking."

About Schmidt depicts retirement as more than a tragedy: retirement pushes the protagonist into a journey of self-discovery, some of it painful, much of it exhilarating, as he finds a new life for himself. While retirement may not be the very best time in life, by God's grace, retirement need not be the worst.

Still, for many who are aging, as for King Lear, life's most difficult decades begin at sixty-five. Most suicides are by men; the highest rates for male suicide begin at fifty and continue to rise through age seventy. In this decade American suicide rates for men and women over fifty have risen markedly.[8] Keep those stark figures in mind the next time you hear sentimental claptrap about retirement.

Retirement isn't what it used to be. The median age for retirement in America declined to fifty-seven in the early 1990s from a high of seventy-four in 1910, when the expected life span was about fifty and neither Social Security nor pension plans existed.[9] Those who did not die at fifty continued to work because they had no choice; retirement was an unknown concept. Today's median retirement age is about sixty-two. Only a small percentage of Americans (5–10 percent) work beyond age seventy.[10] Voluntary retirement becomes more attractive when we have both critical masses of retirees with economic security and social expectations that retirement is a positive experience.

Differences in class, race, gender, and economic security that separate us throughout life become even larger and more detrimental in our last years. To speak of the elderly without accounting for those differences falsifies the subject. Still, we have learned much about general paths of aging, and these insights can inform a broad range of congregations who want to help members negotiate the challenges of retirement.

When workers are forced to stop working earlier than planned or earlier than they want, retirement is seen as a curse rather than a privilege. Compulsory retirement is an arbitrary and unnecessary rule that's usually based on age discrimination stereotypes rather than on careful evaluation of what a person is contributing to the company. The main function of compulsory retirement rules is to protect administrators from having to make informed and sometimes painful assessments and decisions about employees.

I know of a medical center where doctors were forced to retire at seventy. Mandatory retirement made sense to some of the doctors, who expressed gratitude that the institution made a decision about their retirement for them. Others, varying across their particular fields of medical practice and their personal abilities, pushed back. Some medical residents testified to the value of having a few experienced, wise practitioners to train them in diagnostics. The medical center decided to end mandatory retirement at seventy and to institute yearly reviews of all doctors over seventy, making retirement decisions on a case-by-case basis.

When my theological mentor, Karl Barth, was forced to retire from his faculty position in Basel, he moved his seminar to a local tavern, where the students flocked to receive Barth's wisdom.

Work—getting up, going out, and making a contribution to the larger good—is our major means of social interaction. Work keeps us active and in touch with the young. Ceasing from work thus presents the former working adult with a challenge: How shall I stay in contact with and keep exercising responsibility for others now that I no longer have a job to decide for me? What is the rationale for getting out of bed in the morning?

The Work of Retirement

In his book *Finding Meaning in the Second Half of Life: How to Finally, Really Grow Up*, James Hollis, using Rohr's two-part life schema, says that success in the second half is often dependent on the work we've done in the first. The first half accrues "growth, purpose, and meaning," which will be used to negotiate the challenges of the second half.[11] "What does the world ask of me, and what resources can I muster to meet its demands?" sets the agenda for the first half.[12] Hollis says that the "fantasy of acquisition" dominates the first half, "gaining ego strength to deal with separation, separating from the overt domination of parents, acquiring a standing in the world, whether it be through property, relationship, or social function," and building "a sense of ego strength sufficient to engage relationship, social role expectations, and to support oneself."[13]

The primary task of successful retirement is somehow coming to the realization that retirement is not only giving up and ending a way of life but also finding a passage from one form of life to another. It is possible for a person moving into the second half to see that retirement from one set of responsibilities and cares frees them to explore another set of obligations and to assume another set of concerns. We are surprised to find that as our time grows shorter, sometimes our time to explore ourselves and our world expands.

Retirement calls us to assume new narratives, moving from the story "I used to work, but now I have stopped working" to "Once I did this work and then I stopped doing it, so I am now free to do other work."

Let's be honest. Some of us retire from jobs that are meaningless. In our working years we may have invested too much in our jobs, attempting to imbue significance in a job that the job could not bear, vainly trying to receive satisfaction from a career that delivered little joy. Now, in retirement, we are free not to expect so much meaning from a rather meaningless job and to assume more fulfilling work.

Yet moving from working at a job into the jobs of retirement is not only movement into another stage of life; retirement is undeniably a movement into the last stage of life. We have not merely endured the bodily changes that come with the acquisition of years; we are entering the final years. This means we are no longer members of the generation in charge, which may be very painful to those of us like Lear who have derived a great deal of meaning from having authority and influence. Having observed the retirements of a number of fellow clergy, I know that the sidelining that accompanies aging may be most difficult for those who have enjoyed being at the center of attention. The worst part of retirement, confessed a retired Methodist pastor, "is that I've got just as much to say but no longer have that blessed twenty minutes every week to say it in a sermon."

It is possible for retirement to be liberating for those who have borne the heavy burdens of being in charge. I was cast by the church into a demanding job with heavy responsibility for the lives of others. Having retired from being bishop, I now enjoy having more choice over my areas of responsibility. While retirement is the loss of certain

sorts of power, it can also entail the acquisition of different, more enjoyable empowerment.

If it is true, as it was for Lear, that one of our greatest fears in aging is loss of control, perhaps we ought to prepare ourselves for that inevitable eventuality. We should look for those occasions when we can be dependent, when we can put ourselves in the care of others and relax and go with the flow. We manage fear by facing our fears and by experiencing fear-inducing circumstances. Might we treat our fear of lack of control the same way?

"This Thanksgiving for the first time I'm going to sit back and let my daughter-in-law handle coordination and preparation of the family's Thanksgiving dinner," a woman proclaimed. "It's her trial run for taking charge when I'm not responsible for Thanksgiving the rest of my days."

The Economics of Retirement

Christianity is an embodied, incarnational faith. We Christians demonstrate our unique brand of spirituality when we concern ourselves with economic matters and with questions about the just distribution of God's material gifts. It would be tempting to talk about aging either as a mostly bodily and medical change or as a purely emotional, psychological, social, or attitudinal challenge. Yet the Christian faith—in the eternal Word became flesh (John 1:1)—will not allow us to act as if the economics of aging is beyond the bounds of theological concern. Body and spirit, the mundane and the divine, are joined in Jesus Christ.

I interviewed a woman who works as the coordinator of her town's senior center. She provides a marvelous network of social services for the aged.

"What's one thing that would improve the lives of the aged with whom you work?" I asked.

"For most of them, two hundred dollars a week would dramatically improve their situation," she replied. Some of the problems we treat as psychological, medical, or spiritual are economic.

Aging exposes and aggravates economic inequalities a person has endured for decades. A widespread social injustice in our country is

the gap between the affluent aging and the nonaffluent aging. More than a third of the private wealth in the United States is held by 1 percent of the population, as aging Bernie Sanders says, and the elderly are overrepresented in this 1 percent group.[14] However, the majority of older adults have insufficient savings to meet even a modest medical or economic emergency, and most will need assistance from government, friends, and family. Almost a majority of Americans have no retirement savings (though many have equity value in their homes). Nearly 4 percent of Americans have no Social Security benefits to aid them in their last years.[15]

Aggravating these inequities is an economy that makes being in community difficult and turns our purportedly civilized society into Thomas Hobbes's *bellum omnium contra omnes*, a war of all against all. We assume that the best senior care is best offered by the best paid professionals, that there's not enough to go around, and that the source of good care is a well-designed economy. By feeding us a narrative that we are what we produce, a capitalistic culture can leave those no longer contributing to the GDP feeling purposeless and extraneous. Inherently adaptive, market driven, and innovative capitalism is at odds with those whose main contribution is passing on, nurturing, and protecting tradition. If productivity, rationality, and efficiency are considered to be the prime human contributions, then there is little for the aging to do. Elders become functionless and redundant. In a traditionalist or at least tradition-loving society, the old have something to contribute to the young, something the young do not have that can be given to them only by the old. When the aging are viewed as noncontributing, they are dismissed as those who are full of boring, irrelevant, repetitive stories that nobody wants to hear.

On the contrary, Deuteronomy 6 arises out of a culture that values the contributions of the aged. The way of the Lord is given to Israel, but the Lord knows that God's people will need one generation teaching another in order to keep the way of the Lord refurbished in the hearts of the people: "In the future, your children will ask you, 'What is the meaning of the laws, the regulations, and the case laws that the LORD our God commanded you?' Tell them: We were Pharaoh's slaves in Egypt. But the LORD brought us out of Egypt with a mighty

hand. Before our own eyes, the LORD performed great and awesome deeds of power against Egypt, Pharaoh, and his entire dynasty" (vv. 20–22). A tradition-valuing, transgenerational culture says that the function of elders is to recite and to teach God's ways to the young.

The maximum annual Social Security benefit for a single person who retires at age sixty-six is a little less than $32,000. Most recipients don't qualify for the maximum benefit. The average benefit is about half that. The cost of living for an older single person who rents a residence is about $24,000. Social Security comprises about 90 percent of income for 22 percent of older couples and for 45 percent of older singles.[16] While these Americans may not be in danger of starving, they will testify that their lives are severely circumscribed by a lack of funds.

Only about half of households with people over sixty-five enter retirement with savings. Half of those households have a defined benefit retirement plan apart from Social Security, and 36 percent live in a mortgaged home. This means that about 60 percent of older Americans are categorized as poor on the basis of income. When home equity is considered, the home equity for older Americans at the poverty level is about $120,000, so about 10 percent of the forty million Americans over age sixty-five fall below the poverty line.[17]

The economics of retirement looks vastly different for the affluent. During the past couple of decades, some of the elderly have become much richer, while younger adult cohorts have become poorer. Many older Americans did well for themselves in their housing and in the stock market and stashed away more of their earnings than those who follow them. While their younger cohorts are still making money in their work, there is a widespread sense that the elderly are generally more affluent and are fiercely protective of their government benefits (called "entitlements" by conservative politicians) from any legislated diminution. By working longer than other generations, many Boomers are not leaving room in the job market or for advancement for younger generations. Many elderly voters have a conviction that if their fellow older adults are in need, they are in need because they foolishly failed to prepare financially for their retirement.

Social Security taxes are a major means of equalizing some of the wealth disparity in the United States. Most Social Security benefits are subsidized by the young because they are paid for by future taxes.

Social Security taxes are now about 6.2 percent, with another 6.2 percent paid by an employer on the first $18,000 of income.[18] Social Security is the primary way America forces people to save for retirement. It would seem to be good government policy to do everything we can both to encourage and to require people to prepare for their post-earning years. Therefore, it may be a Christian responsibility to vote for an expanded Social Security system, both in funding and in future benefits. While preparation through Social Security may be repugnant to those who favor smaller government and less government benefits, this could be the easiest way to help the indigent elderly and to relieve some difficult generational stresses in the future.

Critics of Social Security and Medicare blame the deterioration of care for families and children on the "graying" of the federal budget. It's true that by the 1980s, more than half the federal domestic budget was being spent (mostly through Social Security) on the elderly.[19] Older voters were accused of placing the financial burdens they were incurring on their children and grandchildren; the hard-earned tax dollars of the young were being spent on unduly golden retirements of the elderly. The 2018 tax reform gives some credence to this point of view. Republican tax policy reformed the taxation structure by preserving benefits for the elderly, by postponing and ceasing environmental protection, and by incurring massive debt for future generations of Americans. Those who lament the alleged "graying of American political power" (Trump is my age, though his coiffure has escaped this graying trend) have some evidence on their side. We elderly are voting for those who promise to protect our retirements, to shore up the present without much thought for the future, and (without admitting it) to pass on the bill to our grandchildren.

Legacies and Estates

King Lear is a warning to us that one of our most fateful decisions related to retirement concerns our legacy. Retirement and the prospect of the end of our lives brings out the worst and the best in us, magnifying our faults and our virtues. We need not have as large an estate as Lear's to do, like the raging king, great damage. Sometimes, the smaller the estate, the more fierce the family battle. Despite my

pastoral efforts to work reconciliation, a brother and a sister to this day refuse to speak to each other because their mother's cherished bedroom dresser was given to one and not the other.

Frequently, a vain or lonely parent, like Lear, comes to view adult children as those with hands outstretched waiting for the parent to die and the will to go into effect. The parent is then tempted to threaten to withhold resources in order to gain more attention from the children. On the other hand, an adult child who nurtures memories of past pain inflicted by the parent or resentments arising from the burden of caring for the parent in their last years may view the parent's estate as the just restitution to which they are entitled, as did Lear's greedy daughters, Goneril and Regan.

A couple had a little farm that they lovingly nurtured throughout their lives, often saying, "This will belong to our children when we die." When both of them died within a few months of each other, I watched their surviving children squabble and put the farm up for auction to strangers rather than see any one sibling occupy the land. Their parents' funerals were the last gatherings of the family.

"John and Mary worked so hard to leave that farm to their children," someone in the church said, "only to have that farm, after their deaths, become the undoing of their family."

When my wife, Patsy, and I met with our attorney to draw up estate plans, our attorney said, "Do what you want with what you leave behind, but as for me, having seen so many otherwise good children ruined by the prospect of a rich inheritance, having seen so many families torn apart by fights over the estate, I'm telling my own children that they will receive a reasonable part of my estate, but I'm settling most of what I've got on a community foundation."

Realizing that as Christians we are under a mandate more demanding than the "family first" credo, that loving our grandchildren is not the extent of our ethical responsibilities, Patsy and I took the largest portion of our estate and formed a charitable foundation to be administered by our heirs when we're gone. We've provided for our children (most parents, if able, do that), but after we're dead, we hope to dispose of our property like Christians and provide for someone else's children.

This aging generation will leave behind the largest transfer of wealth ever. Whereas some of the elderly suffer from poverty, others

bear the responsibility of estates. A big estate can lead elders to suspect that their loved ones are treating them well because of their expectation of a future reward, not because they love them. A large estate can also bring out bad behavior in elders as they make excessive, Lear-like demands on their children, saying, "Act as I command or you're out of the will."

Transference of accumulated wealth raises ethical questions for older people with means. Should we wait until death to dispose of our financial holdings? In our estate planning, should we strive for equality in passing on resources to our children, treating each heir equally? A good case can be made for distributing earthly goods (and an estate is nothing more than that—*earthly*) sooner rather than later. Once we have accumulated enough to support ourselves into old age, why not experience the joy of parting with as much of our resources as possible now, rather than putting it off until after our deaths?

Perhaps Warren Buffett and Bill and Melinda Gates, with their intentions to distribute their vast wealth beyond the bounds of their families, should be our models. Parental generosity can be a witness to our children: as a Christian, nothing that I have is exclusively mine; I deserved none of it, as everything belongs to God. Jesus rearranges our notions of family and has given us responsibility for the needs of others beyond the bounds of our biological kith and kin.

In our distribution of portions of our estates to our families, should we consider the differing needs and abilities of our children and grandchildren? The principle of perfect equality isn't much of a guide. God gives us the gift of discernment. Most parents love all their children equally but also distinctively, honoring each child's needs and gifts. On the one hand, perhaps we should distribute according to need, giving more resources to the adult child who has a child with special needs or to the child who has had less economic opportunity than the others. On the other hand, such unequal distribution can be tricky, as children may feel that their siblings have jockeyed for this special treatment through fake displays of filial affection. *King Lear* is a cautionary warning of the dangers of unequal distribution of an estate to one's children. Is your family one of sufficient honesty and Christian formation that you can distribute your estate unequally without fostering resentment?

Freedom *for* Rather than Freedom *From*

We have good reason to fear the trials of retirement. Being forced by retirement to quit the work that gave us meaning and purpose raises the fear that we will be lost without it. Downsizing to a smaller home in a different neighborhood means saying goodbye to people we have enjoyed. Will we be able to muster a reason to get out of bed each morning? Will we have value to anyone any longer? Retirement's accoutrements can include concerns about being past exclusively with other older people and thereby segregated from younger generations, worries of financial insecurity, and FOMO—that is, the fear of missing out, for those of you not hip to Millennial acronyms. No wonder anxiety rises at the prospect of retirement.

Yet following Scripture's twofold sense that aging is not only a sometimes challenging, difficult time of life but also a divine blessing, we also must celebrate retirement's gifts. It is a sad commentary on our inadequate theology that we cannot affirm retirement's grant of blessed Sabbath rest. Most of our forebears would gladly have exchanged their burdens of having to work until they dropped for our First World retirement dilemmas. Here is a short list of some of the blessings of retirement: availability to help children and grandchildren, time to reconnect with friends and family, release from the burden of having to hold things together in a job, time to communicate with letters and email, extrication from some of the annoying hassles of working life, flexibility to sleep whenever desired, freedom to read and learn new things, liberty to say yes and no to offers, and opportunity to travel.

More than one early retiree has been surprised at receiving disapproval and even hostility from their coworkers, as if those who are still working said, "What gives you the right to turn your back on the career for which I'm making so many sacrifices and to which I'm giving my life?" Though the early retiree didn't mean for their retirement to be a critique of the work life of others, it was perceived in that way.

Freedom from work requires us to answer, "What am I now free for?" When we were actively working, our time was in the hands of others. We didn't spend much time asking, "What will I do today?"

In retirement we are free to "take time," which means not only free-dom but also new responsibility. If a person has had demanding, time-consuming work, having so much discretionary time can be a burden. One is now in a period of indeterminate length without an agenda imposed by society, faced with an array of choices about how to use time and resources, how to find purpose, and how to maintain relationships.

Odd that we often think of youth's "growing up" as a matter of accepting responsibility for the course of their lives when "growing old" is equally demanding, requiring us to be responsible for the use of our time as the time of our lives grows shorter, placing on us a sense of urgency to use well the time we have left. At work, we did not have to concern ourselves with what to do with time or find people with whom to interact: all that was readily available, done for us. Thus, retirement creates uncertainty and forces us to plan, to choose, to take responsibility. Retirement can be a time of new beginnings and a revival of interests that we had to put on the shelf in earlier life. Some retirees experience a new sense of urgency—time is limited, and if we are going to accomplish our goals, we had best begin now if we are to catch up with things, invest ourselves to the fullest, deal with unfinished business, overcome some perceived deficit in personality, or expand our horizons. In short, the bucket list syndrome.

What Paul said to new Christians ought to be said to those of us entering retirement: "You have stripped off the old self with its practices and have clothed yourselves with the new self, which is being renewed in knowledge according to the image of its creator" (Col. 3:9–10 NRSV). Retirement doesn't so much take away our self as it gives us a different sort of self. Having spent so much time exercising creativity—making, doing, achieving—we are now free to imitate our Creator in taking creative Sabbath rest.

Kenneth Calhoun wrote a delightful story, "Nightblooming," that tells of a young, aspiring jazz musician who encounters a group of older adults who "found themselves retired" and who reacted to their retirement by saying, "Now's finally the time to form a band!"

> You should see the instruments they fished out of attics and basements. Not so much the instruments themselves—horns haven't changed

much over the years—but the cases. Some are covered with flesh-tone leather, boxes made of wood with rusty hinges, lined with red velvet. When they crack them open, it looks like they're pulling metal bones from the insides of a body.

The dudes are severely elderly, these Nightblooming Jazzmen. They wear white belts and bow ties, polyester pants pulled up high. Our angle is we're old, they say.[20]

The Nightblooming Jazzmen have found that a chief gift of retirement is *freedom from* in order to be *free for*. Go ahead, form a jazz band, be like George W. Bush and take up painting, travel, or sit on a rock and look down on the valley. You are free. True, for Christians, freedom is a contested concept. We are never truly free, if freedom means the freedom to live only for ourselves. As Christians, we are baptismally named, claimed, called, attached, and commissioned by Christ. Our "freedom" may therefore be freedom from the cares entailed in our vocation (needing to earn money, care for our families, etc.) in order to have freedom for our chief Christian vocation—discipleship.

In an interview with her oldest grandson, Senator Barbara Boxer said, "I am never going to retire; the work is too important. But I am not going to be running for the Senate in 2016."[21]

For one faithful person, retirement freed him from his career so he could devote himself more fully to his vocation. The week after he retired from his engineering job, he offered himself for service to the church, saying, "Now that I no longer have a job, I'm free for full-time Christian service." That's the spirit!

Preparing for Retirement

During my time as a pastor, I wouldn't perform the marriage of a couple I had not counseled. The purpose of this time of reflection together was not to tell them what they were getting into. How would I know that? My goal was to help them think about marriage as Christians. We talked about marriage as living out the implications of their baptism. I asked them how their marriage would support and encourage their vocation to discipleship.

What would it mean for me as a pastor to prepare the people of my congregation for retirement? The most successful retirement is premeditated in order to take full advantage of a recent privilege of a small portion of humanity. How can the church help folks think about retirement as Christians? As a preacher, my job is "to equip the saints [of any age] for the work of [all sorts of] ministry" (Eph. 4:12 NRSV). A main means of equipping is preaching, week in and week out, forming people whose faith in Christ enables them to negotiate the challenges of following Jesus. Through preaching, the Christian story is laid over our stories; we learn to look at life through the lens of Scripture. We thereby think like Christians, radically reframing words such as *freedom*, *dependency*, and *control* in light of Jesus Christ and his mission.

After the death of her husband, which was preceded by the deaths of both of her parents, a woman said to me, "I never noticed how much of Scripture is concerned with the plight of widows and orphans. Now that I'm both widowed and orphaned, I'm a more astute Christian than I was before. Life shoved me to the center of the Christian faith."

As I moved toward retirement, I received invitations from my bank and my employer to participate in preretirement planning. All these seminars focused on financial management. Why didn't my church gather some of us to think like Christians about this life transition?

As a pastor, I always convened my graduating high school seniors for an evening of pizza and discussion of the topic "Being Christian in College." That evening I unashamedly offered them "Rules for Staying Christian on Campus." I asked them, "What information, insights, or support do you need from your church as you launch forth into college?" I suggested that they promise God and themselves that they would read the Bible at the same time each day, pray daily, join a campus Christian group, keep in touch with their pastor during their first days in college, and so forth. Why didn't I convene my senior church members and instigate a similar conversation about their impending retirements?

Part of the pain of aging is being disconnected from the rituals that gave our lives meaning and order. In a period of life with many transitions, the patterned, predictable, purposeful ritual life of the church

can take on greater meaning for us. Can't the church do better than the world's sorry rituals for retirement?[22] When students left for college or on a family's last Sunday as part of our congregation before they moved, we ended the service with a time of blessing in which we formally bid farewell and Godspeed and then laid on hands. Why didn't we do something similar to bid people into the adventure and the tasks of retirement? When someone in my church was thrown into the tasks of bereavement, I would routinely visit them in their home to see if I could be of help. Why didn't I pay them a pastoral visit when they retired from their work to hold them accountable to their vocation?

A SERMON

Here is a sermon I preached some years ago in an attempt to help my congregation think about retirement in a specifically biblical, Christian way.

Retirement: A Whole New Life[23]

> Vanity of vanities, says the Teacher.
>   . . . All is vanity.
> What do people gain from all the toil
>   at which they toil under the sun?
> A generation goes, and a generation comes,
>   but the earth remains forever.
> . . . .
>   There is nothing new under the sun. (Eccles. 1:2–4, 9 NRSV)

Then I saw a new heaven and a new earth, for the first heaven and the first earth had passed away, and the sea was no more. . . . And the one who was seated on the throne said, "See, I am making all things new." (Rev. 21:1, 5)

My text is from Ecclesiastes, one of the Bible's most depressing, cynical books. "Vanity of vanities, says the Teacher. . . . All is vanity."

Have you ever felt like that, looking back on your life? Your accomplishments crumble in your hands as dust. Your great achievements appear as so much chasing after the wind.

No wonder the writer of Ecclesiastes feels this way about his life. "There is nothing new under the sun," he says. Life is just one thing after another, a great wheel in which there is no beginning and no end. Life is, in Shakespeare's words, full of "sound and fury, signifying nothing."[24] Ecclesiastes is one of the only books in the Bible with a cyclical view of history. History doesn't begin or end; it's not going anywhere. History is a great cycle, a circle. There is nothing new under the sun. When there is no ending or beginning, no real newness, life is depressing.

Everyone here will, some of you sooner than later, in some fashion, retire. Let's talk about retirement. I have a problem right from the start. When I preach, I like to preach from the Bible, take a biblical text and work from there. Trouble is, only recently did humanity live long enough or accumulate enough goods to "retire" in our sense of the word. The Bible, particularly the Hebrew Scripture, considers old age, a long life, a great gift of God. But retirement, what to do with our old age or our now widespread long lives, is a relatively recent problem.

I'm unhappy with the word *retirement*. It's a cousin of similarly uninspiring words like *retreat, remove, regress*. Retirement makes it sound as if, in our last years of life, we withdraw from the fray, settle in, settle down, quit moving, quit living, for all intents and purposes. Yet we're learning that each stage of life has its challenges, its different demands and new adventures, including retirement.

I recall a student whom I was teaching in seminary. He was serving his first little church as a student pastor. One day he complained to me about his congregation. "The median age of my congregation is over sixty," he declared. "And you know how old people are."

"How are they?" I asked.

"You know—set in their ways, creatures of habit, slow to change, stuck in their ruts. They don't want any innovation or change in the church."

Not two days before I had read an article on retirement that noted that, of the six or eight most difficult transitions you must make in

life, the most traumatic changes, four or five of them will occur after sixty-five. Transitions like declining health, loss of independence, unemployment, and the loss of a spouse are among the major moves of this last stage of life.

I noted this information to the young student pastor, adding, "Which suggests that it's not fair to say that these older people are refusing to change. They are drowning in some of the most dramatic changes in life. When you've buried the man you have lived with for forty years, or you are forced out of your life work, about the last thing you want is to come to church and have some upstart young preacher say, 'Let's do something new and innovative this morning.' They're sinking in a flood of innovation!"

Bury the woman you lived with for forty years, wake up the next morning unmarried, that's innovation aplenty.

We once thought of adulthood as that time in life when you at last put down roots, hunkered down, burrowed in for the rest of your life, and stayed put. The really important developmental events occurred in infancy, childhood, or youth. We now know that adulthood is best construed as a series of passages (thank you, Gail Sheehy), of shifting challenges that are far from stable.

For some years I have taught a course to first-year students at Duke called "The Search for Meaning." We study the ways various people have found meaning in their lives, a reason to get out of bed in the morning. Students are pushed to articulate their own sense of meaning in life, to write down where they are headed and who they plan to be when they grow up.

I have noted that most of them think to themselves, "I'm all confused and in flux now, but when I am twenty-five, I will have decided who I want to be. I'll settle down, settle in, buy a minivan, vote a certain way, and be fixed forever."

Life is not like that. For instance, I note how odd it is for us to ask students, "What do you plan to do when you graduate from Duke?"

They respond with a sense of finality: "I'm going to be an electrical engineer." Or "I'm going into medicine."

But then we note that the average American goes through *seven* job changes in a lifetime. Someone from the Engineering School told

me the other day that they did a study of their graduates and only 30 percent of them were in engineering twenty years after graduation!

See my point? These students had better be preparing for a more challenging life than merely figuring out what they want to do for the rest of their lives and expecting to stay in that job, fixed with that identity for the rest of their lives.

Is that why increasing numbers of educators are coming to speak of intelligence not in terms of IQ, a fixed intellectual quotient in you since birth, but rather intelligence as *the ability to adapt*? Life is this long series of adaptations, moves, changes, beginnings, and endings, some of them precipitated by the changing state of our bodies, some due to cultural shifts, and some due to the machinations of a living God.

As a pastor, I've watched a good number of people move into retirement. I'm on my way there myself. And though, from what I've observed, there are a number of challenges in the allegedly "golden years," one stands out above all the rest: *retirement is a whole new life*. I'm here paraphrasing from a great book by my friend Reynolds Price, *A Whole New Life*.[25] It's Reynolds's moving account of his struggle through cancer surgery, recovery, and beyond. What Reynolds has to say there is too rich to be condensed, but it's fair to say that one of the most important insights of the book, and the insight that lends to the book's title, is that Reynolds experienced his illness as an invitation to a whole new life.

Reynolds tells how he denied the existence of his cancer, how he was filled with anger and resentment when he realized that he was very sick, and how he struggled in the painful months after his debilitating but life-saving surgery. Here was a once robust, active man, at the prime of his life, the peak of his career, reduced to life in a wheelchair.

But Reynolds depicts his path back as a dawning realization that, in his words, "The old Reynolds has died."[26] His old self was gone. So many of the aspects of his former existence that he loved were gone. He could not get them back. Now he was faced with a choice: he could spend the rest of his life in grief for what he had lost, pitifully attempting to salvage bits and pieces and cobble a life together from the leftovers, or he could begin "a whole new life."

Reynolds chose the latter. He began again. He started over. It was not the life he might have chosen, if he were doing the choosing, but it was a good life, a life worth living. He now enjoys his greatest period of artistic productivity, turning out more novels, plays, and poems than ever.

"Find your way to be somebody else," he advises, "the next viable you— a stripped-down whole other clear-eyed person, realistic as a sawed-off shotgun and thankful for air, not to speak of the human kindness you'll meet if you get normal luck."

Retirement is rarely as traumatic as spinal cancer. Yet I do think there are analogies to be made. From what I've observed, the people who fail miserably at the challenges of the later years are those who are unable to see retirement as a definite transition from one plane of existence to another. They attempt to salvage too much of their former life and drag that along with them into their next life.

I'm haunted by what a woman told me of her mother. Her mother had worked at minimum wage in a garment factory for over forty years. When she retired, her children thought she would be thrilled. She was miserable. She cried. She hung around at the gate of the factory many mornings, vainly hoping they would call her back to work. She even took an assumed name and tried to get hired, representing herself as another person.

That won't work. Your old life goes on without you. They somehow get by down at the office without your services. The school doesn't fall apart after your last day in the classroom.

You can't get the old life back. You need to lay hold of a whole new life. I think those of us who are moving toward retirement (and isn't that just about everyone here?) could do much more to prepare ourselves to make that transition to a whole new life. If our only life is our work, we are in big trouble unless we can find some new life after work. For Christians, to be retired is not to be unemployed or out of work. We can retire from being a paving contractor or a dishwasher, but we can't retire from discipleship. Churches could do a better job of helping our members to prepare themselves and to support one another during the transition into retirement.

My mother taught school twelve months a year. She had time to participate in church only on Sunday mornings. While some of

her friends had time to partake of bridge clubs and go to church meetings, she was too busy. From time to time she expressed disdain for those who had nothing better to do than sit around and play bridge.

When my mother retired, she worried about her new life. What would she do with her time? She took up bridge. She began volunteering at church. Her fear of retirement was replaced by gratitude for the gift of time to use as she pleased rather than at the behest of others.

"I'm living the life of leisure I secretly envied in others," she said.

We need better rituals for retirement. In Japan, for instance, there is a tradition in which, when a woman reaches retirement age, she takes all of her pots and pans and presents them to her daughter or daughter-in-law. From then on, she is expected not to enter the kitchen. That part of her life is over. A new life has begun.

Many Japanese men begin retirement by dressing in a red kimono and doing something adventuresome that they have not done before, like climbing Mount Fuji. People need to be encouraged to do something visible and physical that symbolizes their important transition.[28]

Thomas Naylor and I wrote a book arising out of our first-year student seminar called *The Search for Meaning*.[29] To our surprise and delight, a number of churches have reported using the book in congregational preretirement seminars. We're delighted that the book we wrote with college freshmen in mind has proven to be helpful for those in their sixties. We are reminded that one of the most important skills one can have is the ability to take a deep breath, to look out over one's life as it was, and to start over with a whole new life.

As Christians, we do not believe that history is a meaningless cycle going nowhere, one damned or blessed thing after another. We believe that God is Alpha and Omega, the Beginning and the End. God not only gets us going at the beginning but also meets us at the end. More to the point of the challenges of retirement, God gives fresh beginnings, new days, and new lives. The Bible opens with the Genesis declaration, "Let there be light!" as a new world comes into being and, as today's Scripture has reminded us, closes with the Revelation, "Behold, I make all things new!"

Between here and there, we are asked to make many transitions, each with their attendant pain, uncertainty, and promise. One of the most important of our life transitions is retirement.

My father-in-law spent his entire life as a pastor in a variety of United Methodist churches in South Carolina. Carl Parker had thus lived much of his life in black suits and white shirts playing the role of moral exemplar of the community, doing his duty in the week-in-week-out care of his churches.

When he retired, he bought a camping trailer, and he and Mrs. Parker pulled the little trailer toward New England for a long-awaited retirement celebration trip. Somehow, on the way from South Carolina to New England, he took a wrong turn and found himself driving down the middle of Manhattan, pulling that trailer, lost, not knowing which way to turn.

A car blew its horn at him, pulled up beside him, and the driver shouted, "Old man, I wish you would figure out where you're going or get out of the way!"

Mr. Parker said that he paused and thought to himself, "I'm not going to get out of the way. Don't know which turn to take. I'm a Methodist preacher. But I'm all the way up here in New York, a long way from South Carolina. Nobody here knows that I used to be a Methodist preacher. I'm retired."

So Mr. Parker rolled down his window, looked over at the man in the car beside him, and said, "I already know where I'm going, and I wish you would go to hell!"

Retirement. It's a whole new life.

FOUR

Successful Aging

As a child I loved a little yellow book, *Ponce de Leon and the Fountain of Youth*, the story of a Spaniard who set forth to find the storied fountain of perpetual youth. Instead of everlasting, undying paradise, Ponce discovered Florida.

The Third Pill, a BBC radio drama by James O'Neill, presents Greg, who is late-middle-aged, feeling out of touch, and afflicted with aches and pains.[1] An advertisement pops up on Greg's computer telling about a medical experiment that reverses the aging process. Greg enrolls and begins the trial treatments, and the dark comedy begins. With one pill Greg's gray hair returns to its earlier brunette color. His coworkers comment on Greg's increased energy and output. His wife notices that the wrinkles have disappeared from his face and that Greg has new romantic vitality.

Greg takes another pill and begins again to listen to hard rock music. He buys a motorcycle. When his colleagues at work say that his office cubicle is a mess, Greg quarrels with them and whines, "Why is everybody picking on me?"

When he shows up to take the third pill, the doctors refuse, saying that Greg has already knocked years off his life and that the third dose could be dangerous. Greg throws a tantrum and petulantly demands to be given the third dose of the elixir of youth. The researchers acquiesce. When Greg's fellow employees go to the office the next day,

they are horrified to find a squeaky voiced child of six or eight years old sitting at Greg's desk, kicking the furniture and littering the floor with candy wrappers.

The drama ends when a doctor tells Greg's wife, after her yearly physical, "No, it's not cancer. You're pregnant."

Do we really want a pain-free fountain of youth? Contrary to our fantasies and the claims of pharmaceutical and cosmetic advertisements, there is no everlasting youthfulness. About the best we can hope for is successful aging.

What is "success" at seventy?

Christiane Northrup, MD, urges aging women to aim for nothing less than divinity, a claim that would have confounded even Ponce de Leon. Here are Northrup's dubious "Tips for Becoming the Ageless Goddess You Are Meant to Be."[2]

Tip 1: "Reframe the term aging. Aging is generally used to describe the process of deterioration and decline. . . . Dr. Mario Martinez says, 'Growing older is inevitable, aging is optional.' Pay attention to the words you use when you speak about growing older."

My translation: If you don't talk about aging, it won't happen.

Tip 2: "Update your beliefs. Your beliefs are far stronger than your genes. . . . For example, do you believe that After 40 it's all downhill or All the good men are already taken or You can't have great sex after age 50? Until you bring these beliefs to consciousness, they can adversely affect your biology."

In other words, if you refuse to believe you are old, you aren't.

Tip 3: "Age Proof Yourself NOW! The physical effects that we cumulatively call 'aging' . . . can be prevented by lifestyle choices."

Really? Although a healthier lifestyle is a good idea at any age, no matter what you eat, the death rate still runs 100 percent.

Tip 4: "Stop trash talking about age. And stop blaming your health problems on your age. Your body believes every word you say. . . . I suggest that 21 be your last 'milestone' birthday. If you don't tell your body your age, it won't know."

Our bodies are not that dumb. Usually, your body is the first to know that you are old.

Tip 5: "Resolve to get younger next year. There is a huge difference between biologic (the age of your cells) and chronologic age (the age on your driver's license). By implementing lifestyle improvements, you can quite literally reverse the clock and grow biologically younger. . . . Live agelessly! When you embrace the innate vitality of an Ageless Goddess, your body and spirit will reflect it for the world to see."

And they call Christians naive and credulous!

Inane Optimism, Barren Pessimism

Fear of aging encourages self-deceit. Woody Allen defined old age as "about ten years older than I am now." (Allen also purportedly said, "I recently turned sixty. Practically a third of my life is over.") While no grave damage may be done to those who laugh at Allen's wit or who gullibly embrace Dr. Northrup's self-deceiving, goofy pop-paganism (peddling age-defying fantasies has made her famous), *Christians* thinking about aging will avoid the seductive lure of both inane optimism and barren nihilism. Self-deception—whether dishonest cheerfulness or paralyzing pessimism—may be particularly tempting in old age. Still, if you're a truth-loving Christian who would settle for success in aging that's short of divinity, read on!

Advice on successful aging has a long history. In the first century BCE, Cato the Elder gave guidance to his younger comrades in Cicero's *On Aging*:

> Friends, we should resist old-age; we should compensate for its defects by watchful care; we should fight against it, as we would fight against a disease; . . . we should do regular moderate exercise; and we should eat and drink just enough to replenish our strength, not so much as to crush it. Nor, indeed, should we give our attention only to the body. Much great care should be given to the intellect and the mental facilities. For they too, like lamps, grow dim with time, unless we keep them supplied with oil.[3]

We can give "watchful care" to our aging by overcoming misconceptions and prejudices about cognitive decline among the aged, such

as misconceptions that older people have less brain capacity, suffer from diminished brain power, are slow to learn new things, and are forgetful.

There are also unproven generalizations about physical factors, such as that older people have mobility problems, suffer from poor eyesight, and are deaf.

Add to these lists the misconceptions about the attitudes of the elderly, such as that older people live in the past and abhor change, have lost interest in today's world and current trends, are frightened to go out, and are distrustful of others.[4]

Successful aging involves embracing the realities of aging without accepting false generalizations. In their book *Successful Aging*, gerontologists J. W. Rowe and R. L. Kahn offer a number of myths that have been disproven by current research.

1. To be old is to be sick.
2. You can't teach an old dog new tricks.
3. The horse is out of the barn—meaning it is too late to reduce the risk of disease and disability or to reap the salubrious effects of exercise.
4. The secret to successful aging is to choose your parents wisely.
5. The lights might be on, but the voltage is low—implying that older people suffer from inadequate mental capacities.
6. The elderly don't pull their own weight and are a drain on the economy. (This ignores the over three million home care laborers who are mostly unpaid and constantly on call, to say nothing of the millions of aging who are the backbone of volunteer programs. Then there are the many competent elderly who are excluded from the workforce, even though they would rather continue to work.)[5]

Rowe and Kahn define successful aging as "avoidance of disease and disability, maintenance of physical and cognitive function, and active engagement with life."[6] What is missing from Rowe and Kahn's threefold definition? Christian gerontologists James Houston and Michael Parker add a fourth category: "positive spiritual growth and development."[7]

Sometimes critics of ageism replace stereotypes of the elderly as brittle, conservative, detached, senile, poor, and sick with currently popular (and equally false) stereotypes—older couples jumping out of airplanes or bouncing along zip lines. These positive stereotypes too easily privilege the affluent elderly over the impoverished elderly and tend to deny the realities of aging. They come with an incipient demand that all aging people be robust, sexually active, vigorous, self-reliant, and frenetically recreational—that is, old people should be young. The health of the young is handed to the old as an assignment, a fantasy of the good life they must strive to make reality. The aging must surf the web and submit to experts (like Dr. Northrup), must become active participants in refusing to age, should regard aging as their worst enemy, or must buy their way into elegant retirement settings that confirm their breathless pursuit of an "active lifestyle." Grim pessimism gives way to an unrealistic optimism that fails to see elderhood as a God-given form of life with its own trials and benefits.[8]

Because we live in a scientific, mechanistic culture, there is a tendency to view aging as a problem to be solved or as a plea for better social policy. Therefore, we focus on questions of when and how older people ought to move out of the labor pool and how we can avoid poverty, prevent disease, and work the health care system to our advantage.

While Christianity is an incarnational faith—physical and fiscal concerns are valid—the Christian faith has more interests than the merely material. Framing discussions of old age in a simply naturalistic way testifies to our lack of scriptural imagination. One of the gifts of the church is to stoke, fund, and fuel our imaginations. In approaching aging as an exclusively materialistic or social policy problem to be solved, we separate chronological aging from any larger story within which to make sense of elderhood and become sidetracked by debates over means without thoughtful consideration of ultimate ends. As Christians we have a grander narrative that fits our aging lives into an account that's larger than ourselves and sets our little selves within the pageant of God's vocation for us and God's salvation of the world.

Into Aging with a Truthful Story

Arthur Frank says that our imaginations are gripped by a myth that
determines our views of health care: "I was in health yesterday. Today
I am temporarily sick, but after medical intervention, tomorrow I'll
be healthy once again."[9] Aging rebukes this myth. Not everyone who
is ill gets well; aging often comes with chronic pain and illnesses.
Then there's the problem of death's inevitability.

Here's a more truthful account of health: everyone who is well
today can count on being sick sometime in the future, and anyone
who recovers from an illness will, sooner or later, have more illness
and probably more pain, and, even if they don't, everyone dies. Because many of the physically debilitating aspects of aging cannot be
"fixed," the "I was in health, then I got sick, but tomorrow I'll be fixed
and healthy again" story is a fantasy that plays into our self-deceit
about the omnipotence of modern science and medicine. Aging is
not an illness, a tragedy, or a problem awaiting a solution; aging is
the price we pay for life, which is a greater gift than we deserve.

Poet A. R. Ammons, reflecting on aging, admits, "The people of
my time are passing away . . . well, we never thought we would live
forever (although we did) and now it looks like we won't."[10] So if we
can't live forever, what is our story?

The Christian faith is based on a story more truthful than the fairy
tales of the world. We Christians claim that the scriptural narrative
of the death and resurrection of Jesus Christ gives us a means for
making sense of our lives. Rather than the "I was in health, then I got
sick, but tomorrow I'll be fixed and healthy again" fantasy, Christians
learn a story that goes something like this:

> God gave me the precious gift of life. My life is on loan from God.
> Even more valuable than my life, God in Christ called me, gave me a
> vocation to discipleship, whereby my life is caught up in the purposes
> of God and I am utilized by God in God's salvation of humanity. I am
> not a god or an immortal angel; I am a finite being, an animal who is
> subject to the limitations of being a creature who is not the Creator.
> My life is not my own. I live on borrowed breath. The eternal signifi-
> cance and sustenance of my life is up to God and not to me. While
> I have life, in whatever physical or mental condition I find myself, in

whatever circumstances I am cast, I am called to glorify, to serve, and to enjoy God and God's good gifts and to use whatever gifts God has given me in service to the needs of others. Eventually God will take back the life with which God has entrusted me so that I might be given the gift of glorifying and enjoying God forever.

Loss

No matter how good the stories we live by are, we haven't told the truth about aging without speaking of loss as an undeniable, persistent aspect of aging—"sans teeth, sans eyes, sans taste, sans everything." While losses can be experienced throughout life, they greatly accumulate during our last years. We outlive friends, we are the only surviving sibling, we are forced to move from beloved, predictable places, and we run out of time to accomplish all that we would like to undertake.

Donald Hall tells the truth when he writes, "To grow old is to lose everything."[11] While visiting parishioners in a nursing home, I asked a ninety-two-year-old woman if she would like to have prayer before I left her room. "No," she said. "I'm mad at God. God's taken everything from me but won't take me."

"If only I could walk once more in the street in front of my house in Greenville," sighed another nursing home resident that same day.

By evening, in my study, even I said to myself, "I'm going to run out of Sundays before I do justice to all the Scripture that ought to be preached."

Some losses are necessary in order for us to enter the second half of life with confidence. "We cannot live the afternoon of life according to the program of life's morning," said Carl Jung, "for what was great in the morning will be little at evening, and what in morning was true will at evening have become a lie."[12]

Loss is the risk we take, and sometimes the price we pay, for loving. Loss and loneliness are the twin fruits of love. Losses accumulate, social engagements and supportive people fall by the wayside, the world passes by, and we feel deserted. Most of the downsizing we experience in aging is involuntary, making our losses even more difficult to bear. Friends depart. Familiar landmarks disappear. If a

spouse or partner dies, we fear it might be said of us, "She died from a broken heart."

Yet suffering loss can reposition us to receive something else. I have seen widows move from deep grief over the death of a husband to renewed self-worth.

"Who knows? Maybe now I'm more me than my old married me," a woman said a year after her husband's death.

As we learned when we downsized and moved into a much smaller home in our sixties, some losses can be unburdening, joyfully letting go of superfluous accumulation. Forgiveness is a kind of loss, but many Christians testify that such faithful loss can be joyful release.

The presence of others who continue to love and care for us, even in our loss, is of inestimable value in helping us to live through our assorted bereavements and, to some degree, to reintegrate and go on. God has made us for relationship, and the pain of the loss of relationships is often best assuaged by other relationships. When someone says, "We joined this church because everyone here was so warm and friendly," that's not an inappropriate reason for church.

In delivering Meals on Wheels, one quickly discovers it's not the meal but the visit that brings the recipient the most nourishment.

Because the major narrative of aging involves loss and decline, this narrative can stifle our determination to see opportunities as we age. Aging, and our bleak stories about it, may be a source of the storied midlife crisis. No wonder some have a disorienting crisis at midlife when they're being told that they are now moving inexorably toward the worst time of their lives.[13] Judging from research into people's reports of happiness, it's more difficult to be forty than to be seventy, perhaps because of the looming grim prospect of aging. Surprisingly, reported life satisfaction actually begins to rise after fifty. It's easier to attend your fiftieth college reunion than your twentieth.

Amid the losses attendant upon aging, we have to find a way to, in effect, write a new chapter in our biography. Speaking more theologically, we must embrace the story that God is writing with our lives, learning to love the plot that is taking an unexpected or even undesired turn. Gerontologist James Woodward says that a key to negotiating the realities of aging is to move from an impossible desire for liberation *from* old age (Dr. Northrup and her ageless goddess)

to a joyful embrace of the liberation *of* old age (the Nightblooming Jazzmen).[14] While there are losses in aging, finding a special sort of freedom is possible. We can be liberated from fantasies of eternal usefulness and indispensability to the world and from the misconception of the impossibility of a meaningful last stage in life. Old age can be received as a gift of freedom from an overly self-conscious youth or the rigorous constraints and responsibilities of middle age.

Can we, by faith, come to say, "The LORD gave, and the LORD has taken away; blessed be the name of the LORD" (Job 1:21 NRSV)? Can the Christian faith and its master story give us the means of narrating our lives as, "The Lord gave me one sort of life, but living a long life has meant that much of my earlier life has been taken away, so now the Lord is giving me a new life"?

Aging Bodies

The human body grows up, degenerates, and declines. Aging entails predictable bodily constraints. Research indicates that the brains of healthy older adults continue to work well but more slowly; our brains do not process information as swiftly, and our reflection time increases. These changes in brain functioning may account for why it seems as if time moves faster while we are moving slower. There is also a documentable loss of flexibility in solving problems and thinking about alternatives—aging negatively affects the brain's ability to modify approaches to problems or to easily adapt to unexpected changes in life—and a reduced capacity for multitasking. Most of us older adults note that we have slower recovery from physical or mental exertion and from surgery or illness. We more quickly and more frequently sense fatigue. Yet slower brain functioning does not mean mental incapacity.

In spite of decreased adaptability in problem solving, we aged can take heart that it is possible to teach an old dog new tricks because successful aging requires behavioral change. Aging bodies offer us the possibility to correct our disembodied, docetic theologies and to embrace the embodied, incarnational nature of the Christian faith. A refusal to disparage or to deny physical realities or to paper them over with superficial gnostic sentimentality is a gift of the theology

of incarnation. Because God Almighty took on our aging flesh, we can joyfully adapt to bodily, fleshly limits as well.

You don't have to be an adaptive, innovative person at heart to age successfully, but it helps. As someone cheerfully told me after her mobility and independence were ended following a bad fall, "I am now adapting to a revised lifestyle."

Among the physiological changes of aging are a decrease in cellular water content along with an increase in fat cells in relation to muscle cells, leading to less muscle mass and decreased elasticity; a reduction in bone mass and minerals, making bones more brittle and raising the risk of fractures; and deterioration in the range, flexibility, and composition of surfaces and joints, increasing the likelihood of inflammation, fractures, and arthritis.[15] Changes in the cardiovascular system greatly impact the health of some older adults. These biological changes account for a sense of diminishment in physical abilities among the aging, but they also mean that even modest physical activity has great benefit for the aging body.

"Have you had a fall in the last three months?" has become the standard first question put to me at the beginning of any medical exam, even a dermatological checkup. Falls are the leading cause of fatal and nonfatal injuries in older adults. More than eight hundred thousand older adults are hospitalized each year due to injuries from falls. Mortality rates from fall-related injuries are estimated to be as high as 20 to 30 percent. Fear of falling is a significant cause of older adult inactivity.[16]

In speaking of the physical, bodily aspects of aging, we are not veering from our goal of thinking like Christians. In Christ, God became embodied in our always aging human flesh. Jesus Christ experienced our fleshly suffering and temptations in every way (Heb. 4:15) with a notable exception—the sufferings and temptations attendant with life after thirty-three.

Should we regard the physiological changes in our aging bodies as restraints and disabilities, or should we see them as predictable aspects of being over sixty-five? James Woodward finds it interesting that when asked, "How is your health?" the majority of older adults judge themselves to be "healthy," even though they are often less healthy than at any other time in their lives. Perhaps these adults have successfully

expanded and adapted their notions of health. They have learned that a decline in physical abilities is not necessarily connected to a decline in other abilities, that decline is not synonymous with cessation.

"I can still go anywhere I really need or want to go," quipped a septuagenarian as he hobbled up the church steps, "with the exception of Mount Everest."

Concepts like health and wellness are complex, multidimensional, and sometimes even contradictory. "Good health" looks different for different people. Sometimes our notions of wellness are merely a commentary on the wiles of life in a consumerist society that tells us it's possible to buy our way into a life worth living. Woodward says that it's futile to attempt to deny or fend off old age, to defy the inevitable changes in identity that aging entails. However, he also believes that we can come to a place where we can embrace physical changes as part of who we are.[17] Can God give us the grace to see our aging bodies and minds not as cruel biological fate but as God-ordained ways of being human?

We aging can take heart that medical research indicates that physical decline related to aging may not be as steep as we once thought and that a number of measures can be taken to minimalize or at least delay debility. These steps can be beneficial in slowing the deleterious effects of bodily aging: calorie reduction (fewer calories for the body to process), exercise (any is better than none), a nontoxic environment (eliminate smoking, alcohol, and a fall-prone setting), management of stress, and ingestion of more fruits and green vegetables and less meat, salt, and sugar.

Older adults are wise to be suspicious of some of the (seemingly monthly) announcements of dramatic benefits to be had through various dietary measures. There is no conclusive scientific evidence of the benefits of antioxidants. While celiac disease is a serious disorder, many who do not have celiac disease believe that restricting gluten makes them feel better, though there is little scientific evidence for other conditions of gluten intolerance. The placebo effect is real. If eating kale makes you feel better, by all means, eat kale.

Remember Geritol? There is no scientific evidence that it helps those who drink it daily, and yet thousands continue to believe it helps.

As far back as the 1930s, a rat study found that rats who were fed half of the calories fed to other rats did better in all aspects of aging (except for wound healing and viruses). Many researchers believe that a reduction in calorie intake is the single most important factor in extending longevity in laboratory animals, but few physicians believe it's a realistic strategy for humans.[18] We'll never know if dietary restriction dramatically helps human aging—humans lack the willpower for a dramatic, voluntary reduction of calories, and as Scripture teaches (Gen. 3:6), we tend to succumb to food temptations. The best advice seems to be that for all post-middle-age adults, fewer calories, achieved through eating less or brief bouts of fasting, is a good idea.

Normal, predictable aging will not be defied. The internet is full of wild but scientifically unsubstantiated assertions of the discovery of *the* nutritional key to halting the ravages of time. Aging cannot be defeated, only somewhat resisted, so it is wise to beware of exaggerated claims regarding the benefits of super foods.

Exercise positively impacts senior bodies and minds, but it is not magic. Regular, sensible exercise does not seem to affect longevity but does improve the quality of life in the aged. Physical debility is accelerated by disuse of our bodies. Exercise can't control or stop aging; however, exercise can lessen the slope and the speed of physical and mental decline.

The goal in regard to diet and exercise should not be an increase in longevity but rather an augmentation of healthy years and a concomitant decrease in sick years. Sickness is a more significant factor in longevity even than exercise. If we cured cancer, we could add three to four years to Americans' longevity; a heart disease cure would win us an additional six to seven years. Here's an incentive for longevity: people who live past ninety tend to consume fewer health resources, go into nursing care only at the very end of their lives, and depart quickly.[19]

Stress can have negative health consequences for the aged, but a lack of all stress, leading to social, physical, and mental inactivity, can be deleterious. Relieving the aged of all sources of stress isn't wise, particularly the stress that is induced through normal interaction with others. Stress—if rightly managed and seen as encouragement

to keep moving, to keep contributing, and to keep relating to others—can be beneficial.

"Having to raise my two grandchildren, even when I'm sixty, has added a decade to my life, whether I wanted it or not," said a grandmother recently. She may be right.

You've perhaps heard of some of the interesting research on brain plasticity, the way the brain develops and responds to changing contexts and demands placed on it. It's important to note that brain studies show that brain development can continue into old age.[20] But this does not occur without stimulation. Beneficial stimulation is more than playing brain-training games, which have yet to show much positive effect. The best brain stimulation comes from having connections with and responsibilities for others, as does the grandmother whose brain is forced to help her raise her two grandchildren—whether she wanted to or not—or the church members who must, "Be tolerant with each other and, if someone has a complaint against anyone, forgive each other. As the Lord forgave you, so also forgive each other" (Col. 3:13), whether they want to or not.

Woodward closes his book with practical advice on how to achieve successful aging: learn something new, take the opportunity to be someone different, prepare for death.[21]

Do you note anything missing from Woodward's steps to successful aging? God.

For Christians, the major goad to successful aging is active discipleship, fulfillment of our vocation, service, and Sabbath-like connection with God. The church shouldn't be in the business of promoting excessive self-concern; that is well stoked in this culture without help from the church. Instead, the church should neither excuse anyone from active witness to the faith nor treat the normal aches and pains of aging as if they were an injustice or a form of martyrdom.

The church must teach people of all ages to see older adults as a God-given resource.[22] For the young who have not experienced the joy of taking responsibility for the needs of anyone else, caring for the aged can be an aspect of God's vocation. For the aging, an increase of years can be seen as an opportunity God offers us to enjoy some of life's blessings that we may earlier have neglected, an occasion for us to witness to all God's people that Jesus Christ can be faithfully

served in any season of life, even in a time replete with physical decline, pain, and ill health.

Gray hair is often seen as a sign of wisdom. I once read a story about a young actor who was asked why she wanted to be in a film directed by a ninety-year-old. She replied with something like, "Clint Eastwood's wrinkles and weathered face show how much life has taught him."

Studies of aging highlight the importance of cultivating a positive frame of mind. Of course positive thinking cannot compensate for the ill effects of poverty, pain, or poor physical or mental health in old age. That's one of my misgivings about Richard Rohr's popular *Falling Upward*. Rohr's cheerful self-help book on aging makes successful aging mostly a matter of an upbeat mental attitude. He thus panders to a desire for personal control. "No one can keep you from the second half of your own life but yourself. Nothing can inhibit your second journey except your own lack of courage, patience, and lack of imagination. Your second journey is all yours to walk or to avoid."[23] Norman Vincent Peale *redivivus*.

Telling myself the lie that I'm a seventy-year-old with a twenty-five-year-old body and brain, far from helping me negotiate the challenges of aging, makes me feel as if any of my discomfort with aging is my own fault, a failure to achieve a positive attitude.

An exclusively affirmative depiction of aging, with praise for the energetic and good-humored elderly as exemplars of successful aging, ought to be chastened by admission that a blissful old age is often dependent on material and situational factors for which the cheerful elderly can take little credit and that are not enjoyed by the majority of their aging cohort. For a Christian to be too cheerful about life may be evidence of a disregard for the plight of those who have not been blessed with health and wealth.[24]

For those who would like a less moralistic, more realistic take on life's "second journey," I commend Mary Sarton's powerful though bleak little novel, *As We Are Now*. Sarton's character Caroline Spencer, who at seventy-six is consigned by her family to a "home," rages like Lear that she is in nothing more than a concentration camp for the old.[25] Caroline speaks of aging as a journey that is like visiting a strange, unknown land that isn't understood until one gets there.

Rohr's talk of the second journey being all ours to walk or to avoid is the message that we independent, affluent, control-loving, privileged persons love to hear. We enjoy thinking of ourselves as capable of overcoming all life's obstacles by our sheer grit, overlooking how much of our agency and independence has been given to us through our economic, educational, and social privileges rather than through our personal virtues. As Christians, we are who we are in part as a gift of God. We are God's people. The church is curiously missing from Rohr's book.

Rohr paints a rosy picture of the second half of life as a serene time when we wise and magnanimous people allow our basic goodness to flourish, leaving behind those sour elderly who have a bad attitude. He speaks of the second half of life (a phrase he picked up from Jung) as the "crowning" time of life, a summit from which we look down with charity and magnanimity on all with a bright, luminous gaze. It's easier to think of old age as the crowning time of life if one is not completely dependent on the beneficence of the Social Security system.

Yet in fairness to Rohr's positive thinking, much evidence shows that even people with physical and financial disabilities can be helped by the cultivation of a positive general disposition. A key factor in happiness is having a modicum of control over one's life and some sense of independence and agency. Though we don't have complete control over our finances or our health, we do have some modicum of management of our attitude. If Rohr is right that frame of mind and general disposition can make a difference in how we go through aging, then the church—a place where our imaginations are stoked and funded and where our inclinations and desires are formed, re-formed, and cultivated—surely has a role to play, which must be the reason why Rohr's work is so widely embraced by my own church.

The Grant Study

In 1947 researchers began the Grant Study by studying men who graduated from Harvard in 1948. (Only men were at Harvard then.) Then researchers returned to these subjects throughout the course of their lives and thereby produced our most thorough and important

longitudinal study of college-educated men. George Vaillant, a widely
published Dartmouth psychiatrist, mined the data from the research
and interviewed the subjects of the Grant Study who were still living—
men now in their eighties—to uncover the factors associated with
successful male aging.[26]

Vaillant defines the goal of successful aging this way: "To . . .
retain human dignity despite the ravages of mortality."[27] As Vaillant
notes, while this is a task for anyone who faces imminent death, the
successfully aging demonstrate that mortal life can be good, right
to the very end.

The Grant Study shows that long marriages are good for emotional
well-being in the last decades of life. Through marriage, Vaillant
theorizes, some of our inherent narcissism is overcome with empathy
and love and our defense mechanisms and social intelligence improve.
Perhaps this validates the church's claim that the best way to love one
another is by making and keeping promises "for better, for worse, for
richer, for poorer, in sickness and in health" in youth or in old age.

Alcoholism is a major detriment to aging bodies, says the Grant
Study, suggesting that the virtue of temperance has a biological
benefit.

The Grant Study notes not only stability but also surprising change
in our personalities as we age. The course of life shapes the self, and
the self shapes life's course. Coping mechanisms enable the aging to
adapt their thinking and feeling in beneficial ways. Old habits and
patterns of relating to others can be modified. A very ambitious and
demanding person may in later life become more serene and reflective. A relatively solitary individual may at last have the time and the
inclination to venture forth into community.

While King Lear reminds us that real personality change is rare in
people of any age, the men of the Grant Study show that some aging
people change their disposition to better align themselves with their
changed circumstances. Sometimes they change because they want
to stay connected with the norms among younger cohorts. They
modify their life patterns to fit in with contemporary lifestyles in
order to maintain links with their children and grandchildren. Vaillant asserts that changing interaction patterns with younger cohorts
can be a major influence on older people. That's another reason why

it is good to be in the church: churches provide the most significant multigenerational interaction opportunities for many of us.

Sometimes aging gives us the freedom to express aspects of our personality that were repressed or set aside because of certain life demands and family responsibilities. The mother who always presented an exemplary, official demeanor to her children may become more accommodating and fun loving in old age. The father who was always away and on the road with his job now has time to be the perfect elementary school volunteer. Adaptability, flexibility, and creativity are not only required to have a successful last quarter of life but also necessary for those who aspire to serve and worship a living God.

Affluence aids successful aging. The Grant Study found marked differences in the last decades of life for the comparatively rich and the relatively poor. The rich live longer than the poor, free of concern about getting by from one day to the next. Queen Elizabeth's long life may be more attributable to her royal financial holdings than to her prudent lifestyle.

Successful aging is linked to intellectual curiosity and growth. Ruel Howe quipped that you don't grow old, rather "when you cease to grow, you are old."[28] A paradox of aging is that, while there is physical decline and multiple loss of abilities, the last decades of life can bring more social engagement and more extensive intellectual interest. Programs such as Road Scholar and OLLI (Osher Lifelong Learning Institute) show that seniors are an expanding, eager market for travel and lifelong learning experiences. Ironically, we older people who are short on future life often have more time for growth and study as well as a greater sense of urgency. "If I'm going to learn more about opera, I need to get started now," said my wife, Patsy, at seventy.

Education is an important factor in aging, not so much because of what is learned, says Vaillant, but because the achievement of a high degree of education demonstrates traits of perseverance and goal setting. Reading interest and fluency contribute to successful aging.[29] A higher education level also adds to positive personal regard.

Politically, liberals negotiate the challenges of aging better than political conservatives, Vaillant claims, because liberals are more

likely to be open to new ideas and to approve of the younger generation's behavior. In the Grant Study, liberals tended to have had highly educated mothers and to have gone to graduate school. They displayed creativity and used sublimation as a defense (diverting an instinctual activity, such as sex, into a higher and more socially productive activity, such as education). While conservatives are cautious of novelty, they make more money, play more sports, and are twice as likely to be religious as liberals, all of which can aid aging.[30]

Vaillant was surprised by factors that were not as important as we might think. Ancestral longevity and genetic inheritance are not as important as popular wisdom suggests ("Choose your parents wisely"). Psychosomatic distress earlier in life neither contributes to nor deters longevity.[31] A high cholesterol count doesn't seem to be important. Even a bleak childhood is not a significant factor in successful aging, according to Vaillant.[32]

Here are the eight factors that *did* predict healthy aging: not being a smoker or stopping smoking while young; an adaptive, coping personality (poor Lear); mature defenses; an absence of alcohol abuse; a healthy weight; a stable marriage; some exercise; and the acquisition of some years of higher education. Vaillant also stresses agency: "Whether we live to a vigorous old age lies not so much in our stars or our genes as in ourselves," a thought that echoes Rohr.[33]

There is an increasing awareness, stimulated by research like the Grant Study, that social factors may be as important for successful aging as physical factors. Stimulation provided by the psychosocial environment has beneficial effects on the elderly. Connection with younger cohorts is important. It is never too soon and never too late to begin the physical, intellectual, and socially connective work required for successful aging.

Aging Out of Control

Throughout Vaillant's work is his recognition, based on the Grant Study, that one of the challenges associated with aging is having to cope with having so much of life out of our control. No matter how hard we try, how careful our eating habits, or how much we study, much of our lives is already determined genetically, physically, and

emotionally, a truth that is particularly unpleasant for Americans who like to think of their lives as personal projects, self-constructions.

From what I have experienced, loss of control due to aging is a greater challenge if a person has (1) been a pastor whose parishioners' affection and friendship were freely offered, (2) been a bishop whose authority and power were bestowed rather than earned, (3) been a writer whose work schedule was at his own discretion, (4) enjoyed good physical and mental health throughout his life, and (5) always had enough money to buy everything he needed and much that he wanted.

Though Vaillant gives short shrift to the role of religion in successful aging, I see a potentially positive effect of the Christian faith on older folks who feel they are losing control over their lives. Think of the Christian life as training in having our lives out of our control. Our lives are not our own. We don't have to self-concoct the significance of our selves. Who we are, what we ought to do, and what we mean are God-given gifts, not personal attainments. There is freedom in answering "What is the significance of the life I've lived?" with "God only knows."

The typical losses of aging, the sense of being out of control, give us the opportunity to recollect Jesus's curious statement that we cannot enter God's realm unless we "turn [our] lives around and become like this little child" (Matt. 18:3). Many of the aging learn that turning back toward the vulnerability and neediness of childhood is not something that we decide; it is what life does to us. Everyone who lives long enough looks small, vulnerable, and out of control someday. That's no fun, but in the words of Jesus, our reduction and diminution place us in range of the kingdom.

Is it any wonder that some older adults attempt to take matters in hand and self-terminate or direct someone else to terminate them?

In his letter to the elderly, Pope John Paul II tackled the issue of euthanasia. The pope lamented that

> in recent years the idea of euthanasia has lost for many people the sense of horror which it naturally awakens in those who have a sense of respect for life. Certainly it can happen that, when grave illness involves unbearable suffering, the sick are tempted to despair and

their loved ones or those responsible for their care feel compelled by
a misguided compassion to consider the solution of "an easy death"
as something reasonable. Here it should be kept in mind that the
moral law allows the rejection of "aggressive medical treatment"[34] and
makes obligatory only those forms of treatment which fall within the
normal requirements of medical care, which in the case of terminal
illness seeks primarily to alleviate pain. But euthanasia, understood as
directly causing death, . . . regardless of intentions and circumstances,
. . . is always an intrinsically evil act, a violation of God's law and an
offence against the dignity of the human person.[35]

Though I'm not so sure that euthanasiasts should be judged so
harshly, it's true that euthanasia can play on the deceit that we are
in charge, that our lives are our possessions to use as we will. The
irony, of course, is that dying is about as out of control as life can
get. Is it in our hands to judge when our lives are no longer worth
living and when our continued living is without meaning to others?
Are we given mastery over how our lives end? The same could be said
about end-of-life directives, meticulous preplanning of funerals, and
the distribution of our legacies. While these practices can be evidence
of a healthy confrontation with our mortality, in what ways do they
give us the illusion of control precisely at the time when we are totally
out of control? Remember Lear!

Nevertheless, as Thomas Moore puts it, "Aging is an activity. It
is something you do, not something that happens. When you age—
active verb—you are proactive. If you really age, you become a better
person. If you simply grow old passively, you get worse. . . . You will
be unhappy as you continue the fruitless fight against time."[36]

Vaillant highlights the ways that mature defenses are an intelligent,
creative way to exercise agency in our lives in spite of our loss of
control. Altruism, anticipation, humor, sublimation, and suppression
of negative feelings make strong, positive contributions to successful
aging. (Vaillant previously wrote a fine book on the importance of
coping mechanisms, The Wisdom of the Ego.[37]) These defenses help
increase our resilience and ability to negotiate life's challenges without propagating the myth that we are in control. Though we can't
control the trials that come our way, we can choose our responses to
the contests presented by our aging.

Regret

The poet T. S. Eliot lists three ills of aging: ills of the body, ills of the world, and ills of the past when one is apt to feel "the rending pain of re-enactment of all that you've done, . . . of things ill done and done to others' harm."[38]

Some older persons are consumed with remorse due to life paths taken and not taken, fractured relationships, and regrettable life choices. Dealing with regret requires deciding how to think about things that shouldn't have been done or should have happened but didn't. The intensity of sorrow is often dependent on the distance between what we would have preferred to have happened in life and what actually happened.

Sometimes the best cure for regret is to introduce ambivalence toward what we would have preferred. The prized achievement that we thought we simply had to obtain can be reframed, viewed in a way that enables us to see that the coveted goal was not so worthy anyway. This introduction of ambivalence acts as a counterweight to the backward, downward tug of regret.

Still, for Christians, the gift God gives us for dealing with regret and remorse is more than the cultivation of ambivalence toward the mistakes we've made. Nearly every Sunday the pastor invites us to "confess our sin to Almighty God," an invitation for everyone to un-burden and leave their regrets at the altar. Jesus commanded us to forgive our enemies, and sometimes our greatest enemy is our vain attempt to live our lives without mistakes and failures.

Learning to Love the Life God Gives

I believe that a fundamental secret of successful aging is learning to affirm the lives God gives us in the face of regret that God didn't give us the lives we thought we needed to live happily. As Rabbi Abraham Heschel put it, aging "is not a defeat but a victory, not a punishment but a privilege."[39]

If you are a goal-oriented person, you are accustomed to post-poning joy and satisfaction into the future. But then you wake up one day and discover that your future is shrinking. More yesterdays

than tomorrows. Successful aging requires finding a way to love our lives today, regardless of whether or not our cherished goals were reached or valued relationships were maintained. Excessive investment in specific life projects can be a setup for sadness. Therefore, many of us must find joy in noninstrumental, goal-less experiences. The pleasure of travel or attendance at parties and athletic events is that they have no higher purpose, no goal other than sheer, gratuitous, momentary, pointless joy.

Aging gives those of us who have goal-oriented, telic personalities the opportunity to become contemplatives. Brilliant John Stuart Mill was a precocious child (he allegedly mastered Greek by age three). In his late twenties, Mill had a nervous breakdown and was forced to find activities unrelated to his ambition. Mill asked himself, "Would achievement of my ambitions make me happy?" He decided that reaching his goals would not lead to contentment. Mill stopped allowing his goals to determine the value of his life and began living in the moment and enjoying himself and the life he had.[40]

In our last decades of life we realize that we are going to miss out on the realization of some of our aspirations and may have to relinquish some of the things we most enjoy. Still, this time in life can be not only a time of simplification and limitation but also a period in which our scope of interests expands and we are given opportunities that we have been previously unable to enjoy. In focusing on the essentials, are we going back to basics or are we moving forward to whom God always wanted us to be? With the freedom given in retirement, some pursue completion of their bucket list. As T. S. Eliot said, "Old men ought to be explorers."[41]

Simplicity can become the elderly's chief virtue. Our lives are often in turmoil because we're busy striving to create, to assemble, and to accumulate. In old age, complex lives can whittle down to the basics; we are free to reclaim the essentials. William May, in his book *The Patient's Ordeal*, says that ritual—a love of the predictable and the familiar—often characterizes the lives of the elderly "not merely because memory lapses into the familiar, repetitive grooves, but because the Pilgrim has at long last, learned to travel light . . . to live by simple truths and simple gifts."[42] The prophet Micah describes the person who focuses on the basics:

He has told you, O mortal, what is good;
   and what does the LORD require of you
but to do justice, and to love kindness,
   and to walk humbly with your God? (6:8 NRSV)

After a guest speaker at our church extolled the joys of divesting ourselves of some of our superfluous material goods and living a simpler lifestyle, one of our older members testified, "I've spent most of my adult life accumulating stuff, collecting, buying, and getting. Then the Lord saw fit to take it away from me, and my life got radically simplified. Now, as I enjoy my little room at the retirement center, I'm surprised by how good it feels. Makes me wonder if this was the simpler life God intended for me all along."

Reflecting on his loss of sexual desire, Sophocles said he felt "like a slave escaped from a cruel master."[43] Aging, when viewed as more than physiological deterioration, can be seen as a peculiar freedom. Sexual desire that jerked us around for so much of our lives may be quelled as we age. We can also find ourselves free of our lust for social status, along with anxieties over prestige or fame, as our drive to impress others or to make a name for ourselves weakens. Free of the weight of many of our adult responsibilities, we may view aging as life's last great adventure and develop a capacity for playfulness. While there's not much research on the benefits of playfulness, what does exist indicates that "playfulness in later life improves cognitive, emotional, social and psychological functioning and healthy aging."[44] At last there's time to devote to a cherished hobby in which we lose ourselves, free of excessive self-concern or the need to be productive. Time to join the Red Hat Society and make up for the sobriety of youth.

"In our first marriages," explained a couple of octogenarians during our premarital counseling session, "we married for love with responsibilities. Now we get to marry just for love."

"Your relationship surpasses even the irresponsible goofiness of teenage love," I said to them. "It's wonderful!"

The Godfather (part 1) ends with the brutal Mafia don, played by Marlon Brando, happily playing games in the garden with his little grandson. Though Don Corleone lived badly, scoundrel though he

was, he got a contented dying anyway. As writer Tom Robbins put it, "Never too late for a happy childhood."[45]

The twelfth-century Chinese poet Lu Yu, in his poem "Written in a Carefree Mood," speaks about old age as the recovery of the child within. He describes how a nearly seventy-year-old can act just like he did as a boy: he heads to school with a "battered book" under his arm, "whooping with delight when he spies some mountain fruits."[46]

In his memoir, *The Summing Up* (written at age sixty-four!), Somerset Maugham noted that old age frees us of certain passions that caused mischief in earlier life. "Old age has its pleasures, which, though different, are not less than the pleasures of youth."[47] Mary Pipher says that "the old like verbal and physical affection and, unlike the young, are under no illusion that they do not need love."[48]

Delight can be a companion as we rejoice when younger friends move into positions where they can make special contributions and flourish. We've given them a helping hand up and now can relish our protégés' accomplishments. Fewer cares and responsibilities weigh us down, so we at last have time to stop and smell the roses. Relatively trivial things can be acknowledged for their triviality as we are given world enough and time to focus on matters of greater importance. Stripped of our own ambitions, we more fully delight in the achievements of others. Gratitude, which may have been in short supply in earlier stages of life, now blossoms in us, and we say with the psalmist,

> the boundary lines have fallen for me in pleasant places;
> I have a goodly heritage. (Ps. 16:6 NRSV)

Empathy is another reward of old age. Looking back, we see that life can be tough for everybody. That's why the aged are often more generous, less severe in their judgments, less envious, kinder, and more compassionate than the young. Age gives perspective on the ups and downs of life. We take the long view. Pondering our own struggles to grow up, to become established in our marriage or job, we may have greater sympathy for the struggles of the young. Having enjoyed the benefits of good health, we may be given particular sensitivity for younger people stressed by ill health.

"As a young man, just starting out, I went hungry for nearly a month," said an older man to me after service one Sunday. "I swore to God I would do my part to feed others when I got the chance. Don't turn away anybody from our church door who says they're hungry. You give them what they need; I'll gladly repay."

When my late friend and writer Reynolds Price heard that President Clinton could be impeached for his wrongdoing, Reynolds sent a note of consolation: "Dear Mr. President: I've done worse. Reynolds."

Toward the end of his life, crusty old Malcolm Muggeridge wrote, "When I embarked I worried about having a cabin with a porthole, whether I should be asked to sit at the Captain's table with the most attractive passengers. All such considerations became pointless since I shall soon be disembarking. The world that I shall soon be leaving seems ever more beautiful. Those I love, I can love even more, since I have nothing to ask of them but their love; the passion to accumulate possessions, the need to be noticed and to be important, is so evidently absurd that it can no longer be entertained."[49]

Christians are given the capacity to be honest about life's ending. Awareness of our mortality can add value to the present time. My late friend Peter Gomes, minister of Memorial Church, Harvard, often testified to his great delight of waking up each morning and saying to himself (and to the Lord), "Well, I have awakened to another day. This day, any day really, becomes good when it is an unexpected gift. Thanks be to God."

When my friend Peter slipped away to "the undiscover'd country from whose bourn no traveller returns,"[50] I gave thanks to God that Peter's faith had enabled him to savor each of his last days as a surprising bequest.

Perhaps honesty about our mortality is fruit of a sense of God's eternality. To believe that God is in and yet beyond time, that God is eternal yet reaches out to us in our temporality, can be a comfort to older people. Looking back, we see things we should have done differently and would have done differently if we knew then what we know now. There are problems that will not be solved and mistakes that will not be righted in this life. So much is beyond repair here, now. That's when God's eternality is our consolation. We are given

the long view. A Scripture-engendered sense of divine eternality may account for the irony that many aging people report that in a time of physical decline and a shrinking personal world they feel they have an increased spiritual and intellectual capacity.

As he aged, my father-in-law (Carl Parker, the same one who, in retirement, pulled a collapsible camper through Manhattan) talked a great deal about the weather. "How's the weather up there?" was his greeting when we phoned. I wonder if the elderly talk so much about the weather not because they have nothing better to talk about but because they have learned to take life one day at a time, appreciating the present, marveling at the weather, fair or foul, living in the moment, appreciating even mundane meteorology.

We enjoyed taking my mother on family trips when our children were young. Stuck in a long line at an amusement park or languishing in stalled traffic, we marveled at my mother's seemingly endless capacity to notice even the most humdrum detail of our surroundings and comment.

"What an interesting tree that is," she said as we sweltered on the freeway in Los Angeles. "It's rare to see a palm growing that straight and proud." Being on our way out of the world makes the mundane more dear.

By the grace of God we can receive gratitude for otherwise routine tasks. The person who had to rush through the preparation of meals now has time to enjoy spending an afternoon putting together a gourmet dinner for friends. A retired, high-powered business executive told me, "My greatest joy these days is serving on my church's altar guild. I who always had to be up front and in charge have now learned to cherish anonymously polishing the brassware and arranging the flowers so others can worship."

These days, when I encounter a flight of steps, I walk up them gratefully, remembering friends who are now unable to climb. If I am still able to take the stairs, I have a moral imperative to do so.

Called into Aging

For Christians, the chief freedom that comes with aging is the freedom to give ourselves more fully to our vocation, our partnership

with God in God's ongoing work in the world. Having raised children and provided for a family, we are free to raise someone else's children, to provide for the needs of those who are beyond the bounds of our biological family. Having been burdened by responsibilities for our own economic well-being, we are free to assume responsibility for others, using our resources on behalf of someone whose needs are greater than our own.

Christians believe that older people are not simply a collection of bodily ills but instead are people with God-given capacities of mind and spirit, people who never outgrow accountability to God. Salvation is tied to fulfillment of vocation.

Jesus Christ, in his cross and resurrection, rearranges our definitions of "success" and "failure." The basic call to life in Christ is, in the words of the Westminster Confession of Faith, the delightfully nonutilitarian summons to "glorify God and enjoy God forever." This rather playful, noninstrumentalist vocation suggests that successful aging for Christians somehow involves rediscovering our vocation to glorify and enjoy God, in spite of everything, in the last quarter of our lives. Even as we must learn to love the body that we have, to love the friends and family that are ours, and to be grateful for this stage of life, so we must practice loving the God who has decreed that human life is bounded.

Numbering Our Days

The psalmist prays,

> So teach us to count our days
>   that we may gain a wise heart. (90:12 NRSV)

The church that teaches us to count off our remaining days is the church that helps us to wise up and appreciate the days we have left, using them for no better purpose than the glorification and enjoyment of the God who will one day lovingly take back the life that God lovingly gave.

It's wisdom to know that our days are numbered. Realizing that our time is short, we do good now rather than putting it off until later.

And yet it can also be argued that fear of death breeds destructive actions that are bad for us and our neighbors. Many of our wars are fought out of fear that we or our families are in mortal danger. Fear does not bring out the best in us. When fear grips us, our worries become more narrow, and we're even more self-absorbed and suspicious of others, which may help to explain why many of the elderly are exaggeratedly self-concerned.[51]

In a *New Yorker* cartoon an old woman stands before an easel in her room, painting. She looks over her palette and peers through the little peephole in her securely locked door. The scene she paints on the canvas before her is one of chaos—bandits, brigands, and criminals charging toward her. What a worldview! The elderly have the greatest fear of being victims of violent crime and yet are the least victimized by violent crime.[52]

The philosopher Adam Smith imagines a charitable person who hears of a tragic earthquake in China. Immediately, he resolves to make a generous gift for the victims of the earthquake. But then he gets the news that disease requires the amputation of his finger. In a moment, all thoughts of others vanish and he is concerned totally with himself. Fear, pain, and illness, as intimations of mortality, tend to drive us inward.[53]

Whether numbering our days brings out the best or the worst in us is dependent in great part on whether we understand our days as gifts of God, a trust from God, a vocation to be undertaken that we may glorify God here and now so that one day we might glorify and enjoy God forever.

"Don't you know that your [aging] body is a temple of the Holy Spirit who is in you? Don't you know that [even in your last years] you have the Holy Spirit from God, and you [elderly] don't belong to yourselves? You have been bought and paid for, so honor God with your [elderly] body" (1 Cor. 6:19–20).

FIVE

With God in the Last Quarter of Life

In 1839, the American artist Thomas Cole painted a series known as *The Voyage of Life*, now displayed in a room of its own at the National Gallery in Washington, DC. In the first scene, *Childhood*, a smiling infant emerges into a lush, Edenic landscape full of potential. In *Manhood*, an adult pilots a boat on a turbulent river with swirling currents beneath and dark clouds above. Threat is all around, yet the muscular man, with hand on the tiller and eyes fixed on the river, steers the boat onward with confidence, energy, and determination.

In *Old Age*, a stooped, white-bearded old man is out on a cold winter night trudging beside the river toward where the river empties into the ocean. No life is seen, only dark clouds and a featureless ocean ahead. An angel looks down maternally on the old man, pointing him toward a golden city of lights far off in the distance. Whereas there is promise and adventure for childhood and adulthood, there is nothing for cold, exhausted old age but passive rest followed by a nebulous, distant eternity.

A major task of the contemporary church is replacement of these widely held conceptions of old age with images less pagan and more Christian. In Cole's paintings, the child, the adult, and the elder are each alone in a sometimes promising, often foreboding landscape. There is no visible human companionship and God is only hinted at by an angel. The best we can hope for, in Cole's rendition of the

end of life, is a faint, solicitous angel pointing us toward a celestial realm, ethereal and indistinct.

Christians believe that the God who walks with us, who leads us onward, is in the boat with us as we drift into our last decades of life. Jesus said, "I don't call you servants any longer. . . . Instead, I call you friends" (John 15:15). In our last years, friends we have made throughout our lives can become more important than ever, including the Son of God, who calls us his friends.

Thus there is truth in theologian Eugene Bianchi's claim that "aging is more of a spiritual than a biological journey."[1]

The Importance of the Social

Though many of the challenges of aging are physical, consequences of having an aging human body, some of the most difficult changes are social and relational. The latest research on aging reveals the remarkable import of social networks, friendships, and socialization as positive contributors to successful aging. Loneliness may be more detrimental to the health of older adults than diabetes. As bad as smoking is for our health, almost as deleterious is social isolation. George Vaillant even cites studies that show that loneliness can rob us of five years of longevity.[2]

Writer Dan Buettner visited "blue zones" where people live remarkably longer. He became quite enthusiastic about eating beans, citing research that indicated that beans can be beneficial for longevity. Yet after further study of the Seventh-day Adventists in Loma Linda, California, and the residents of the Japanese island of Okinawa, Buettner decided that more important for successful aging even than diet is continuing socialization.

In America, we divide our lives into two parts: our work life and then everything else. Buettner notes that people seem to age better in societies where retirement is virtually unknown, where older men keep advising the town council on its business and older women typically care for children and do most of the cooking, thereby making essential contributions to the well-being of the family.[3]

Vaillant says that although he is a physician who is concerned about the perils of alcohol abuse, sometimes alcohol encourages so-

cialization. "Friends are always more fun than good habits! Before and after age 50. Cultivate the richest social network you possibly can. Your life will be better for it," even if alcohol is involved.[4]

Christians live out the truth of John Wesley's dictum: "Christianity is a social religion; to turn it into a solitary affair is to destroy it."[5] Jesus gathers a group of disciples; his mission is no solo affair. Thus Christianity has always maintained that salvation is a corporate, social, group experience. Christian worship is inherently socializing—loving friends around the table. If we are to worship and serve Jesus Christ, we must do so in the company of others, making friends with those who are befriended by God. Simone Weil says that at any time in life there is nothing more salubrious for Christians than "friendship with the friends of God."[6]

God Calling Young and Old

As a child, I relished the story of the call of little Samuel when he was in service to old Eli (1 Sam. 3). God comes to the inexperienced kid, awaking him in the middle of the night with, "Samuel, Samuel . . ." rather than disturbing the sleep of the theologically trained, professional priest. At some point—say, the summer I became fifty-one—I began to resent this story. Why would God give revelation to the untrained kid that God withheld from the aging priest?

First Samuel says that the call of the prophet occurred in a dry season for spirituality. "The LORD's word was rare at that time, and visions weren't widely known" (1 Sam. 3:1). Finally, God appears—at last a vision is given—but not to the priest, old Eli, "whose eyes had grown so weak he was unable to see" (v. 2). When an epiphany occurs, it is given not to the senior citizen Eli but rather to the untrained, uncredentialed kid Samuel. He hears his name called. Samuel presumes Eli has summoned him. Eli tells the boy that he didn't call him and instructs him to go to his cot and lie down. Though Eli had been living with and working for the Lord for years, young "Samuel didn't yet know the LORD" (v. 7). A second and third time Samuel is called. "Then Eli realized that it was the LORD who was calling the boy" (v. 8). So Eli, who had years of experience with the Lord, tells Samuel, "Go and lie down. If he calls you, say, 'Speak, LORD. Your servant is listening'" (v. 9).

Though advanced in years, suffering from poor eyesight, and not the beneficiary of much recent revelation, Eli has something to contribute to this epiphany: he can help a new generation make friends with God, aiding them in interpreting their ambiguous spiritual experience as God's vocation.

The story takes an ominous turn, at least for the aging, weighted, poor-sighted priest. The Lord calls Samuel to become a prophet, a spokesperson for God, though the message that Samuel is to preach is not good news for Eli's family: "I am about to do something in Israel that will make the ears of all who hear it tingle! On that day, I will bring to pass against Eli everything I said about his household— every last bit of it! I told him that I would punish his family forever because of the wrongdoing he knew about—how his sons were cursing God, but he wouldn't stop them. Because of that I swore about Eli's household that his family's wrongdoing will never be reconciled by sacrifice or by offering" (1 Sam. 3:11–14).

God afflicts Eli for the blasphemy of his sons. If it is true, as I have heard said, "You're only as happy in retirement as your least happy child" (what is more out of your control than your child's happiness?), Eli is about to become a very unhappy older adult.

In a poignant scene, the next morning old Eli asks young Samuel what the Lord said to him. Samuel is fearful to answer, but Eli encourages him to tell him about the vision; Eli is willing to hear God's truth. So Samuel tells all. We don't know Eli's reaction to the threatening vision. We know only that little Samuel grows up and enjoys a great prophetic career in which "none of his words fall to the ground" (1 Sam. 3:19 RSV). I ask again, "Why would God bless young Samuel in ways that God did not bless faithful Eli?"

Toward the beginning of Samuel's adult ministry, the Philistines kill thousands of Israelites in a disastrous battle. Eli's ne'er-do-well sons Hophni and Phinehas had the bright idea to lug the ark of the covenant to the battle, hoping to gain magical protection for the Israelites. In the calamity that follows, the sons of Eli are killed and the victorious Philistines steal the holy ark. Poor Eli lives long enough to see his sons responsible for the loss of everything he has cherished and worked for.

A messenger is sent to Shiloh to tell the bad news to Eli, who is "sitting up on his seat by the road watching" (1 Sam. 4:13 NRSV).

Old Eli has clearly aged out of the game, sidelined from the battle, where he sits and waits in anxiety because "his heart trembled for the ark of God" (v. 13 NRSV). There's aging for you: retreat from the battle, sitting beside the road watching the world go by, disappointed and abandoned by progeny, fearfully awaiting word that everything has gone down the drain.

"Eli was 98 years old, and his eyes stared straight ahead, unable to see" (v. 15). He is told what happened. Hearing the bad news of the deaths of his sons is a blow, but when Eli is told of the fate of the ark of God, the text says, "Eli fell backward off the chair beside the gate. His neck broke, and he died because he was an old man and overweight" (v. 18). It's a sad end for the forty-year ministry of Eli.

To my mind—as an aging, formerly active, heavy priest—a chief question for us seniors who are attempting to live with and worship Eli's God is this: "Are we willing to go through aging with so interesting and demanding a God?"

Typical of Scripture, the story of Eli is simply reported without moralization, explanation, or regret. The most thought-provoking character of the narrative isn't grieving old Eli or even up-and-coming young Samuel. The most interesting actor is the author—the God who is in conversation with both Eli and Samuel. Toward the end of our lives, sometimes there is judgment and sometimes blessing, some things work out well for us and others go badly. Our children please and displease. And through it all, a true and living God is free to come and go among us, sovereign, able to reveal or not, calling whom God calls, assigning parts to play in the pageant of God's salvation.

We know how very important friends, social contacts, and interaction with others are for the last quarter of our lives. Yet it is the conviction of the church that of even greater import is our relationship with our most challenging Friend, the One who created us and continues to work with us and to summon us to service even in our old age.

Simeon and Anna, who step on stage and play their parts in welcoming the baby Jesus, Elizabeth and Zechariah, and Abraham and Sarah are not as interesting as the God who speaks and works through them. The central character of the drama is the God of Israel and the church who delights in calling older adults.

In the rest of this chapter, we will explore some of the benefits and the challenges of theological existence, the joy and the pain of lives lived into their last years with faith in the God of Eli, Abraham, Sarah, Zechariah, and Elizabeth.

The Agency of the Aging

Philosopher Martha Nussbaum, in her reflections on the challenges of aging, says that "one of the most damaging of all stereotypes about aging people is that they have no agency; they are just victims of fate." Nussbaum warns, "To rob aging people of agency and choice in the way one describes them is to dehumanize and objectify in a particularly insulting manner."[7]

As a Christian, I'm a bit troubled by Nussbaum's exaltation of human agency as the hallmark of humanity. We Christians believe that we have value because we are created, loved, called, and cherished by God. Our self-worth is due to God's loving agency, not ours. Still, morality implies agency. We generally don't hold people responsible for actions over which they had no control. Ethics is involved in those circumstances in which we ask, "What ought I to do?" Thus the ability to effect change, to impact our situation, to respond, and to exercise agency is a mark of our humanity. Is the inability to act and to effect change in ourselves and our world an inevitable loss of aging?

Harvard's Erik Erikson, in *Identity and the Life Cycle*, says that a major crisis for many elderly is the gap between what they hoped to do in life and what they actually accomplished. If people can creatively deal with that gap, says Erikson, they can reach a high degree of integrity where they can be at peace in a time of life when they are no longer able to accomplish much. If the aged are unable to resolve that conflict, they slip into despair. Later observers corrected Erikson's stark binary by stressing that recognition of a gap between what people hoped to do in life and what they actually did can spur them to strive to give meaning and purpose to the last years of their lives that may have been lacking in earlier years.[8]

Erikson assumes that our aspirations arise solely from within ourselves and our personal ambitions. That's not the Christian view. Through God's vocation, commandeering, and enlistment, ordinary

saints are given agency as human extensions of God's divine agency—assigned roles to play in God's work in the world, given something to do for God. Whatever God wants to do in the world, God in Christ has chosen not to work alone.

Through baptism, Christians are not only washed and redeemed but also called, summoned to play our bit parts as coworkers with God. In baptism, we are given lifelong agency as disciples. In a time of life when the purposefulness and meaning that were derived from a job or from caring for a home and family are taken away, the church's conviction that disciples are expected to love and serve God no matter their age can be one of the great gifts of our faith.

One of the challenges of caregiving is to care for the elderly without robbing them of agency. In her discussion of the pros and cons of assisted living arrangements for seniors, Nussbaum says, "We know that an aging individual, as well as the health care system, is better off if assisted living does not infantilize the person, but allows controlling decision-making to remain in the hands of the individual as much as possible."[9]

As part of my training to be a pastor, I took a quarter of clinical pastoral education at Wesley Woods in Atlanta, a care and recuperation facility of the church. At that time, Wesley Woods followed what was called "reality therapy" in which patients were given maximum opportunity to care for themselves and stay in touch with reality. When I, as a student chaplain, entered a patient room, a prescribed dialogue would occur: "Good morning, Mrs. Sheppard. I'm Chaplain Willimon. Do you know what day it is? What time is it?" I would then persist, "Where are you? Tell me the names of your children," and so forth.

We were even encouraged to ask patients questions like, "What is the name of the president of the United States?" The goal was to keep aging minds in reality rather than to aid and abet them in sinking into confusion.

I'm unsure of the effectiveness of this reality therapy in fending off dementia. One man said to me, "Dammit, if you have trouble remembering the name of the president, write it down! I'm not responsible for your forgetfulness!"

I witnessed older persons brought into Wesley Woods on a stretcher, incontinent, unable to feed themselves, totally dependent on caregivers.

Their loving families said things like, "Mama was spilling food on herself when she ate, so we began feeding her." The philosophy of the staff was not to infantilize the patients by spoon-feeding them but to encourage them to feed themselves, even if it took all afternoon.

Within a matter of weeks, many patients were functioning much better. Their families had loved them into passivity and helplessness, robbing them of agency. We must allow and encourage the aged to do as much for themselves as they can and not rob them of the simple joys of self-care, no matter how limited. Above all, as we care for the elderly, we must keep reminding ourselves of the centrality of Christian vocation: Jesus Christ calls ordinary people to discipleship and thereby gives them agency—without regard to their age or stage in life.

Responsible Aging

With agency comes responsibility. The elderly ought to be granted as much agency as possible and then held responsible. The church need not give people a pass on their immorality, abusive behavior, or sins of racism or greed just because they are old. The Fourth Commandment's decree to honor our elders does not mean to honor their mistakes of judgment, abuse of others, or sins.

To tell the truth, Christians are apt to be shaped more by the mores and influences of North American culture than by Scripture. We grow old the American way rather than as Christians. In the literature on gerontology, there is little criticism of the attitudes, prejudices, and biases of older people. Older folks are given a free pass, morally speaking. Yet to rob people of moral evaluation and responsibility is to rob them of their God-given agency. Moreover, it implies that the elderly have no accountability to God. We Christians must be self-critical throughout our lives. My church begins worship on most Sundays with a corporate confession of sin with no age limit on personal and corporate acceptance of blame and responsibility. Some older people have racist views, and those views should not be patronizingly overlooked simply because they have been held for decades. Cruel or abusive behavior must not be excused with "He's just being a dirty old man." The dismissive "silly old fool" is not found in Scripture.

"What gives you the right to cut the taxes that will fund my genera-tion's Social Security?" a twentysomething asked my seventy-year-old senator just after the senator's absurd comment that "climate change is fake news."

Even in our advanced years, we are still called to discipleship, and service in the name of Jesus often entails radical, unceasing personal reformation and sanctification. Older people must be held account-able for their words and deeds, and they must listen to truth-telling younger friends whose honesty God uses to encourage us to greater faithfulness. Sitting passively in the pew—refusing to tell the gospel story, to evangelize, to submit to correction and rebuke by brothers and sisters in the church, and to be engaged in Christ's mission—cannot be an option for aging Christians. Irresponsibility is ugly in a Christian of sixteen or sixty.

Not all elderly are passive, powerless recipients of care; many of the elderly continue to enjoy mobility, material resources, and mental capacities that enable them to be active givers of care and generous responders to the needs of others with their time and money. Pas-tors should not consign an older member of the church to the list of "homebound" if in most activities (other than church attendance!) that person is active. Being on a fixed income is not reason enough for a person to be excused from financial support of the church's ministries. As a preacher, I need to preach with the conviction that while there's life, it's never too late for a Christian to cultivate gen-erosity, courage, selflessness, and love.

Back in the sixties, it was fashionable for sociologists to interpret aging through the disengagement theory. This theory speculates that as people grow older, both they and the society in which they live agree on their gradual withdrawal from earlier social ties, roles, and responsibilities. The elderly deal with aging by disengagement and de-tachment from active life as their world shrinks to themselves and their own needs. I vividly remember the pastoral care textbook that told us seminarians that the chief factor in older adult experience is contraction: the aging person disappears from the community to safe confinement in the home, then to life limited to one room in a nursing facility, then to a bed, finally to a coffin, where the family disengages from the older person who disengaged from them.

Disengagement theory has been criticized as a demeaning view of older people, not only at odds with the data on how older adults actually age but also failing to match a more Christian view of humanity. Martin Luther defined sin as "the heart turned in upon itself."[10] Christ teaches his disciples to engage, to love their neighbors, to feed the hungry, to go into the world, to teach, to heal, and to witness without setting age limitations.

Earlier we noted researchers' amazement that when asked how they're doing, most of the aging reply that they are doing well "for my age." Many report that their health is good, even though they face serious health challenges. Does sanguinity about health demonstrate that these elderly are being unrealistic, or does it show that they know enough of God's will for their lives to believe that they are obligated, even amid the health challenges of aging, to positively preserve some sense of agency and responsibility?

There's some truth to the old saw "You are only as old as you feel." Attitude counts. Philosopher Christian Miller cites studies that indicate that an attitude of gratitude has documentable health advantages. People who believe that their lives are gifts—looking back, things have worked out well—tend to enjoy better physical and mental well-being. Miller believes that by cultivating feelings of gratitude, we can live longer and better.[11] Paul's exhortation to "give thanks in every situation" (1 Thess. 5:18) appears to be not only good theology but also good medicine. At our fiftieth college reunion, I asked a classmate how he overcame his alcoholism as late as age sixty. He replied, "I just decided to be happy."

After a visit to a woman in a nursing home (whose adult son was alienated because of her constant complaining and sourness), I said to the son, "I think your mother is depressed. She ought to be examined by a doctor." A mood-altering drug was prescribed. The son later said, "My mother's last years of life were a sheer joy to her and to her family."

However, we should be wary of efforts to drug or to moralize in order to encourage sour, complaining, and angry older adults to look on life more positively. Many older adults have good reason to feel sad. Sometimes older adults, like people of any age, do not handle life's disappointments and regrets in a positive way. It's threatening

for younger people to hear their elders express regrets, disappointments, or anger toward the very projects in which younger people are
investing themselves. Aging can be challenge enough without always
having to be pleasant and upbeat about the realities of growing old.[12]

In *Keep Moving*, Dick Van Dyke, the popular entertainer (writing
in his mid-nineties), says that the most important advice for seniors
is simple: keep moving.[13] The brain craves familiar, effortless ruts and
sends powerful messages to stay put and continue to plow familiar
furrows. For Van Dyke, keeping moving is a moral imperative for the
aged. If we can move, we must. We have a responsibility to ourselves
and to our friends (and to God) to keep moving as long as God grants
us the ability. Being able to boast, "Here all my needs are met; I don't
have to lift a finger" may not be best for the well-being of a resident
of a retirement facility.

The average human life span in the United States is now about
eighty years. Yet the maximum human life span is 120 years. Humans
have one of the largest gaps between average life span and maximum life span when compared with other animals. Lifestyle habits,
the intent to keep moving, diet, time spent interacting and intercon-
nected with others, fulfilling responsibility for someone other than
ourselves—in short, all the choices we make throughout the course
of our lives—sometimes don't impact us until our last decades, when
our chickens come home to roost. The bad habits that we successfully managed in earlier decades get the best of us in our last years,
reducing our longevity.

Most of us don't think of our medical problems as connected to
morality, having long since disposed of the notion that good or bad
things happen to us because of our good or bad actions and attitudes.
Still, an administrator of the Medical School once swept his hand
across the horizon of the vast Duke Medical Center and said to me,
"Well over half of the patients in those hospital rooms are there due
to their lifestyle choices." Agency entails responsibility, and unwise
lifestyle choices are apt to bear their bitter fruit after age sixty-five.

"It's irresponsible for you to refuse to use the handrail on the
stairs," one of my friends said to me.

Even with health problems, the majority of the aged are still able
to manage their own households. Over a third of those living beyond

eighty-five years can be described as fit for independent living, some with only minimal and occasional assistance.[14] There is no hard-and-fast rule for the relationship between aging and physical health. Indeed, there is much variability and variety, possibly due to the differing ways these adults have responsibly exercised their agency or, to put it in a more Christian way, due to the differing ways these adults have stepped up to the gifts that God has given them and to the tasks that Christ has assigned to them.

As we have noted, aging can be experienced as an acceptance of a life that's increasingly out of our control. Loss of control can be particularly painful for controlling personalities. The challenge is to be honest about those factors over which we have control, to let go of those areas over which we have no control, and to have the wisdom to know the difference. If wisdom is required for truthfulness about the God-given agency and responsibility of the aged, as well as our limits, that's good; the philosopher G. W. F. Hegel said, "The owl of Minerva [Roman goddess of wisdom] flies at dusk."[15]

Generation to Generation

For Christians, aging is a test of character, a time for witness and therefore an invitation for each of us to be a teacher, to hand over what we have learned to another generation. We have less time to live, yet most of us find, in our last decades, that we have more time to give. Not only do children who are tutored by the elderly in after-school programs show remarkable progress (because of older adults' patience, focus, and gift of time?), but the older adult tutors also show measurable positive changes in their physical and emotional well-being. In giving, we receive, as someone has said (Luke 6:38).

Among the lessons elders can teach the young are these: the joy of forgiveness, the gratification to be received through Christian service to others, the worth of people even when they have dementia, the limits of wealth, and the delight in the old, old story of God with us. On top of that, older people can show the rest of the church how to die.

Younger people gain from being in community with older adults, yet sometimes responsibility flows from the young to the old. I was in a little congregation where the pastor called forward those who

were seeking baptism. An old man hobbled to the front. The pastor embraced him and said with excitement in her voice, "Our young adults group met George in their ministry with those who live on the streets of our town. Until last month, George was living under the railroad trestle off Elm Street. Due to his liver disease, George has only a couple weeks to live. And guess where George has chosen to spend his last days? Here with us!"

The congregation broke into applause.

"George, why don't you tell the church why you want to be baptized?"

George thanked the congregation for their care of him and told them that they made him want to die with Jesus. He had gotten to know the church because of three or four young adults who helped him get medical care. What a credit to this congregation that someone wanted to spend his last days with them. "One generation shall laud your works to another, and shall declare your mighty acts" (Ps. 145:4 NRSV).

Remembering

One of the most prophetic, faith-engendering acts of the church is remembrance. It is sad that older adults are full of memory and yet are subject to memory loss, particularly short-term memory loss. The aging find that the present becomes harder to recall, while the past becomes more easily recollected. Of people over sixty-four, 10 percent suffer from dementia; dementia rates rise to 32 percent in people over eighty-four.[16] I vividly remember my first parishioner to be diagnosed with Alzheimer's disease. Since my pastoral role mostly involved talking, listening, and thinking, I was terrified to see a beloved personality slip away due to loss of memory, and I was in anguish because of my inability to help.

James Woodward gives some guidelines for visiting people with dementia: don't rush your visit, introduce yourself and give some information about yourself every time you meet, sit on the same level as the person you are conversing with, speak slowly and simply but don't patronize or infantilize, allow time for the person to reply, don't be afraid of sustained pauses, ask only one question at a time,

visit earlier in the day when the person is less fatigued, and use touch when appropriate.[17]

For the aged, it is usually pleasant to remember, to recollect, to reminisce, and to continue to engage some of the questions and projects that they worked on in the past. The stories of Elizabeth and Zechariah, Simeon and Anna push us to remember that we have more future with a living God than past; God keeps us leaning toward the future, expectant and hopeful that though our lifetimes are ending, God is forever beginning, creating, and venturing. Throughout our lives, it's a challenge not to tuck God comfortably within the past, to make of God a distantly remembered relic rather than a presently resurrected Lord. As Jesus said, God is God of the living and not the dead (Mark 12:27).

History need not enslave. We are free lovingly to recall the past but not to idolize the past. The good old days weren't good for many; that we fail to remember some of the pain of the past may be testimony to the graciousness of forgetfulness. Sometimes the way we recall the past demonstrates our self-deceit.

Every Sunday when the Bible is brought into worship and we read from it and thereby submit ourselves to the wisdom of the ancients, we show the centrality of memory in the Christian life. Scripture holds in memory some of our greatest truths about God and our best adventures with God so that we don't have to. Much of the church's life is in response to Jesus's "Do this in remembrance of me." Yet with a living God who is eschatologically active in the redemption of the world, tomorrow could easily be better than yesterday. One benefit of the Christian practice of forgiveness is that it enables us to begin again rather than to be constantly bound to the past.

Elders' capacity to spend so much of their conversations dredging up the past can be annoying. Maybe aging Christians ought to give ourselves a "remembering budget," budgeting the time that we spend on projects from the past and giving ourselves more fully to undertakings that enrich the present and the future, not only because present and future time for us is dwindling but also because God is with us most vibrantly in the present and the future. In our recollection, self-discipline is required. If, when others are kind enough to pay us a visit, we dominate the entire conversation, repetitiously

talking about the past or itemizing our aches and pains, the visit will not likely be repeated.

Suffering

Many of the elderly suffer chronic pain. One of the odd claims of the cruciform Christian faith is that suffering can be redemptive. Somehow the pain of Christ is related to the mystery of the atoning work of Christ, and somehow our pain is part of Christ's atoning work. Paul complained about his painful "thorn in the flesh" but kept on preaching anyhow (2 Cor. 12:7). Christ never implied that following him meant freedom from suffering. In fact, he commanded each of us to take up our cross daily and follow him (Matt. 16:24–26). In aging, some of us will receive what we asked for when we sang the old hymn, "Draw me nearer, nearer, nearer blessed Lord to the cross where thou hast died."[18]

The suffering occasioned by cross-bearing is the pain produced by discipleship, whereas the suffering of the elderly tends to be bodily pain due to the natural processes of aging. Still, the Christian faith neither denies nor promises relief from all pain. Paul dares us to "take pride in our problems, because we know that trouble produces endurance, endurance produces character, and character produces hope. This hope doesn't put us to shame, because the love of God has been poured out in our hearts through the Holy Spirit, who has been given to us" (Rom. 5:3–5). Paul's boasting is not based on a general conviction that all suffering is worthwhile or that pain is positive in its effects but rather because of "the Holy Spirit who has been given to us," we can expect even suffering to be used by a redemptive God.

A little later in his Letter to the Romans, Paul urges endurance in suffering that is based on hope in God's promised future.

> I believe that the present suffering is nothing compared to the coming glory that is going to be revealed to us. The whole creation waits breathless with anticipation for the revelation of God's sons and daughters. Creation was subjected to frustration, not by its own choice—it was the choice of the one who subjected it—but in the hope that the creation itself will be set free from slavery to decay and

brought into the glorious freedom of God's children. We know that
the whole creation is groaning together and suffering labor pains up
until now. And it's not only the creation. We ourselves who have the
Spirit as the first crop of the harvest also groan inside as we wait to
be adopted and for our bodies to be set free. We were saved in hope.
If we see what we hope for, that isn't hope. Who hopes for what they
already see? But if we hope for what we don't see, we wait for it with
patience. (8:18–25)

While this passage speaks of an eschatological hope of future relief
from suffering due to the "coming glory that is going to be revealed
to us," it also candidly acknowledges "the present suffering" (v. 18).
Aging bodies sometimes experience "slavery to decay" that causes
occasional "groaning" (vv. 21–22). Sometimes our suffering becomes
anguish as we regret events from the past or our lack of accomplishment. While there is little of Buddha's dictum that "life is suffering"
in the life-affirming good news of Christ, there is acknowledgment
by Jesus that suffering is the price we pay for embodied life and that
some suffering arises from the world's hostility to Christ and his
followers (Matt. 5:11).

Unfortunately, in our therapeutic culture we have moved beyond
noble attempts to relieve the pain of physical suffering or the agony
of mental anguish and bought into the myth that all suffering is un-
necessary, meaningless, and avoidable.[19]

In a small congregation during prayer requests, a person asked,
"Pray for Mama. She has been in pain. I just don't know what this
good woman has done to deserve this."

"His mama is the oldest member of our congregation," the host
pastor whispered to me, "ninety-six years old."

While we ought to pray for the alleviation of someone's suffering,
are there theological dangers in considering pain to be an undeserved
intrusion in a long-lived life? Is the toward-the-end-of-life suffering of a
ninety-six-year-old an injustice? What did Mama do to "deserve" a life
that is twenty years longer than the lives of her fellow church members?
Probably as little as she did to "deserve" this suffering at the end.

There is a prejudice abroad that all suffering is without meaning
and that the prospect of death is inherently bleak and unimaginable.

Christians therefore must find a way to live well without denying suffering and death as aspects of life. Only God is eternal. At every stage of life we are dependent, not on our efforts but on the grace of God. The suffering of Jesus helps to redeem our suffering by knowing "Christ and the power of his resurrection and the sharing of his sufferings by becoming like him in his death" (Phil. 3:10 NRSV). Jesus has not only been through suffering and anguish worse than ours, he is known by his active compassion for sufferers. Where there is suffering, there is Christ.

One caveat: while a theology of redemptive suffering may help with our own anguish, aches, and pains, we should be loath to apply it to the suffering of others. It's not for me (even if Paul did it) to tell some sufferer, "Rejoice, your suffering is a gift from God to draw you closer to God." Still, one can humbly offer a suffering friend the hopeful assurance that, even in suffering, God is there.

Much research is being expended on end-of-life health issues. Is this effort truly health care, or is it immortality fantasy? I fear that some of the impetus for this research comes from our negative attitudes toward suffering and death. Though the goal of palliative care is positively stated as "improving the quality of life," one has the suspicion that the point of much of this care is drug-induced banishment of human pain.

"Because of America's opioid epidemic," said my doctor recently, "our hospital now says upfront, 'Recovery from your surgery is bound to involve some pain. We promise to manage your pain as part of the natural healing process, but recovery without pain is impossible.'"

How can Paul proclaim that he's "happy to be suffering for you"? Paul can boast of happy pain because he is "completing what is missing from Christ's sufferings with [his] own body. [He's] doing this for the sake of [Christ's] body, which is the church" (Col. 1:24).

Though there is no equal correlation between the suffering of Christ and the suffering of Christians, and though the cross of Christ neither explains or explains away all suffering, Jesus's way of suffering service offers us Christians the opportunity to make sense of our suffering and even to see our pain as an expression of our discipleship and thereby to make a witness to the world, which thinks that all suffering is without meaning. Though suffering is rarely a gift of

God to the sufferer or anybody else, the way that we suffer can be a gift to others, our testimonial that life can be lived even in life's pain.

We should certainly avoid suffering, but suffering must not be avoided at all costs. We worship a God who lovingly suffered for us as "a man who suffered, who knew sickness well" (Isa. 53:3). Aging provides the church a grand opportunity to rethink and to reform the life of the church and the lives of individual Christians who are part of the Body of Christ. By the time we are old, while it is not too late to take measures in order to age well, aging is easier if the church has been preparing us all our lives for pain, for aging, and for inevitable death.

Rather than isolate sufferers and hide from view those who are dying, the church compels us to be connected with the suffering of others. Just as Christ was "a man of suffering," Christ embodies suffering love so, where there's suffering, there's Christ, and where Christ is, we want to be.

In all stages of life, Christ must be granted room to work, to work even in our suffering, even in our worst of times, and especially there. There's no way to avoid human suffering, our own or others'. We are animals. More significantly, Christians are walking the way of the cross with Christ. When we suffer, we can take heart in the knowledge that Christ has been there and in knowing that when we find ourselves in pain, we find ourselves with him.

As a pastor, I feel privileged to have seen many dear people suffer and die. I say "privileged" because when it comes my turn to go through pain and death, I hope I'll be able to show what I've learned, asking not, "What have I done to deserve this?" but rather saying, "Now it's my turn to give back the life that God has graciously entrusted to me."

Dependence

Christianity is training in dependency, learning to acknowledge that our lives are tied to the gifts of others and that our salvation is utterly dependent on God doing for us what we cannot do for ourselves. One of the most radical, prophetic acts of my church occurs when

we come forward for the Eucharist and are compelled to open our hands to receive the body and the blood. That openhanded physical gesture of emptiness, need, and dependency is countercultural.

Mary Pipher says in the opening of her book *Another Country: Navigating the Emotional Terrain of Our Elders*, "Aging in America is harder than it needs to be."[20] Aging is difficult in a culture that is obsessed with autonomy and self-construction. (No wonder we are a society of widespread loneliness.) The dependence that usually comes with aging and terminal illness can be a Christian witness to the mutual dependence that God intends for us throughout the Christian life. The fond fantasy of the elderly is to remain independent. Yet networks of interdependence (like the local congregation) sustain human usefulness and purpose.

I've stressed that we elderly need not passively waste away in health care facilities; we can be active agents. How much of my stress on agency and initiative betrays how I have bought into less-than-Christian notions of autonomy and independence? Do appeals for the aged to take charge of their aging and get their heads straight about the second half of life contribute to the problem of aging rather than solve it? What do we do in cases when, due to physical deterioration or dementia, there is a dramatic lack of agency? In a culture that worships individual autonomy, the dependence and need of the elderly reveal the lie of human self-sufficiency. Christians are called prophetically to proclaim that Jesus Christ has made everybody interdependent.

> Then the king will say to those on his right, "Come, you who will receive good things from my Father. Inherit the kingdom that was prepared for you before the world began. I was hungry and you gave me food to eat. I was thirsty and you gave me a drink. I was a stranger and you welcomed me. I was naked and you gave me clothes to wear. I was sick and you took care of me. I was in prison and you visited me." (Matt 25:34–36)

Not only do the elderly lose their independence but so do the caregivers to the ill and aging. If autonomy is the mark of a good life, then those who tie their lives to others by providing loving presence and care for the ill and the elderly are diminished. Christians can help

their fellow Americans recover the relational character of the good life as opposed to the ideal of the solitary hero or the self-sufficient loner. We are not simply "interdependent"; in a specifically Christian point of view, Christ makes us "mutually dependent." Not only are we subject to God for what we need in order to live, but God has also created us to be dependent, connected to one another, empty-handed as we stand before our sisters and brothers in the Body of Christ. "The parts of the body that people think are the weakest are the most necessary," preaches Paul (1 Cor. 12:22).

Sometimes in our losses God moves us to gratitude for the gifts of friends and allies. Is it possible that our losses are also God's way of ripping some of our idols out of our hands so that we may more fully worship and give ourselves to God? Maybe loss, while a painful part of life and love, can be an occasion for a redemptive God to work with us to enable us to be more grateful for and more truthful about our interconnectedness and interdependence. "Naked I came from my mother's womb; naked I will return there" (Job 1:21).

Loneliness

Loneliness is a state of longing, a feeling of emptiness that is a major aspect of life among the aging, particularly those who age in a culture that bows before the idol of individuality and autonomy.

Loneliness is evidence that God has implanted within us a desire for interaction with others, a longing for loving connection.[21] Sometimes loneliness is proportional to the amount of loss a person has suffered. In other people, loneliness accompanies self-alienation, disappointment, and self-rejection. To be elderly and alone does not automatically mean that one is lonely. Sometimes loneliness can be experienced as grace-filled solitude, a gift, a privilege. The move from loneliness to softer, kinder solitude can be a learned skill of the aged. Thus Richard Rohr says that one of the tasks of successful aging is to learn to be "happy alone" and that the cure for loneliness is to cultivate "the disciplines of solitude."[22]

I know a man who had a very public life as a prominent pastor. I doubt that in his retirement he feels lonely. He has learned to relish solitude and to enjoy being out of the public eye.

A myth of aging is that older adults have no sexuality.[23] While sex and romantic love among the aging are a reality, love among the aging can be complicated. Older people carry baggage into their relationships. Aging people have a past and also a present that often includes ex-spouses and children. The opinions of the children about the marital relationships undertaken by their parents or grandparents can make those relationships difficult. Sometimes stepchildren find it tough to include their aging parent's new partner in a new and blended family.

The Netflix series *The Kominsky Method* is a funny, insightful (some critics say "sad") look at two men who deal with the challenges of aging. After three failed marriages, Sandy Kominsky (Michael Douglas) has nothing to occupy his time except rather ridiculous attempts at affairs with younger women. His friend and agent, Norman Newlander, in deep grief over the death of his wife, is at least steadied in his last years by his Jewish faith. As Newlander repeatedly tells him, Kominsky's bungled affairs show that sex, as good as it can be, is not up to the task of saving us from despair at the work necessary for aging well.

Still, romantic love and sexual activity during the last years of life may be a testimonial that God has created us for community, communion, and partnership and has given us desires that do not end at sixty-five.

In the churches I've served, I've been surprised by a number of divorces of couples over sixty-five, sometimes accompanied by the statement, "I'm retiring. Why not get out of the marriage that has made me unhappy for so long?" Others said, "I liked being married to him when he was on the road most of the week, but can't handle having him home all the time looking over my shoulder."

On the other hand, I have also known three couples who had been divorced for some time but who got back together and cared for each other in their last years, choosing to spend those years together rather than apart.

That so many aging persons choose not to remarry after the death of a spouse may be a testimonial that when marriage has ended by death, the surviving spouse may not feel that he or she is consigned to inevitable loneliness but rather can now have a different sort of

life. As a widow said to me, "I loved being married to Tom, but now that Tom is gone, I have no desire to be married to anyone else. Been there, done that."

Others, having enjoyed being married to someone, actively work to stay connected socially and, sometimes, romantically. "I've learned one thing about myself in thirty years of marriage," said one widow. "I enjoy men. I don't like living alone. Pastor, bolster yourself for a round of premarital counseling."

Grief

Grief tends to be an intensely personal experience. As a pastor, I've advised grieving persons, "Grieve as you grieve, not as someone tells you that you ought to grieve."

Although grief among the elderly involves some of the same tasks and is assuaged by some of the same comforts as loss during any time of life, many older people seem to have resources for doing grief work because they have had more experience with loss over their years of life.

First Timothy 5:3 asserts that taking care of widows, women whose husbands have died (or may have been martyred), is a key activity of the church. While marriage is the norm for most aging men, nearly half of women beyond their sixty-fifth birthday are widows. Statistically, older widows tend not to remarry, which may indicate that not all widows are inevitably lonely and unhappy or that initiating romantic relationships and matrimony in our last years isn't easy.[24] Again, it's not helpful to make generalizations about how people grieve or should grieve.

Widowhood requires a person to ask, "Who am I if I am no longer a spouse?"[25] Sometimes the task of widowhood is establishing a new lifestyle or restructuring friendships. The loss of a spouse and the attendant grief must not be seen as a pathology. The grief testifies to love and is a necessary path one must walk after loss toward recovery and readjustment.

As a young pastor attempting to minister to an older woman whose husband had suddenly died, I witnessed other widows giving comfort.

"Sure, this is a blow to you, an adjustment," one said. "But you will come to see the bright side of all this." What?

Said another, "We go to Atlanta shopping three times a year and take a cruise every spring. It's sad that George has died, but welcome to our club!"

(While their comfort may have been reassuring, as their pastor I immediately set out to give this post-marriage club an agenda more important than shopping.)

Gender Differences in Aging

Women live longer than men. The mortality gender gap appears to have social as well as biological reasons. Men in our culture are more prone to have accidents and diseases that could have their roots in men's competitiveness, high-risk activities, and drug and alcohol abuse. Women appear to show greater flexibility and resilience in aging than men. Perhaps that will change with more economic opportunities for women—accompanied by more stress and strain—and with men learning to function in a wider array of roles.

Nearly three-fourths of the elderly poor are women. This disproportionality may be due to the way Social Security is structured, to the pay gap between women and men, or to how women are often penalized through divorce. An economically unjust divorce settlement sometimes does not bear its bitter fruit until old age. Most of the negative burdens of the aged poor, widowed, and those living alone are more characteristic of women than of men.[26]

Aging men often have a deep ambivalence about the aging process, feeling that they have lost purposeful activity and personal significance. Because men often receive less social support in their work in secular settings, the support they receive in the church may be even more important as they negotiate the challenges of aging. Women have less access than men to secular sources of power, prestige, and resources; therefore, they may more highly value the access to power, influence, and leadership that's given them in the church (or feel a special resentment when their church does not grant them this access).

Perhaps that is why, compared to older men, older women are more likely to attend church, pray, and report that religion is important to

them. Some research indicates that in the last years of life there is a shift away from the stereotyped roles for men and women to an emphasis on finding wholeness and integration in life. Some researchers even say that in older age gender is psychologically transcended.[27] In aging, some of the limitations imposed on people by social constructs of gender roles can be overcome as men enjoy caregiving and nurturing and women assume more authority in the governance of finances in the household and leadership in church and civic organizations.

Church Participation

There are over 350,000 Catholic and Protestant Christian congregations in America. About 70 percent of Americans consider themselves members of some religious denomination. Nearly 40 percent of the aged claim to attend weekly worship. Ninety percent of adults age sixty-five and under report a religious affiliation. Eighty-four percent of fifty- to sixty-four-year-olds are religiously affiliated. Among African American and Latinx adults in these age groups, the number is about 5 percent higher.[28]

A Barna study in 2002 revealed that approximately 89 percent of older people pray, and about half say they read the Bible during the same week. Fifty-five percent have attended religious services in the past seven days.[29] While older adults may struggle with diminished levels of activity in many areas of their lives, they are the most active religious age group in America.

"Amid an attendance recession," one pastor preached to her congregation, "we're counting on those of you over sixty-five to step up your church attendance. We need you present with us for prayer and praise! Now more than ever! Maybe you can't set up tables for the weekly food giveaway. At least you can show up for worship!"

There is now a *Journal of Religious Gerontology* that regularly reports that older people are deeply immersed in religion. A 1999 study showed that 79 percent of people between the ages of sixty-five and seventy-four claim that religion is "very important." Some research indicates that people do indeed become more religious with age, though there are multiple patterns of religious involvement in the later years, just as in the prior years.[30]

I'm unsure what to make of claims of the beneficent effects of religiosity on elder health. For one thing, it's tough to control for factors outside of a person's religious practices. A fifty-year-old active Mormon who is also a lifelong abstainer from alcohol is probably a candidate for greater longevity. Yet how do we separate his religious beliefs from his abstinence?

Research indicates that religious interest increases with age, but why? George Vaillant notes that the Grant Study found an increase in religious involvement among the subjects of the study, but those who were active in religious practices "manifested nine times as many symptoms of depression, and spent three times as many years disabled, or were dead before age 80." Vaillant theorizes not that religion is bad for mental health but that the depressed and anxious are more likely to seek religious comfort.[31]

Vaillant found scant relationship between physical health and religious involvement. He also found no difference in mortality and no difference in rates of smoking or alcohol abuse among the religiously inclined. Mormons, Seventh-day Adventists, and evangelical Christians live longer than their atheistic neighbors, but they use tobacco and alcohol less. Vaillant's verdict is that "abstinence from drinking and smoking play more of a role in increased longevity than religious devotion itself."[32] Still, "Looked at from a psychosocial perspective rather than a strictly medical one," says Vaillant, "religious devotion remains one of humanity's great sources of comfort, and for many replaces the use (and abuse) 0of alcohol and cigarettes."[33]

Strikingly, Vaillant hypothesized that religious involvement would lead to enhanced social support, but he found little evidence among his Grant Study men that this was true. Still, Vaillant thinks that religious involvement could be a comfort to the lonely—God loves us even when people don't.

"An impressive body of research suggests that attendance at religious services protects against premature mortality," admits Vaillant. However, he found no direct, causal effect. Cigarettes and alcohol are important factors, but they are often only self-reported in studies attempting to link religious observance to physical health. Vaillant wonders if these studies tend to take place in the Bible Belt, where agnostics tend to be "social outliers" anyway. "In samples where

healthy social adjustment usually includes clear religious involvement, such involvement is likely to correlate with warm relationships, social supports, and good physical health. Evidence of that correlation, however, does not reflect a direct causal relationship between religious involvement and health."[34]

In 1998, my colleague Harold Koenig founded the Duke University Center for the Study of Spirituality, Theology, and Health. (Pastors and church leaders can find the center's reports on ongoing research, regular newsletters, and insights at https://spiritualityandhealth.duke .edu.) Koenig and his colleague, Douglas Lawson, assert a verifiable connection between religious involvement and better physical health in the elderly: "A steadily growing body of scientific evidence indicates that religious involvement is associated with better physical health, a greater sense of well-being, less depression, and a reduced need for health services, including hospital stays. Hundreds of research studies conducted at our leading institutions seem to indicate that religious beliefs and practices help people of all ages deal better with stress, increase their contact with helpful social-support networks, and discourage activity that has a negative impact on their health: drug and alcohol abuse, smoking, and high risk sexual behavior, which all contribute to disease and disability."[35]

Koenig believes that "religiosity also encourages responsibility, commitment, and concern and generosity toward others." Religious faith and practice enhance the willingness and the ability of elders to provide nonprofessional "healthcare and sustain their emotional support of others on a volunteer basis." Koenig thinks that volunteer elderly caregivers may be the "pivotal factor preventing the complete degradation of our health care system in coming decades."[36] Volunteering is a major contributor to purposeful retirement for many, and as we have noted, there are mutual benefits. Most elderly volunteer through their place of worship, leading Christian gerontologist Neal Krause to declare that "spirituality is the most important motivating factor in senior citizen volunteers."[37]

Research on aging and religion has had the greatest trouble not in defining successful aging but in defining religion. How does one distinguish between religion and spirituality, or religion and a general philosophy of life? Researchers have also had a tough time differen-

tiating between participation in churches and participation in other altruistic civic organizations. How do we know whether or not the older adults who are more involved with religion than those who are young are more active in religious activities simply because they have more time?

Normally, the way research evaluates age differences in religion is by comparing and contrasting levels of religious participation. How do we measure when a person is being "religious"? Research shows that older people are "more religious"—that is, more religiously involved in religious institutions—than younger adults.[38] But not all religious leaders would be comfortable saying that mere frequent church attendance equates with deep faith.

Krause, when researching aging and religion, looked not simply at indicators such as frequency of church attendance and prayer but also at church-based social relationships. Krause found a high degree of church-based social relationships among the elderly. He admits that there are multiple trajectories of religious involvement over the life course and that generalizations about how people age religiously are difficult.[39]

It's tough to separate the effects of religious involvement that can be attributed to God from those that can be attributed to an individual's desire for relationships within the Christian community. Perhaps we need not disconnect these two factors; Christianity is a communal, social, incarnational faith. Krause and Koenig highlight the centrality of social relationships in the church and attribute positive health correlations to these relationships.

Research on race differences among older people shows that older African Americans are more deeply involved in religion than older white people are, and the beneficial effects of religion on health and well-being appear to be more evident among older black people than older white people.[40] Perhaps the Christian faith has provided these black believers with support in the face of the evil of racism, accounting for why the church is still a central factor in African American society in a way that it is not in predominantly white culture. Some observers believe that African American congregations are more supportive of their elderly than non–African American congregations. Many black people are proud that religion helped their ancestors

deal with the horrors of slavery and that their churches were at the forefront in dismantling racial segregation in America; therefore, elders are honored.

I am reluctant to make too much of data that say religion is good for our health. Who wants to be utilitarian or an instrumentalist about our faith? Jesus Christ is Lord whether or not worshiping him helps our blood pressure. And while I know that causality can never be determined conclusively with survey data, Koenig's research does seem to confirm what many of us believers have experienced as a gracious by-product of our religious participation: religious and church engagement help us negotiate life's transitions, including the challenges of aging.

Economics

When Hurricane Katrina swept through New Orleans, over one thousand people died, and most of those who died were economically disadvantaged. What's more, 74 percent of those who died were over sixty years old, and 50 percent were over seventy-five, though the elderly constituted only 11.7 percent of the New Orleans population.[41] We have not honored the elderly if we have not confronted the economic systems that oppress them.

For persons of color, aging presents a cumulative economic disadvantage. Limited access to health care, jobs, and education shows up negatively in the bodily experience of older adults. In the United States, one-third of older women live below the poverty line, but for women of color, that number is over 50 percent.[42]

Those of us who have white privilege and who live in an affluent country get to choose all sorts of expensive treatment options and worry about medical dilemmas that are more a function of our affluence than of the improved quality of life produced by our expensive medical care. Sadly, many health dollars go into cosmetic surgical procedures for the affluent aging while many elderly lack access to basic medical care, immunizations, and safe water throughout the life cycle. In our American health care system, those who have accumulated more money get more opportunities to choose how they will age.

Visiting an ailing octogenarian in my congregation as she lay in the hospital, I asked for what she wanted me to pray.

"Pray that my young doctor will leave me alone. That silly boy intends to subject me to therapy that he alleges would give me another two years! If I were twenty, I would take him up on the offer. Why consume resources that could be used on those who are younger? It's not 'health care'; it's death denial. No thanks. I've had enough."

Economic issues not only raise questions about a more just distribution of resources but also prompt us to remember Jesus's judgments about the perils of wealth. Wealth, in the teaching of Jesus, is a problem, not only because it tends to be distributed unequally and produces a sense of entitlement and privilege among the rich but also because it is an encouragement toward idolatry and a corruptor of character. Wealth enables us to make even good health care an idol as we allow our fear of dying, rather than our fear of God, to dominate our imaginations. Visiting the sick and caring for the dying are difficult in a world in which most of us work most of our lives and have little time to expend in care for others. We would rather earn money to pay for care of those we love than do the caring. The burden of the elderly is a problem, not so much because there are so many more elderly in need around us but rather because we are living lives of self-aggrandizement in which there is little time to respond to the needs of others. In short, the crisis in elder care is a call for the church to help us think not only about the aging but also about the inadequate ways we have constructed our lives on mammon rather than on God.

Greed is ugly at sixteen or at sixty. Jesus had some choice words for those who vainly say to themselves, "You have stored up plenty of goods, enough for several years. Take it easy! Eat, drink, and enjoy yourself" (Luke 12:19). We might call someone wise who prudently planned for retirement and stored up treasures for himself; Jesus, in this parable, calls him "fool" (v. 20). The church at its best saves us from foolish lives.

Politics and Social Policy

The challenges of aging are neither purely personal nor exclusively related to getting along well with one another in the church. There are structural, political, social policy reasons for why many find aging

difficult. We need those who require care and their caregivers to have more independence, choice, dignity, and control over care. There must be fair access to care and development of preventive services. Health care services should be evaluated on the basis of performance, quality, and waste. Somehow we must come up with resources to care for people with dementia without overwhelming health care systems. And we need to encourage seniors to be active and healthy in their habits and exercise programs.

A society fails to be minimally just if it doesn't secure a basic level of human rights and capabilities for all of its citizens. Drug companies should demonstrate that they are truly reinvesting their profits in research. Health care workers ought to receive just compensation for their labor. Health for the aging is not just about treatment for sickness but also about nutrition, recreation, exercise, and wellness care for injuries. The elderly must be granted access to parks and recreational facilities. Public transportation is extremely important for the well-being of the elderly. The dominance of the car in our culture and the corresponding lack of safe bikeways and walkways are significant challenges for older people and evidence of poor social policy.

Being a Burden

Thinking about aging as a Christian enables the church to confront the widespread American myth that it is possible to live our lives without being a burden, free from being anyone's responsibility. Christians are those who have taken on the burden of Christ's yoke in response to his invitation to come to him, all who are weary and burdened, to receive rest (Matt. 11:28). Strange that Christ promises rest and unburdening by asking us to wear his yoke and take on his burden, for his yoke is easy and his burden is light (vv. 29–30). Christ calls us not to totally unburden ourselves but rather to cast off the baggage that the world puts on our backs in order that he may lay on us his yoke and his burden. Rather than free us from all burdens, Christ gives us burdens worth bearing, lives worth living. Paul characterizes burden-bearing as a "law" of Christ: "Carry each other's burdens and so you will fulfill the law of Christ" (Gal. 6:2). Think of Christianity

as training in the assumption of burdens that the world tells us are not our responsibility but that Christ makes our means of serving him.

To take on the yoke of Christ is to be yoked to his Body, the church. We not only are given responsibility for others but also must learn how to be the responsibility of others. Which is more difficult: to give help or to receive help? In our culture, it is grace to be able to say to another, "I need your aid," to allow someone to fulfill Christ's command to "carry each other's burdens." Christianity teaches us how to be a burden to others to whom we have no connection other than baptism.

"Is it fair for you to move your mother into your apartment and assume total responsibility for her?" I asked one of my church members.

"She did that for me when I needed her. Thank God I get to care for the one who cared enough to bring me into this world." Such is the reasoning of those who have taken on the burdens of Christ.

When I praised a woman in my church for showing up at the nursing home every day to care for the needs of an older man from our congregation who had no family nearby, she said to me, "Just this morning I thanked Joe for allowing me to love him in this way. I fail in so many ways to be a faithful Christian. By allowing me to help in his time of need, Joe enables me to be so much better than I would have been on my own."

In Christ, none of us can say, "I'm on my own." We, a burden to a loving God, are called to assume the burdens of others and to let Christ make us a burden to them. The church ought to give us experiences of this burden-bearing as preparation for aging. It is good for us to train our children and grandchildren to be caregivers and to give them opportunities to be with aging persons. To give care and to receive care can be downright prophetic acts in a society that exalts independence over interdependence.

Because of the dread of growing old, there is a widespread rejection of the gift of years. Some opt out. The suicide rate is high among the elderly, particularly elderly men. Suicide rates for the elderly are high in a climate in which we have nothing to do with our dependence, our suffering, and our dying. In baptism, however, our lives are shown to be God's possession and our bodies gifts in service of God and the world. "I have been crucified with Christ and I no longer

live, but Christ lives in me" (Gal. 2:20). Appeals to the sacredness of life are not the point. Life is not our possession to be preserved at all costs or expended as we see fit. Nor are debates about "quality of life" much help. Many times, arguments for physician-assisted suicide imply that our suffering has no meaning for ourselves or for others. These ethical debates must be resolved by Christians first asking theological questions like, "Who has God created us to be?" and "What are human beings for?"

A SERMON

Here's a sermon I preached some years ago in an attempt to help my congregation think about these matters.

The Blessedness of Being a Burden[43]

> How can we thank God enough for you, given all the joy we have because of you before our God? (1 Thess. 3:9–13)

In my pastoral care of people who are in the last years of their lives, I have noted that when people face declining health or physical infirmities, it's not death they fear; it's the dying. What they fear is a long dying. More specifically, they fear "becoming a burden on my family." Our prayer is to end our lives in such a way that we will never be a bother to other people by the manner of our leaving.

I've got a couple of children; do I want to be a burden to them in my old age?

Well, why not? They have been a burden to me. True, I did not give them birth, but I was there, close by, and I had to pay for it. Then the diapers, of which I have changed a few. And the sitting in sweltering hot sun at swim meets. And the PTA meetings! How many times I've had to rearrange my schedule to accommodate them. They were a daily burden to us for about twenty years. Even though they've fled the home, I still worry about them. Why should I bother being a burden to them for the couple of years of my dying?

Being a burden is what it means to be in a family. It's part of the price we pay for loving and being loved.

We live in a society that, under the tutelage of the philosophical mistakes of people like John Locke and Thomas Jefferson, tell us that we live under some invisible "social contract" where we autonomous individuals have decided to come together in contractual agreement with one another in order to better gratify our personal desires. Maybe that is enough for a nation; it certainly isn't enough for a family. Being a family means to have claims on one another. Love tends to seek out burdens rather than to avoid them.

Love teaches us that we are never more human than in those moments when we joyfully burden ourselves with other people. To avoid or reject such burdens is to turn our back on our own humanity.

It is the nature of love to expose us to the needs of others, to have our lives interrupted, detoured, and, in general, disrupted by another. We are at our best as we respond to such unchosen, undecided, unplanned demands, interruptions, and encumbrances.

To say that your life is totally free of the bothers and burdens of other people is another way of saying, "I am lonely. I have no better purpose for my life than my life." On one occasion, Jesus told us, "Come to me, all who labor and are heavy laden, and I will give you rest. . . . For my yoke is easy, and my burden is light" (Matt. 11:28, 30 RSV). I find it interesting that Jesus at that moment did not say, "Come to me, all who labor and are heavy laden, and I will relieve you." Rather, he said, "Come to me and I will put a yoke around your necks and place a burden on your backs that you have not previously borne." Sure, his yoke may be "easy" and his burden "light," but a burden is a burden. Jesus seems to have taught that the burdened life is the abundant life.

Think of the church as training in laying down so many of the burdens that our society places on our backs—financial success, the relentless attempt at unbridled personal autonomy, and the constant care of ourselves—in order to bear burdens that we would never have borne before we met Jesus.

I remember that Sunday when, at the close of the service, this woman in my church came up to me and said, "Aren't you bothered that we don't really pray for anybody except ourselves? We pray for those among us who are in the hospital, who are going through difficulties of various

kinds. Didn't Jesus tell us to pray for our enemies? Doesn't Jesus expect us to consider as brothers and sisters people we don't even know?"

She was right.

This doesn't mean that attempts to make a living will or advance directives are bad. Nor does it mean that we are wrong to seek help and assistance in caring for those parents or children whose lot in life makes them peculiarly vulnerable and in great need of intense and constant care.

It means that Jesus compels us toward a deep awareness of the interdependence of human life. Not one of us is an island unto ourselves. Our children need adults who are willing to order their lives to care for the needs of children. We older adults need children who are willing, as adult offspring, to order their lives so that they have the blessing of returning some of the love to us that we showed to them when they were dependent. And all of us need to be needed. It's the way God put us together.

Christians are crazy enough, looking at ourselves and others through the eyes of the self-giving love of Jesus, to refer to such "burdens" as God-given blessings.

One of the reasons we flee from the burdensome care of those who are dependent on us is that their sickness, mental or physical infirmity, or incapacity is a reminder of a truth we have so many ways of avoiding—namely, that *all of us are dependent*, that all of us in our lives march toward some final incapacity. Most of us hope that we may die in such a way that we may never know that we are actually dying—quickly, painlessly, with no messy leftovers. The truth is, most of us will die attached, not simply to some medical machine but to other people.

The last days of our lives are even more dependent and burdensome to other people than our first days as infants. I hope that my children, my spouse, and my friends will have pity on me when I am in such circumstances. I expect that they will be far more patient, and wiser, in caring for me in this state than I have been with them. My being a burden to them is the price they pay for love.

And because of their Christian faith, they have been told, if not by me then at least by the Bible, that they are indeed their brothers' and

sisters' keepers. Jesus told a story that says those who have loved the most burdensome, "the least of these," have also loved him (Matt. 25).

A man in my church spent most of his life unmarried. He loved to dance. At a ballroom dancing convention, he met a lively woman who shared his love for dancing.

They were always in church on Sunday mornings, but on most Friday or Saturday nights, they danced. I'm talking ballroom, square, South American—you name it, they danced it.

Then one day he called from the hospital to say that her fever was a sign of a terrible illness of the central nervous system. In just a couple of days, she was bedridden, never to walk again. Certainly, never to dance again. Victor changed his work schedule so that he could be home four days a week to care for her. He secured some wonderful care from other persons to help with her. For *six years* he watched over her, loving her, helping her to adjust, organizing parties and dinners at their home where guests gathered around her bedside and laughed and talked, because this brought her joy.

When she died, the church gathered and gave praise to God for her life and witness, and for Victor's as well. During the service, I embarrassed him by making him stand as I said, "Victor, you know how proud we are of you. As your pastor and preacher, I want to take some credit for the way you have lived your life during this difficult time. This church doesn't have many successes. We give thanks to God that you're one of them."

After the funeral and committal, Victor said to me, "Difficult time? That isn't how I would put it. Sure, there were days when I wondered if I could keep going, if I would be able to do for her all that was needed. But you forget. I spent forty years of my life alone. I spent most of my life without anybody who needed me. She made my life count. She gave me a reason for living. She was always much more of a gift than a burden."

I pray to God for such character. I pray for you too. One day may somebody be a great bothersome burden for you. And one day may you be a burden to another as well, thus being the means of someone finding life, and that abundantly.

In the name of Christ, amen.[44]

Bodies

Aging reintroduces us to our bodies. Through much of my life I've treated my body as if it were a car. It gets me from here to there. And when there are malfunctions, I want the problem fixed quickly and effortlessly. Older people are likely to be consumed with bodily health issues because, for older people, suddenly the bodies that we may have neglected—or, conversely, been fastidious in tending—remind us that we are creatures. No matter how good we have been to our bodies, abstemious in our habits, our bodies begin to show signs of age. So there is much conversation about the virtues of our doctors and the search for the surefire cure. As one preacher put it, we engage in "organ recitals" as we detail the liabilities of our aging bodies. When we're in our cohort, we can always talk about our bodies since that's the one thing that unites us.

Yet to despise aging bodies is to despise both our Creator and ourselves as God's creations. We deny our kinship with animals and repudiate our animal weaknesses and vulnerabilities, including our animal-like physical degeneration. The human body decays and smells as it decays. Therefore, to confront aging bodies is to confront tangible, physical truth about ourselves.

Are there limits for the medical treatment we should seek to alter the appearance of our aging bodies? Are facelifts okay? I don't know much about the ethics of cosmetic surgery, but Martha Nussbaum gives some helpful guidelines: we should not use cosmetic procedures as substitutes for exercise and good diet. You must find a way to make peace with the "you" that your body has become. It's sad when Botox, badly applied, prohibits us from smiling. Cosmetic surgery may be a waste of resources when there are better things to do with our money. Surgery is always risky and can have a long and difficult recovery period. Nussbaum says we should be guided by the principle that "looking better is what we're talking about, not looking younger."[45]

The Body of Christ is made up of different kinds of bodies, including older, aging bodies. God's vocation addresses us throughout the life cycle but in diverse ways depending on our stage of life. At twenty, I felt called to be a pastor. At seventy, I still feel called to be

a pastor, but I am not called to be the pastor I was at twenty. Paul talked about the church, the Body of Christ, as being made up of diverse vocations, without any one part of the Body being superior in its functions to another. Our work for God is largely dependent on, and often restricted by, what our bodies can do at a given age. Aging requires us realistically to adapt to what our bodies can do for God at a particular time in life. Our response to God's vocation must be repeatedly renegotiated as we prayerfully ask ourselves, "What is God doing with my life and my body now?"

Death

Church is one of the few places in this death-denying culture where we can actually talk about the end. Church is where we name what is important and what is unimportant, where we are given a lens to look at life *sub specie aeternitatis*, a position from which to take the long view. Our lives are bounded, terminal. God has created us as finite creatures who will die. Psalm 90:3–12 speaks of human mortality as an aspect of God's wrath on our iniquity, part of the distance between us and God.

> You return people to dust,
>   saying, "Go back, humans,"
>   because in your perspective a thousand years
>   are like yesterday past,
>   like a short period during the night watch.
> You sweep humans away like a dream,
>   like grass that is renewed in the morning.
> True, in the morning it thrives, renewed,
>   but come evening it withers, all dried up.
> Yes, we are wasting away because of your wrath;
>   we are paralyzed with fear on account of your rage.
> You put our sins right in front of you,
>   set our hidden faults in the light from your face.
> Yes, all our days slip away because of your fury;
>   we finish up our years with a whimper.
> We live at best to be seventy years old,
>   maybe eighty, if we're strong.

> But their duration brings hard work and trouble
>   because they go by so quickly.
>   And then we fly off.
> Who can comprehend the power of your anger?
>   The honor that is due you corresponds to your wrath.
> Teach us to number our days
>   so we can have a wise heart.

While death may be a fact of our lives, it is also a sign that the world did not end up as God intended. Though Scripture does not look on aging as an evil or an injustice, that is not the case with death. Jesus certainly agonized over his own death as he prayed in the Garden of Gethsemane to be granted a way out. Jesus grieved at the tomb of his friend Lazarus (John 11:33–37). Judith and Richard Hays say that the New Testament confronts death with the affirmation that "God will overcome the power of death by the resurrection of the body at the last day. The resurrection of Jesus is both the first fruits of his final resurrection and the sign of the eschatological resurrection, in which all Christ's people will share,"[46] remembering Paul's words in 1 Corinthians 15:20–28. And yet we still grieve at the thought of confrontation with "the last enemy" (v. 26).

Christians must find a way to combine honesty about our dying with hope of our resurrection. Resurrection hope lies at the heart of the way Christians embody the practices of growing old. Jesus triumphs over death and, in one great, victoriously loving act, takes us along with him in resurrection. This affirmation frees us from the paralysis that often comes with the fear of death. We need not deceive ourselves about death, nor should we allow the thought of death to overpower our imaginations. The Christian faith gives us the ability to look at death directly but also relatively. Indeed, one might think of Christianity and its funerals, its practices and rituals like baptism and the Lord's Supper, and its reading and preaching of Scripture as training in how to die in the name of Jesus. "Since we believe that Jesus died and rose, so we also believe that God will bring with him those who have died in Jesus. . . . So encourage each other with these words" (1 Thess. 4:14, 18). That statement could be repeated every time the church gathers.

"The truth about life is that we shall die," said writer Philip Roth, just before he died. (Roth spoke of aging as a "massacre."[47]) One reason for stigmatizing the elderly or avoiding attendance at their funerals is that we live in a death-denying culture that is loath to be reminded of life's limits or death's ubiquity. If we reject the assurances of the Christian faith, why not deny or deceive ourselves about death and refuse to face death as a part of life since almighty death has the last word on life?

Death may be "the last enemy to be brought to an end" (1 Cor. 15:26); still, it is an enemy vanquished and being put down by the resurrected Christ, an ultimate defeat to which we can bear prophetic testimony right now by the way we live our lives.

In a death-denying world, older Christians can be teachers, serving as examples of how to age and die well. The young can honor the vocation of the elderly by asking them to tell their stories and by promising to remember and to retell their stories after the elderly have died. As Cicero said, "The burden of age is lighter for those who feel respected and loved by the young."[48]

We must not give death a victory it doesn't deserve. Despair is not permitted among those who know the truth about our end as eternal fellowship with God. The young can remind the old that aging is not an excuse for irresponsibility, indifference, or nihilism. The old can show the young that if we live our lives in fear or denial of death, we deprive ourselves of both living the good life and dying the good death. The Christian faith gives us something worth living for and a divine-human relationship worth dying into.

Without resurrection hope, one is forced to concede that Franz Kafka was right: "The meaning of life is that it stops."[49] Christians know the truth not only that life is terminal, that it stops, but also that even mortal life can have meaning because life with God is not over and done with until God says it is.

The dying of many older people is consumed with regret for things done and left undone. Regret is bound to be present where there's death because too many modern Americans believe that our actions are the only actions, our agency is the only agency. We believe we must strive and produce because solely by our efforts do we ensure that our lives are worth living. We think it's an injustice for creatures so wonderful

as ourselves to age and die because it's up to us to make the world turn out right. We've got the whole world in our hands. Amid such delusion, even the most accomplished lives are bound to feel unfinished and regrettable when God is inactive and everything is left up to us.

So as we come to the boundary of our lives, it's good to be reminded that Jesus asserted, toward the end of his earthly life, "My father is still working, and I am working too" (John 5:17). We are creatures who are loved by an active Creator; we are not lonely, frantically driven sole creators. To believe that God is eternal though we are not is to have hope that though our earthly, human work is coming to a close, God's work is continued by God and by God's creativity among coming generations. As Charles Wesley purportedly said, "God buries his workers but carries on his work."

Moses lived to the ripe old age of 120 and still died without entering the promised land (Deut. 31:1–7). Martin Luther King Jr. recalled Moses's death before his life work was completed in his "I've Been to the Mountaintop" sermon the night before he died, confident in his resurrection faith that though his work for racial justice in America was incomplete, God's intentions are not forever defeated. Though King would not get to the "promised land," he had faith that by God's grace, his people would.

Paul admits that death causes grief. We grieve, but because of Christ's continuing victory, we "won't mourn like others who don't have any hope" (1 Thess. 4:13). Nor do we age like those who don't have hope. The God who related to us and summoned us in younger days continues to summon and to employ ordinary people to be the Body of Christ in motion, regardless of age, preparing us for our ultimate vocation—to die in the Lord.

For those of us who have lived out a natural life span, our goal should be palliative care of suffering, not a vain attempt to extend life through Promethean medical interventions. Suffering is the price we pay for the gift of embodied life. Medical resources should not be expended in vain on heroic efforts to achieve an eternal life that only God can give. Death is not an unjust intrusion into life nor a pathology that through extensive, expensive research may be conquered and cured. Death is the way that God set up human life, a boundary that can be overstepped only by God.

When Pope John Paul II refused to go back into the hospital during his final illness, he let himself die. That's not euthanasia; it's withholding heroic treatment, an acceptance of the inevitable, and a refusal to make an unrealistic attempt to postpone the end. As Psalm 90 says, we should "number our days" (v. 12)—know that we are terminal—in order to find a way to wisdom.

When I served as bishop, I discovered the empowerment in knowing the day and the hour when my episcopacy would end, when I would hand over my few achievements and all my frustrations to a successor. Knowing my termination date lent urgency to some of my projects. It also helped to lessen some of the stress caused by my opponents and critics: "There will be a day in August of 2012," I would tell them, "when the Lord will deliver me of you and you will be free of me, though I doubt you will be much happier."

Contemplating the reality of our dying can have a similar effect on our living. We older adults may not know the exact date of our termination, but God gives us opportunities to realize that one day our days will end and that we must entrust our work into the hands of our successors and our lives into the hands of the loving God who gave us life.

Besides, nothing in the Christian tradition leads us to regard biological life, its continuance or its comfortability, as an absolute good that must be sought at all costs. Aging and dying look quite different from the standpoint of the church, the communion of saints.

Memory

On All Saints' Day the church gathers with the dead. We name all those who told us about Jesus and who walked with Jesus in such a way that we wanted to walk with Christ too. The communion of saints comprises the church. Remembrance of and gratitude for the saints keep the church from being reduced to the merely present moment and the church's membership from being limited to those who currently sit in the pews. The church recalls its dead through time, honors their bodies in its funeral practices, and looks forward by looking back. Thus, the church is a community of memory. Memory enables us to see God acting through time, making historians of us all.

In my attempts to lead my church to greater vitality, to reach out to the next generation in order for the denomination to have a future, I learned the importance of having people in the room who could remember when the United Methodist Church was not in decline. Without those who remembered when the church was more faithful in its mission and evangelism, the church was in danger of acquiescing to death and decline as our fate.

When history is considered to be superfluous bunk, the gifts of continuity that the elderly bring to a congregation are undervalued. My first week as the new pastor of a congregation, I always visited the older members first. This won me points. After my visit, these folks would phone their friends and say, "Our nice young pastor visited me today." More importantly, I would say to them, "Tell me how this congregation got to where it is today. What do I need to know about this congregation in order to be an effective pastor here?"

In Plato's *Republic*, Socrates says, "I enjoy talking with very old people. They've gone before us on the road by which we, too, may have to travel, and I think we do well to learn from them what it is like."[50] The stories about the past, told by the elders, point the young into the future. The Christian community can move forward by being critiqued by the memory of the community. To gather on Sunday and to submit to the discipline of remembrance that is entailed in the reading of Scripture is to risk prophetic judgment on the present church. At the same time, we ought to admit that memory can be unreliable, corrupted by nostalgia and sentimentality. Christian community can become closed and introverted, bound to the past that was or never really was.

Sometimes elderly tellers of tales keep a congregation stuck in unhealthy narratives of the congregational past as they tirelessly (and tiresomely) reiterate past injustices or controversies in the congregation.

"This church is still suffering from the damage done here by Pastor Smith," said a church member during her new pastor's first visit to her apartment.

"Pastor Smith?" she asked. "When did he serve here?"

"From 1958 until 1962," she said. "Bad years for us."

"I was in junior high then," the pastor responded glumly.

Though I'm uncertain how wisdom is attained, it's clear to me that the acquisition of years does not correlate directly with the

accruing of wisdom. "No fool like an old fool," we say. Do we have any evidence to suggest that our election of a president who was over seventy meant that we were electing a wise person? King Solomon was wiser as a young person than when he grew old and became as foolish as King Lear. Vaillant surmises that Jefferson, Gandhi, King, Mohammed, Lincoln, Tolstoy, and Shakespeare all reached the pinnacle of their wisdom between ages thirty and fifty.[51] Still, Methodist that I am, I must add that John Wesley labored in the vineyard of the Lord right to the end, praising God through his ninety-first year.

I remember, as a child, that my mother loved watching a TV show called *Life Begins at Eighty*. Host Jack Barry led a panel of octogenarians who answered questions sent in by viewers at home. *Life Begins at Eighty* died in 1956 and had no successors. What does that tell you about the public's thirst for the wisdom of the aged?

Vaillant cites a study called the Mature Reflective Judgment Interview, which found that there is an increase in wisdom up until age thirty-five. After that, researchers found no strong evidence for further wisdom growth.[52] Yet, who would deny that judges, baseball managers, cooks, and pastors can grow in wisdom with decades of seasoning? That pop movies portray and adore the Obi-Wan Kenobis, Gandalfs, and Dumbledores suggests a widespread longing for wise elders, a role I'm only too happy to play! Virginia Woolf, in *Mrs. Dalloway*, says of one of the elders in her story, "The compensation of growing old . . . was simply this: that the passions remain as strong as ever, but one had gained—at last!—The power which adds the supreme flavor to existence—the power of taking hold of experience, of turning it around, slowly, in the light."[53]

Not all elderly are wise or have wise stories to tell. And yet congregations are dependent on having a few wise among them to narrate the good and the bad. A new church pastor, when asked what he most needed to succeed at a church plant, replied, "I never felt I would be saying this. I've spent much of my ministry complaining about traditionalist, conservative, older people in my church. But right now, our trendy twentysomething church could use about a half dozen traditionalist, history-bearing elders to help us steady ourselves and move forward." Older people, at least some older people, must

be good at telling stories in order for a community to nourish and refurbish its identity and thereby to survive and thrive.

"Change is unsustainable when it is not rooted in the core identity and basic stories of a congregation," says veteran church observer Lovett Weems Jr.[54] Dean Greg Jones speaks to those of us at Duke on the need for "traditioned innovation," combining two words we don't often hear together. If an innovative pastor wants change to stick, that pastor had better honor the traditions, stories, and enduring values of a congregation (i.e., listen to the stories told by the elders).

When I was bishop, I was surprised to hear some of my older pastors complain, "The bishop is prejudiced against old pastors." I was sixty-five myself. How could I think negatively of older people? As I reflected on their complaint, I had to admit that, in my drive to innovate and improve the church, I had run roughshod over what many of them loved about their churches. When I said, "We ought to change *x*," they heard me devaluing the institution they had given their lives to produce. Perhaps if I had aimed for innovation that was "traditioned," more of the change I wrought would have endured.

Some of us like to think of ourselves as "progressive." Every day we are getting better and better in every way. But this notion of progress, this naively optimistic view of history so prevalent in the West carries with it an incipient rejection of aging. Labeling ourselves progressive implies that we are leaving behind something that is less important, inadequate, and backward and progressing toward something of greater value.[55]

"Progressive Christianity" implies that somehow we are moving onward from insufficient ideas to better ideas, from benighted, superficial faith to more advanced, more satisfactory faith. The Western notion of progress and forward development of history could be a source of some of our debilitating stereotypes of elderhood. Christ is not a historical figure that we can rise above or go beyond; he is the Lord of all, whom we are still trying to comprehend and to catch up with. Christians believe that time does not rise in an upward spiral, an ascending ramp, but rather has a beginning and an ending with God.

The meaning and significance of our lifetime is not solely within our hands. Time is constantly being punctuated and guided by God's

activity, *kairos*, when the grace and judgment of God turn our time into God's time. At every stage of life, including the last, our *chronos* can become God's *kairos*. God is determined to have us at each stage of life, especially the last.

Church is inherently traditional and tradition-bearing; we need not thoughtlessly jettison the wisdom of the saints from the past. Yet church is also where we are always being drawn toward a living God; we need not cower before the new and the innovative.

When I go to the doctor's office, I must fill out my health history on an electronic tablet. Nearly all my shopping is online now. When I resumed teaching at Duke Divinity School after being bishop, I was required to take two days of classroom technology training. It's somewhat comforting, in a fast-paced technological age, that church is the one place in my life that is essentially unchanged. Forgive me for being really peeved when my pastor substitutes "Edelweiss" for the traditional tune of the Doxology.

Theologian David Matzko McCarthy reflects on the interplay, and sometimes the tension, between continuity and change in the Christian community.[56] Confronted with physical decline and the loss of loved ones, we aging are tempted to attempt to maintain a sense of sameness and continuity. We spend so much time recalling the past in a vain effort to save the people and the relationships that we loved from the ravages of forgetfulness. Little wonder that many older persons love their church as a place where memory is valued and encouraged and the pews are securely bolted to the floor.

And yet we worship and serve a resurrected, living Lord who is always striding before us into the future. McCarthy notes:

> Generational continuity is essential to the church, which by definition includes the unity of all generations, and all times and places in communion with God . . . in a great company of all who have been drawn into God's self-giving. This community always makes us much more than we would have been otherwise. . . . This coming out and going beyond ourselves, is the pattern of grace. . . . Because the church is bound in time, however, change is inevitable and necessary. Issues of continuity and change are, for Christians, issues about the life of the church and its identity as a people of God.[57]

The Christian church lives by continuity, by remembrance, following God into the future by what we know of God's actions in the past. Traditioning—introducing the young to the old, old gospel story; lovingly reiterating the core of our faith; and taking up the habits required for holy living—is a major activity of the church whereby the church makes its existence intelligible. The primary reason for remembering and traditioning is to equip ourselves to keep up with the machinations of a living God.

As I was becoming a bishop, I sought advice from retired bishops. Most of them remembered the episcopacy as a frustrating, well-nigh futile undertaking in which they were constantly thwarted by constituencies as well as by the restrictions of church law.

Yet a few of the retired bishops I interviewed remembered their time of leadership as demanding but rewarding ministry. I asked one, "Why do so many of the retired bishops tell me that the job is impossible?"

"That's how some older bishops excuse their own ineffectiveness," said the wiser retired bishop.

It's good for the young to seek the advice of the aged. And yet our memories should be received and evaluated with a degree of skepticism, for memory can be selective and self-serving, if not self-deluding.

At the beginning of the semester I tell my seminarians, "I've been in ministry a long time. I'm going to share with you some of the lessons I've learned and some of the mistakes I've made. I hope you will find my memories to be helpful. However, not all of my wisdom will have value. You can't serve the church that I served. You'll have to profit from some of my memories and dispose of the rest so that my memories won't keep you tied to the old order, which you'll need to leave behind as you press on."

One reason the aging remember is to preserve a now-disintegrating sense of self. We remember selectively, even desperately, defiantly, having lost a job and some of our friends and family. Remembrance is an act of defiance against injustice, recalling the lives of past victims in order that their witness not be lost. Is my sleep so full of dreams these days because my mind is frantically attempting to retrieve and relive bits of a past that's now slipping away?

Sometimes we must selectively recall because past hurts are too debilitating to be remembered. While the forgiveness that Jesus com-

mands is more complex than "forgive and forget," there is an element of forgetfulness in true forgiveness. We forget past wrongs done to us because we remember Christ's command to forgive our enemies. Nurturance of grudges and remembrance of past slights saps the life out of us, so it's better willfully to forget than to remember.

And yet some of our feverish attempts to hold on to our memories may be a sign that we fear we are being forgotten. We may have bought into the widespread American notion that the way to have a self is constantly to construct, to reconstruct, and to present the ideal self (these days, presented through social media), seeing ourselves as the sum of our efforts rather than as a gift of God's love and vocation. Our hope is not in our or others' ability to preserve the memory of who we "really are"; rather, our hope is that a resurrecting God remembers us. The psalmist prays, "Remember me!" (Ps. 25:7).

In a sermon on Psalm 25:7, "Remember Not the Sins of My Youth, Remember Me," Elizabeth Achtemeier recalled a self-important faculty colleague who had no time to waste with her when she was a struggling young professor; he was writing important books, and she was only a young woman in a man's world. "As he lay dying, I visited him in hospital. Comatose, tubes coming out of his nose. His wife had stacked his four books on the bedside table to comfort him." Achtemeier paused for effect, tilted toward the congregation, stared them down through her granny glasses, and took her voice down to a threatening whisper. "Friends, when you die, you die, and all that you proudly created dies with you. If God forgets to take you along into eternity, *you are without hope.*"

Remembrance of God's remembrance of us is an important insight that can help us when loved ones are diagnosed with or suffer from dementia. In Christian funerals, we remember those who have lost minds and lives and whose bodies have disintegrated. They are remembered by the community and, more importantly, by God. Their existence, though radically changed, ends not if God remembers—that is, resurrects.

God's promised resurrection remembrance of us is our great hope and comfort as Christians, particularly in seasons of life when we are prone to forgetfulness. Sometimes the church remembers on behalf of those who are losing their mental capacities, prays for those who can

no longer pray, believes for those who are being tortured by doubt, and witnesses publicly for those who no longer speak.

Membership in the Body of Christ never comes as a personal achievement but as a gift, an invitation from God, an adoption into the community. The elderly—who feel that their opportunities for individual achievement are diminished—can be living, bodily reminders to us all that our lives are not the sum of our attainments, never our sole possessions, but rather, from birth to death, God's gifts.

SIX

Growing Old in Church

As [Jesus] was teaching, he said, "Watch out for the legal experts. They like to walk around in long robes. They want to be greeted with honor in the markets. They long for places of honor in the synagogues and at banquets. They are the ones who cheat widows out of their homes, and to show off they say long prayers. They will be judged most harshly." Jesus sat across from the collection box for the temple treasury and observed how the crowd gave their money. Many rich people were throwing in lots of money. One poor widow came forward and put in two small copper coins worth a penny. Jesus called his disciples to him and said, "I assure you that this poor widow has put in more than everyone who's been putting money in the treasury. All of them are giving out of their spare change. But she from her hopeless poverty has given everything she had, even what she needed to live on."

—Mark 12:38–44

In first-century Judaism, scribes were devout, pious persons who devoted themselves to worship and to studying Torah. Because they were professional interpreters of Scripture, their advice was sought by anyone aspiring to be part of God's realm.

Yet Jesus is as critical of the scribes as they are of him. Specifically, he accuses them of cheating "widows out of their homes" (presumably

123

to fill the temple coffers). One day they "will be judged most harshly"
(v. 40).

Widows occupy a special place in God's concern for justice, making it all the more sad that the scribes, the interpreters of religious
law, are defrauding those whom the religious law charges them to
protect.

Jesus notes the rich placing their big gifts in the temple treasury,
but he gives special notice to the poor widow who drops in two coins,
all that she has. In noticing the widow, Jesus is once again focusing
on "the least of these." And as he frequently does, Jesus turns the
tables, seeing those who appear to be great as small and exalting
those who are unimportant in the eyes of the world.

But more is going on in this episode than Jesus commending an
older woman for exemplary stewardship. Jesus charges that the temple in Jerusalem is corrupt. In Mark 13:1–2, Jesus's disciples admire
the temple, but Jesus says that the temple will be torn down, stone
cast from stone. The disciples look at the religious establishment and
see beauty to be admired; Jesus sees corruption and disobedience of
God's will.

Jesus sees with sadness the woman's gift together with the hypocrisy and corruption of the scribes.[1] He laments that the religious
leaders will squander the poor woman's gift, even though she is giving them all that she has. Through her self-sacrificial gift, the old
woman is unknowingly propping up a corrupt government-religious
apparatus. But Jesus sees and Jesus knows: the widow is a lover of
God who is being victimized by those who are charged by God to
be her protectors.

Though this older woman is not prominent in the eyes of the
world, Jesus sees her, in all her innocence and goodness. And though
corrupt religious leaders prey on the goodwill of people, especially
poor (older) people, God sees and knows and is working to end this
corruption.

Maybe Mark tells this story as encouragement not to give up. Even
though the elderly poor may be vulnerable to corrupt political, economic, and religious systems, God sees and is moving on their behalf.

In this passage, there is a word of comfort for the vulnerable,
including the aged, who put their trust and their treasure in religious

institutions and those who lead them. There is also a warning for the powerful, who busily administer systems that dominate the poor and the vulnerable, particularly if the systems are God's. God takes sides. Corrupt, insensitive religious leaders, beware.

The church must engage the rising storm of aging, not only because it is a demographic, social crisis but also because we are mandated by Jesus Christ to align ourselves with the disempowered against the powerful, particularly in the church.

It is my passionate conviction that Christian congregations are the ideal location for equipping disciples for their vocations and for helping people negotiate life's transitions, especially the stage of life called aging. I therefore agree with Rowan Greer that "the best care we can give the aged is, when possible, to use their gifts and to love them for what they can give. This means trying to avoid segregating the aged or at least seeking to mitigate the isolation as much as we can. We can strive to enable the aged to keep on serving, to be needed."[2] No better place for this to happen than in your church and mine.

Christian Community

Numerous studies show that older adults who are involved and embedded in vibrant social networks tend to have better physical and mental health than individuals who do not enjoy such close ties.[3] A congregation—those assembled by Jesus Christ to be his physical, bodily, communal presence in the world—is a natural place for significant human social interaction. Neal Krause, who cites many studies on the good effects of church involvement, defines church-based social support as "the emotional, tangible, and spiritual assistance that is exchanged among people who worship in the same congregation."[4] In a culture plagued by detachment, loneliness, and separation, the church's practices of community have become a great gift we have to offer the world.

The church should do all it can to help older people socialize, even when they have mobility challenges. In communities where there is a lack of public transportation, a church van ride service can be a godsend. Technology, such as the internet, provides a potential means of social connection for seniors and enables homebound people to be

connected to the church. It is now possible for every congregation to have contact with homebound members and for seniors to keep up with the life of the congregation through social media.

Congregational culture must move from seeing the aging as those who lack—no job, declining health, slackening intellectual interest— to those who have attained a special status in the Body of Christ, those who have acquired (according to Jimmy Carter) a set of virtues and who have the gifts of longevity, life, and time for service to others.[5] People over sixty-five spend more time volunteering than any other age group, and over 45 percent of all older volunteers help others through religious organizations.[6]

While extolling the joys of life in community, we ought to acknowledge that negative interactions and unpleasant social encounters can erode the physical and mental health of older people.[7] Krause characterizes deleterious exchanges in the church as "disagreements, criticism, rejection, and invasion of privacy" and "excessive helping as well as ineffective helping."[8] When one has spent years supporting a congregation, watching it slowly decline or be torn apart by controversy is no fun. My own denomination is closing hundreds of churches every year. When a church closes, usually the only members left to be displaced and to grieve the death of a congregation are the elderly.

If older people are very loyal to their congregation, negative interactions with people in the congregation can be quite painful. Having lost some of the social connections that brought joy in earlier days, they find negative interactions, division, bickering, and squabbling within the church to be particularly difficult.[9]

Intergenerational Interaction

One of the gifts of many churches is intergenerational interaction. We have become an age-segregated society in which the aging members have no vital role to play (unlike an agricultural society where there is still much for elders to contribute, such as child rearing). Close to 7 percent of the American elderly live in either residential facilities or senior living communities.[10] These communities provide advantages for older people, like an increased sense of security,

neighbors, friends, social interaction, recreation, proximity to care-givers, and freedom from being an undue burden on loved ones. Yet age-segregated communities also have disadvantages, including a lack of diversity of interaction, high cost, and the illusion that one is really living independently.

A serious drawback of these communities is that death is ever present. One reason Christian funerals ought to be held in a church is that mortuaries and funeral homes, or chapels in nursing homes, have only one association: death. When a Service of Death and Resurrection occurs in a church, it takes place amid a host of intergenerational memories from the entire life cycle: baptism, marriage, Sunday worship.

The church is in the meaning-making, meaning-receiving business. A primary instrument of meaning-making is the church's worship. Every Service of Christian Marriage is not just about a bride and a groom. The service is preparation for marriage and supports those already married. In similar ways, the Service of Death and Resurrection is not just for the immediately grieving family. It is also education and preparation for grief and dying for all those present. For the elderly who are in the immediate crisis of aging, as well as for the young who are preparing to age, the intergenerational nature of the church is a great gift.

In Jesus Christ, the Fourth Commandment to honor our elders is not abrogated, but it is reformed through a creative restructuring of the family. Through the baptismal reformation of the family and the formation of a new and distinctive people called the church, the command to honor our elders is expanded, and we are given responsibility for people beyond the bounds of our own generation.

The best way to form intergenerational bonds in the church is by working together across generations in ministry and letting the bonds arise out of our shared work in Christ.

In a study of twenty black congregations in Philadelphia, John Morrison found that these congregations refused to organize themselves by rigid age designation and separation. Members of the church had difficulty telling whether a member was under or over sixty-five. Young people were given the opportunity at an early age to participate in key governing groups. Functional rather than chronological criteria were used to define membership in various cohorts, and there

was much age diversity within the majority of the church's gatherings. Morrison believes that "development of specific senior citizens groups within churches may not be wise. In fact, a number of pastors [whom he studied] felt that age designations or age segregated programs were inherently problematic and should be avoided."[11]

At the conclusion of a congregational study on forgiveness in Jesus's name, I noted how our study had been enriched by having three or four generations of Christians in the discussions. Younger members of the group tended to think of forgiveness as mostly a matter of "not being overly sensitive when somebody does something wrong to you" and of "not making too big a deal out of it." The middle-aged members of the group questioned the practicality and workability of an ethic of forgiveness. "Is Jesus serious?" one asked. The older members of the group agreed to the great difficulty of forgiveness but also told some moving stories about why forgiveness is essential in order to live life without great sadness.

"When I get to be your age," said a younger participant, "I hope I'll be half as honest as you are about how hard it is to follow Jesus."

"I'm sure you will," said the older person. "God has done so many good things in your life already."

A prophetic witness of the church in our day is to push back against our society's tendency to age-segregate and to show how Jesus Christ gives his followers the ability to appreciate one another, to give and to receive differing gifts from one another, and to take responsibility for one another across generations.

Erik Erikson said that successful aging calls for the cultivation of "generativity," the ability to stay reasonably productive and connected to others who are busy engaging with the challenges of life.[12] George Vaillant says that a key factor in the well-being of those over sixty-five is frequent contact with younger generations. It is particularly life-giving for the elderly to be invested in the lives of younger people outside their biological families, supporting and admiring their work, which will outlive them.[13]

Senior Appreciation Sunday is usually a testimony to a congregation's marginalization of the elderly. If aging is a lifelong task for everyone in the church and if all our days, particularly our last, are occasions for witness and ministry, then treating aging as a particularly

tragic time of life or a moral achievement worthy of unusual honor can be counterproductive to fostering a Christian sense of aging. The church owes its aging more than honor; what the elderly most need from the church is continued deployment in mission.

The prophet Micah, condemning Israel's corruption, saw tensions between parents and children as a symbol of Israel's apostasy: "For the son treats the father with contempt, / the daughter rises up against her mother" (7:6 NRSV). Malachi, on the other hand, looked forward to a time when God's faithful people would be united across the generations:

> Look, I am sending Elijah the prophet to you,
>> before the great and terrifying day of the LORD arrives.
> Turn the hearts of the parents to the children
>> and the hearts of the children to their parents. (4:5–6)

Churches need to provide multiple opportunities for interaction between older members and youth. The young must come to terms with the elderly among them and be honest about the ways they may fear being around aging bodies. People skip funerals, warehouse the elderly, and avoid visiting nursing homes in the unacknowledged hope that by evading the aging, they won't have to face the truth that they too are moving inexorably toward their end. "You shall be as I," warns a New England tombstone, reason enough for the young to be wary of the old. As Augustine said, *timor mortis* (fear of death) is the driving force behind much of humanity's best and worst.[14]

In a culture in which there is widespread age segregation and growing friction between Boomers and Gen Xs, Millennials, and iGens, an intergenerational church is a gift to both young and old. A chief role of a pastor is to be a community person whose task is to constantly look for opportunities for unifying practices. Effective pastors encourage the cohesion of the community and work for the inclusion of all. Here are some ways a church can encourage intergenerational interaction.

- Many aging adults must eat alone; mealtimes are often the loneliest times of their day. Church members can regularly eat together with age groups mixed.

- Baptism and confirmation offer important opportunities for intergenerational relationships. Mentor-based confirmation programs are a grand opportunity to pair an older, more experienced Christian with a novice Christian.[15]
- When someone moves into a nursing facility or into a room at a retirement center, representatives from the congregation can visit and offer a blessing.
- When a pastor or lay caregiver visits the elderly in a nursing facility, they can bring young people along.

Many older adults spend a great deal of their time alone, more so than at any other time in their lives. Self-concern, a challenge at any time of life, can be magnified. Bernice Neugarten sums up her research on personality change in older adults: "Although there are important differences between men and women as they age, in both sexes, older individuals seemed to move toward more eccentric, self-preoccupied positions."[16] Some among the elderly feel that if they do not care about themselves, no one will. Depression, anxiety, and difficulty with problem solving can arise out of older adults' excessive self-absorption. Intergenerational connections can help older adults move beyond unwarranted self-concern.

The Christian faith helps to shift the focus away from self. The best ministries of the church draw people out of themselves in engagement in mission, thereby giving people the means to be concerned about someone other than themselves.

Mary Pipher warns that at whatever age we find ourselves, we all have a stake in helping the elderly: "Soon our country will be avalanched by old people, and those people will be us. In a few decades, our solutions to the dilemmas of caring for our elders will be applied to our own lives. The kindness, the indifference, the ignorance, and the wisdom will be passed on. The more we love and respect our elders, the more we teach our children to love and respect us. The more we think through problems today, the more organizational and cultural structures will be in place to handle our generation's needs."[17]

In giving, we receive. By modeling healthy intergenerational interaction—teaching the young how to respect and cherish the old and teaching the old how to support, teach, and encourage the

young—the church embodies its Golden Rule and shows the world that Christ is capable of creating a truly beloved community.

The Gifts of God for the People of God

Among the potential gifts of life within a Christian congregation are these:

- The church helps us think about matters that, for all sorts of reasons, are difficult to think about in this culture.
- The church provides a lifetime of preparation for death.
- The church is a primary location where we deal with losses and seek healing for the pain of loss.
- The rituals of the church provide for the public processing of our fears and our sorrows, setting our anxieties in the context of the full sweep of the Christian faith.
- The church calls certain people elders, potentially making the church a place where there is contact with and formation by the wisdom of the ages as young and old minister to one another.
- In the church's rituals and liturgy we actively practice and encourage remembrance and lovingly guard and reiterate tradition as we corporately submit to judgment by and the witness of the saints.
- The church is where we tell stories, giving and receiving testimony from the living and the dead about the way to a life worth living.
- The church is a location for engagement in confession, forgiveness, and reconciliation.
- The church is a place of thoughtful, imaginative reflection on our lives and our future.
- The church is where ordinary people receive their vocations, where we accept our assignments in the mission of Jesus Christ, and where we are commissioned to participate in his moves in the world that he is saving.
- The church can be a place where we bring some of our self-deluding, self-absorbed nostalgia under control. We can rise

above sappy, sentimental fictions of the human condition and learn to tell the truth about ourselves and the world.

- The church is where we find grace and Sabbath rest and are lifted above our desires to produce, to control, to consume, and to be independent.

- The church is where we are given the grace and the time to look back and sense Providence at work and where we take time to attend to one another, including the elderly.

- The church is where, in a world of lies, we learn to tell and to hear the truth and to be reconciled to God, to ourselves, and to one another.

- In the church we help others name and claim their God-given gifts as the old encourage the young to discover and affirm their vocations.

What the Church Needs to Do for the Aging

"Our congregation is located in a huge retirement area," a young woman said. "We've never been members of such an active church. We've got dozens of ministries—food distribution, medical transportation, emergency assistance, tutoring of kids, study groups around the clock, six services of worship every week. I can't believe our good fortune at having such a great place to be the church. The need is so obvious, the gifts so evident, and the opportunities for mission so boundless because we have so many retired folks with the time and the talents to lead us!"

Only the church would look on the storm of aging, the exponential increase in the number of elderly, as a grand opportunity to be the church. Christians are called not just to be forgiven and saved but also to be in mission. Here are some ways the church can be in mission to the aging.

Support Caregivers

Millions of Americans are engaged in caregiving. Many of these caregivers report that caregiving is the major source of stress in

their lives. In fact, the challenges of caregiving have been called "the twenty-first century's greatest test of character."[18] Families may want to help elderly family members negotiate the challenges, but aging can be hard on everybody. One family out of four is caring for an older relative. For the first time in history, many middle-aged people will have more parents alive than they have children.[19] Our freedom to move to other parts of the country for jobs or lifestyle means that we are geographically dispersed. "Every weekend I spend more time getting to my parents to check on them than I spend time with them," a woman in my congregation lamented.

The average age for caregivers is forty-nine.[20] Many in the "sandwich generation"—those caught between caring for aging parents on one end of the life spectrum and raising children on the other—find large portions of their lives consumed by caring for vulnerable parents who once were their stalwart protectors. Caregivers feel guilty for taking time away from their children to care for an aged parent. Should the resources that the caregiver has saved for future retirement be depleted by paying for the care of an aged parent?

The stress associated with caregiving often comes not simply from the demanding tasks of care but also from the lack of value and reward our culture places on caregiving. The incentive to get out of bed, to start moving, to make a list, and to feel a sense of responsibility can be rewarding for those who find meaning in their caregiving roles. Sometimes the challenge is to find a way to make involuntary caregiving become, to some degree, voluntary—to discover joy in service to another in need.

Few of us can choose the older adults for whom we provide care; nor can we choose who will be our caregivers, which serves as a reminder that our lives are not constituted by our choices but by God's grace. Therefore, a theological task for many of us is to see the aging for whom we care as gifts and to see those who care for us in our need as God's gifts to us.[21]

Whereas most congregations attempt to be in contact with their elderly members, few churches have active programs of support for those who give care to the elderly. Every church ought to know who is functioning as a caregiver. Then to support them, church members can honor the caregivers' around-the-clock care by offering a few

hours of respite. Members of the church can also provide assistance such as shopping, cooking, cleaning, and banking, along with social activities such as visiting, listening, and sharing feelings.

A couple years ago, when I was teaching in Australia, the country was rocked by the news that an elderly woman with Alzheimer's had starved to death after her caregiver husband had suffered a stroke and died. They had been dead for days when they were found, sitting together at their breakfast table. He was her sole caregiver and even though the couple was affluent and neighbors had offered to help, he had refused because he felt that his wife's care was his sole responsibility as a loving husband.

Caregivers may be reluctant to ask for help and neighbors may be reluctant to insist on giving help, but things ought to be different in the Body of Christ.

Provide Retirement Planning

By the late twentieth century, the average number of years of retirement prior to death had increased from three to fifteen.[22] Many of us will spend more time in retirement than any previous generation.[23] Retirement, whether voluntary or involuntary, can be a useful shock that jolts us into the realization that we are indeed aging. In retirement, we are given the gifts of being able to grow, to embrace new possibilities, to find jobs that better fit our gifts and life experiences—in short, to make the transition from (as one rabbi put it) "age-ing to sage-ing."[24]

Unfortunately, planning for retirement has been monopolized by financial advisors. What if, once a year, the church sponsored a celebration/retreat for those who had reached sixty-five? Pastors could also help people devise a theological plan for retirement that answers questions like, "How will I spend my time with God?" and "What new spiritual disciplines will I assume?"

I say again: one can retire from a job but not from Christian discipleship. Those who reach sixty-five should receive pastoral guidance about their vocation in retirement. Wasting the precious time we have been given by being preoccupied with ourselves cannot be an option for those who aspire to age like Christians. "I no longer have a job,

so I can no longer be the person I was; who is God calling me to be now?" is an appropriate question for those moving into retirement.

Discuss Legacy

A moral test of a life well lived and a dying well done is how we make out our will. To whom will we give the material things we've accumulated? George Vaillant says that whereas the task of young adults is to create biological heirs, the task of old age is to create social heirs.[25] Because we have here no "permanent city" (Heb. 13:14), it is fair to ask, "What will we leave behind?" Communally, socially, doxologically, what will be our bequest? Every church stewardship program should have a component that encourages legacy planning, giving that keeps on giving after we're gone. If we have loved a congregation in life, we can ensure that its ministry remains vibrant by our gifts to it in our deaths.

As Christians, we are under obligation to be good stewards of our material goods. "We give Thee but Thine own, whate'er the gift may be. All that we have is Thine alone, a trust, O Lord, from Thee," my childhood church taught us to sing as we brought the offering plates forward on Sunday. Each Sunday's offering is a dress rehearsal for our final offering, handing over to God everything we once thought was ours. If only King Lear could have seen that his power and possessions were not his to dole out in order to sustain his privilege but rather God's gifts entrusted to him for a season and then returned to the giver.

A historian of my church explained our decline: "In its first hundred years, the Methodist Church built institutions to help other people's children. In their second century, Methodists mainly supported institutions to benefit their own families." Most of us in the top decile of economically privileged Americans will leave little behind to anyone other than our children. What we've accumulated could do much good for a wider set of heirs.

John Wesley said famously, "Gain all you can, save all you can, give all you can," with Wesley's emphasis decidedly on "give all you can."[26] Wesley received much money from his publications but made certain that he died poor and directed that only paupers be allowed

to carry his coffin to his grave. Thus he taught his heirs a valuable lesson in legacy.

Plato advises that the most enduring legacy is another person similar to ourselves.[27] As Christians, may we aspire to leave a public witness of our gratitude for the life we were given, the part we played in God's work, our courage in the face of death, and our steadfast hope in the triumph of Jesus Christ.

Eugene Bianchi says that the best legacy we can leave our children "is a personally lived lesson about facing old age and death with courage and grace."[28]

Promote Vocation

We Christians are those who do not have to fabricate their identities by ourselves. We are Christians because we have been summoned, commissioned, enlisted, called by God to join in God's work in the world.

There are interesting parallels between late adulthood and adolescence. The identity question—"Who am I?"—that occupied much of anguished adolescence can also be asked with intensity and poignancy in the later adult years. The question can be particularly painful for older adults who have already achieved certain things and lived enough of life for personality to be well developed if not downright ossified. The person who had a ready answer to "Who am I?" now must answer, "I know who I have been, but who am I now?"

The vocational assertion "It is God who hath made us and not we ourselves" (Ps. 100:3 KJV) sounds odd, schooled as we are in the contemporary American fiction that our lives are our possessions to use as we choose. Yet as Christians, we assert that we are derivative, contingent, created by a God who breathes life into mud (Gen. 2:7) and loans breath only for as long as God wills.

At any time in life, but especially in one's last decade, the typical American question "What should *I* do with *my* life?" is the wrong question. Modernity compels us to write the story that defines who we are, to choose from a variety of possible plots to make a meaningful existence. Christians believe the proper question is not "What do *I* want to do?" but rather "How is God calling me to service?"

Theologian Karl Barth characterized vocation as a "place" where we are met by God's summons. "In any moment we meet the call of God anew, and, hence, in every moment it is as it were, 'just setting out.'"[29] Vocation's power, said Hermann Hesse, is when "the soul is awakened . . . so that instead of dreams and presentiments from within a summons comes from without" and "presents itself and makes its claim."[30] To be a Christian is to be called from without, to be externally authorized, given a role to play in God's salvation of the world. That we are not self-made implies that we are God's property to be called into service as God pleases.

In the New Testament, "calling" or "vocation" refers to discipleship rather than to employment. We can be called to eternal life (1 Tim. 6:12), into fellowship with Christ (1 Cor. 1:9), out of darkness into light (1 Pet. 2:9), and into right relationship with God (Rom. 8:30), but not to a career. Paul was a tentmaker (Acts 18:3), but nowhere is Paul "called" to be a tentmaker. Tentmaking put bread on the table, justification enough for Paul to give it his best. For those who have overly invested themselves in careers or even in parenting a family, the last years of life present an opportunity to recover the joy of more fully giving themselves to discipleship.

Vocation is what God wants from us, whereby our lives are transformed into a consequence of God's redemption of the world. Jesus Christ chooses not to work alone. In vocation, God attaches us to projects and purposes greater than ourselves. Look no further than Jesus's disciples—remarkably mediocre, untalented, lackluster yokels—to see that innate talent or inner yearning has less to do with vocation than God's desire to redeem lives by assigning us something to do for God. As Jesus succinctly says, in a verse that must be rediscovered at every stage in life, "Ye have not chosen me, but I have chosen you, and ordained you, that ye should go and bring forth fruit" (John 15:16 KJV).[31]

While there are good reasons for older people to retire from their careers or the labors of parenting, there's no theological justification for them to think that their responsibilities to Jesus are fulfilled so that now they can focus only on themselves.

As we have noted, aging is often accompanied by much loss. Sometimes God calls us from our losses and helps us regather our sense of

purpose in order to move into a new future with reformed identity and purpose. Grieving our losses can be a call for prayer and reflection to make sense of our situation and undertake the tough vocational work of reconstructing our identity, role, and relationships.

"My children are pressuring me to move. They're concerned that with my bad hearing, it's dangerous for me to live alone," the retired English professor shouted at me across her living room during a pastoral visit.

By the end of the afternoon, I sat in another living room with a father and his teenaged son in crisis. The single parent had a demanding job. When he came home at the end of the day, his son's blaring rock music was more than he could take. They argued about everything and were miserable.

"I wish I could move out of this house!" the son wailed.

"You and me both," sneered the beleaguered father.

Under the influence of the Holy Spirit I said, "Wait. I may have the answer to your problems."

After a bit of negotiating, the next day the teenager moved in with the elderly retired professor. "Your music won't bother me," chuckled the woman. "I'll turn off my hearing aid and you rock away! Now that you are living with me, I can stay in my home."

The three of them— father, son, and older friend—sat together in church on Sunday. These kinds of intergenerational relationships embody God's vision for healthy relationships in church.

We must honestly confront the clash between the American Zeitgeist and the Christian story about aging, nourishing the notion that at any stage in our lives we are still called to discipleship and community. Continuing discipleship usually requires transformation and change in order for us to be faithful. God has created us as people who have a need to serve, a compulsion to give. As Christians, we are commissioned to be Christ's representatives in the world. For the church to be complicit in taking away people's responsibility is sad.

Coach Mike Krzyzewski—a faithful Catholic—spoke at the Duke University retirees' luncheon. He said, "As I look around this room, I see people who were masters in physics, housekeeping, neonatal care, plumbing, roofing. Such wisdom is gathered here. What valuable experience!"

Coach K paused for a moment, leaned into the microphone, and said,

Now you owe us! I've got a friend who coaches a team where only two out of his fifteen players know their fathers. Look, people, the American family is in a mess. We need you. It's not good enough for you to sit back and say, "I raised my kids. I'm not looking after someone else's." Your wisdom and experience are valuable community resources!

Now, I've got notepads and pencils at every table. Write down what you are going to do to make Durham a better place, something you are good at that the world needs. Those of you who are already working to give back to the community, you write down what you are doing. We are going to sit quietly for a moment while you write this down. Then we'll collect them. Now!

For me, it was a grand moment of Christian vocation.

A woman in my church who suffered a terribly debilitating nerve disease asked me, "I wonder what God has in mind for me now?"

"Er, what do you mean?" I asked her awkwardly.

"I don't get out anymore," she said, "but, preacher, I'm perfectly capable of using a telephone." Each morning I would give her a list of people to call—visitors from the previous Sunday, people in the hospital, students away at college, committee members who needed to be reminded of meetings. I ordained her the Minister of Telephoning.

Mary despised being relegated to a nursing home when she broke her hip and was forced into a wheelchair for the rest of her days. She had been a high-powered business executive in her previous life.

She told me, "So I said to myself, 'You've spent your whole life rushing about, never time to sit and talk and listen to anybody. Now's your chance.'"

She asked the nurses to give her a list of folks who were lonely and who had few visitors. Each day Mary "goes to the office" by wheeling herself up and down the halls, knocking on doors, and asking people if they would like a visit. Now's her chance.

Martin Luther's conviction that every station in life can be a calling from God should be applied not to our careers but to the stage of life in which we are living. One could make a case that the Christian calling to stewardship, hospitality, compassion, advocacy, and

social justice can be exercised better during the last years of life than in prior stages. How wonderful to be able to say with satisfaction, after having exchanged a job for a vocation, "This is who I am. For this, I was made."[32]

When I led a delegation from our church to participate in the Moral Monday demonstration at the state capitol, I was a bit disappointed that the only people I could assemble were retired. Then I thought, who is better able to see the ravages of bad government or who is freer to risk arrest at a demonstration protesting a miserly state budget than retired school teachers and public servants?

Though we don't know many details about that place where God bids us in our ending, in our dying we can be hopeful that the God who constantly, resourcefully called us in life will continue to call us in our deaths. As we prepare for death, we have a last opportunity to ask, "What is God doing with me now?"

John Wesley, founder of the Methodist movement, bragged, "Our people know how to die!"[33] Dying well means witnessing to God's grace right to the end and gratefully remembering the manner and the good of one's life and for the church to remember us in the same way.

Grow in Grace

In my own Wesleyan tradition, we stress the power of God's grace working in us, at every time of life, to make us better than we could be without God. Grace is the power of God that enables us to have a more faithful life than we would have had if our lives had been left up to us. The great Wesleyan theological achievement was linking justification to sanctification, salvation by grace to growth in grace, promising not only rebirth but also continuing reconstruction. A living God keeps remaking us even when we think we are done. No one ages out of the adventure of Holy Spirit–induced growth in grace.

Rembrandt painted a picture of his elderly mother. The old woman is not sitting quietly, gazing out the window as the world passes by. She is intently studying a large open Bible.[34] In most congregations of my acquaintance, older adults are the majority of those in study groups. Their participation is not due simply to their having more time on their hands. Aging provokes an intellectual crisis that calls

for reframing, rethinking, and reconsidering the concepts and the principles that guided us during earlier years of our lives. The church can be a great location for thoughtful, intellectual exploration. Older adults need to be students not only because of the intellectual requirements for successful aging but also because we want to "grow in every way into Christ" (Eph. 4:15).

Mainline Protestant church decline is due in part to a corporate failure of intellectual nerve, amnesia regarding the core affirmations of the faith, and distraction that allows the nonessentials to crowd out the essentials. Christians need to read, think, and study their way out of this malaise.

At a church I recently visited, a woman (about my age) invited me to attend her Sunday school class.

"We are studying Mark 1:1 today," she said.

"Just the first chapter of Mark's Gospel?" I asked.

"The first verse of the first chapter," she responded. "At last we have the time to go deeper, verse by verse."

Offer Learning Opportunities

Churches ought to offer a class titled "Thinking like Christians about Aging." Class content could be derived from the chapters in this book. Here is a suggested learning plan using each of the book's chapters and specifying some possible learning outcomes.

1. Aging with Scripture

    Participants will know the way that Scripture is honest about both the challenges of aging and the gift of a long life. They will note the roles that the aged sometimes play in Scripture.

2. The Storm of Aging

    Participants will be able to cite two or three reasons aging presents great challenges for living in the last years of life. They will have greater appreciation for the increasing challenge that longevity presents for our society.

3. Retiring with God

    Participants will better appreciate the blessings of retirement and cite three or four trials of retirement after a career.

They will come to view retirement as a test of character and
an opportunity to see their lives as God's continuing creations.

4. Successful Aging

Participants will be able to define unrealistic fantasies of
aging and to list three or four proven biological, social, and
theological contributors toward successful aging.

5. With God in the Last Quarter of Life

Participants will be able to cite two or three core Christian
affirmations and practices that enable them to think more truthfully and fruitfully about aging in specifically Christian ways.

6. Growing Old in Church

Participants will gain new appreciation for the ways in which
their congregation can be a valuable resource and support for
persons preparing for and living through aging as well as how
their congregation can prepare younger members for aging.

7. Ending in God

Participants will have renewed confidence that God goes
with them as they live through the last days of their lives. They
will be encouraged to see the Christian affirmations about death
and life after life as key theological support for facing the end
with hope.

What the Aging Need to Do for the Church

"Much will be demanded from everyone who has been given much,
and from the one who has been entrusted with much, even more will
be asked" (Luke 12:48). We are created to be givers. Those who are
given the gift of advanced years are called primarily to see themselves
not as passive patients but as agents, not as receivers but as givers,
not as burdensome but as responsible.

A congregation ought to frame its work as a ministry *of* older
adults rather than a ministry *to* older adults. Some aging adults (not
all, but perhaps more than we admit) have the gifts of time, financial
resources, patience, wisdom, experience, and skills that are badly
needed among many in the congregation and in the congregation's
neighborhood.

"I look on myself as the senior networker," said the woman who was her congregation's coordinator of senior ministry.

"What's a 'senior networker'?" I asked.

"Well, I begin with the slogan that older adults are not primarily to be served but to serve. We have more important things to do than a fall trip to the mountains to see the leaves change. I tell them, 'If you want trips with old people, see a travel agent. The church is entrusted with a more pressing mission.'

"So I network, trying to help all the older adults discover and affirm their God-given missions."

"Such as?" I persisted.

"Such as putting a young man who has been out of work for a year with two of my older men who were business guys in their former lives. I told them they have to see this thing through until Thomas lands a job. I have a woman who was a master tailor teaching three of our younger women how to sew. I even have three older adults—all recovering alcoholics—on call as the pastor needs them to care for alcoholics in the congregation."

She is my model for older adult ministry.

In the New Testament, widows are given the task of prayer. A 1999 study revealed that of the 98 percent of older adults who pray, most pray for the well-being of others, especially family members. Of these, 95 percent believe their prayers are answered.[35] The church is a community of prayer, work that nearly all of the aging can do well.

I know a church that has been in the urban church slide for decades. Today that church is beginning a near-miraculous turnaround. The pastor gives all the credit for the congregation's revitalization to a group of older women, the Wednesday Morning Prayer Circle. They had risked praying, "Lord, what can we do to give our church a future?"

The Lord directed them to start a free child care ministry at the church on Friday nights. They put a big sign in the church's yard: "Free, Expert Child Care, Fridays 5–11 p.m." The children get a meal prepared by the women, games, bedtime stories, and movies, and the parents get a free night out as well as a welcoming encounter with the church.

"Those Friday evenings have been used by God to transform our church," said the young pastor.

When the Alabama legislature passed the meanest anti-immigration law in the country, one of the churches that urged me to sue the legislature in the name of Christ (we won our suit, by the way) was a church in a central Alabama town. A group of older members in the church ran a program for latchkey kids who could go to the church in the afternoons and do homework and have fun until their parents got off work. Most of the students spoke Spanish. The program was run by a retired high school Spanish teacher who, though she was not a church member, was recruited by her friends in the church to oversee the program.

The law made the program illegal; it was unlawful to "harbor" or "transport" undocumented people. I'm proud to say that, even in Jeff Sessions's state, these courageous women said, "We aren't stopping this ministry for anybody. What are they going to do? Jail a bunch of eighty-year-olds?"

Here are some other ways aging adults can help the church.

Witness

While it's true that aging can be a time of worry, regret, and loneliness, our last decades can also be, by the grace of God, a time for heightened Christian witness. All Christians are called to testify to who God is and to what God is up to in the world, and to encourage others to hitch on to that work. Yet those who are "old and gray" can have a particular witness:

> They will bear fruit even when old and gray;
>> they will remain lush and fresh in order to proclaim:
>> "The LORD is righteous.
>> He's my rock.
>> There's nothing unrighteous in him." (Ps. 92:14–15)

Older members can "remain lush and fresh." Why? "In order to proclaim." God gives some a blessed, fruitful old age, not simply for personal satisfaction and contentment but for witness.

I still remember being challenged in one of my first congregations by the witness of an older man who never missed a Sunday. Each week he hobbled in on crutches and took his place toward the front

of the church. I once asked him, "Tom, do you have much trouble with pain?"

"Son, I haven't been without pain for the last thirty years after my accident. It takes me at least an hour of prayer and dogged determination just to get out of bed each morning."

Until that moment, I had never heard Tom speak of his pain.

Self-restraint is a virtue when talking about our problems. Effective Christian witness requires skill to know when to speak and when to withhold our speech. When we obsess over our aches and pains, our limited horizon is exposed, showing that our main concern is ourselves. We seniors, like Tom, must be stewards of our pain and misfortune and must show how, even in our pain, God can still be praised.

"I woke up this morning feeling unwell," I told Tom one Sunday, "head hurting, not wanting to get dressed and come to church. Then I remembered you would be sitting in the first pew to the right. Here I am!"

I overheard an older woman saying to another, "My deafness has gotten so bad that I can't make out a word of the sermon."

"If you can't hear, then why do you come?" asked the other person.

"I come to be an example to the rest of you," she said with a giggle. "At least my deafness is physiological. How about you? Ever had trouble listening to the preacher's sermons?"

When one of our older church members was diagnosed with lung cancer, a younger member attempted to console her by asking, "You've lived such a good life. Are you angry with God for this bad luck?"

"Angry with God?" the older woman snapped back. "I'm the one who smoked a pack a day for forty years. I hope God isn't too angry with me!"

Oh, the blessed witness of the elders who "remain lush and fresh in order to proclaim."

The biblical stories of Jacob and Esau at the approach of Isaac's death (Gen. 27) and of Joseph and his brothers at the time of Jacob's death (Gen. 49) show that sometimes at the end family fault lines are rent when suppressed tension built up over years is made undeniable and visible. Some older adults can witness that it is possible, even at the end of life, to engage in the tough work of reconciliation and

forgiveness. There is often a great deal of regret and loss among the elderly, but there is also time for fixing broken relationships and setting things right before the end.

A fair question is "What is the work you need to do before you die?"

When I have been asked if people should plan their funerals, I have sometimes said, "Sure. Plan your funeral. But more important is doing any unfinished business with others so you can have a peaceful passing." Much grief is due to regret over fences not mended and relationships left broken.

It's possible to do work in our later years that we neglected when we were young. It is never too late to say to another, "Can you forgive me?" "I forgive you," "Thank you for what you gave me," "I love you," or "Goodbye." Closure heals relationships, provides opportunities to be obedient to Christ, and enables us to experience the reconciling Holy Spirit in our lives.

Sometimes finishing the work of our lives is difficult because well-meaning palliative caregivers have medicated us into a stupor. It's important for us to say, even in our pain, to those who would offer us mind-numbing drugs, "I want some of my pain assuaged, but I also need to be as conscious and alert as possible to accomplish the work that I need to do before I go."

Elderly people can also be witnesses by reminding us that aging and death are not the worst things that can happen to us. Worse is to die without having lived. Jesus speaks (especially in the Gospel of John) of the walking dead who have yet to live. In the face of death, Christians assert that while death is the final enemy, it is not our most daunting test; life with God is the challenge.

"Let us describe that task of the old, . . . as a task of *witness*," says Oliver O'Donovan. "The old have neither to conform to the young nor to resent them by standing at a distance, but to be themselves *before the eyes of* the young, to live and to die as they have lived hitherto, to make available to the young the experiences they have lived through authentically, standing where they have always stood on important matters, cheerfully adapting themselves, as best they can, in unimportant ones. That is what the young need of them."[36] Let our prayer be that of the psalmist:

So, even in my old age with gray hair,
don't abandon me, God!
Not until I tell generations about your mighty arm,
    tell all who are yet to come about your strength,
    and about your ultimate righteousness, God,
because you've done awesome things! (Ps. 71:18–19)

May God give each of us time enough to tell generations about God's mighty arm.

Step Aside

Earlier we discussed the witness of old Elizabeth and Zechariah and Simeon and Anna. Note that they began the story of Jesus with their prophetic vision of God's future. Then what did these elders do? They moved out of the way and are never heard from again. Let us elders take these exiting matriarchs and patriarchs as exemplars.

At a clergy conference, Lauren Winner, associate professor at Duke Divinity School, and I were asked by an older clergyperson, "Why doesn't the church do a better job of retaining and utilizing our older clergy to serve some of our smaller parishes?"

As an older clergyperson, my heart resonated with this priest's plea. But I remember Lauren responding with, "I'm sorry. I know so many young Episcopal clergy who have finished seminary and have been waiting for years to be sent to a parish. I really hope that some of you clergy who have enjoyed years of fruitful ministry will now consider stepping aside."

The young have the responsibility to enter life and take hold of the world, faithfully fulfilling God's commission. The old have the obligation to be supportive of those who now bear the major burdens of leading the church. We should wish them well . . . and then step aside.

We can witness to what we have found to be true. We can sympathize with them as they take up the burdens we once bore, offering suggestions and encouragement when asked. But we must remember that they don't live in the same world in which we lived. Though they work at many of the tasks we tackled, they must work differently. They must dismantle some of the things we so lovingly constructed.

Through them, God may solve problems we attempted but failed to solve. They are not merely continuing the work we began. The world changes. Christians, young and old, all serve a living God with whom we have more future than past, a God who refuses to stay stuck in the status quo or hemmed in by what was done before. That is why some of the most important service the old can render the young is to step back, bless them, and say, "It's yours now."

The young have their hands full. A chief vocation of the aging is to stand beside the young, to offer them encouragement and consolation as they take up their duties in life's first half. Because sometimes the years bring wisdom, perspective, a sense of proportion, and reliable knowledge, the old feel more self-assurance than the young and therefore can stand beside them during their times of uncertainty.

I know a church that was having a rough time financially. At an anxious meeting of the board, one of the older members gave a brief history of the congregation, highlighting five financial crises (worse than the present) over the congregation's past fifty years. After hearing the history, the pastor said, "Thanks for reminding us of our past. Folks, we're encountering nothing today that God hasn't brought us through before!"

Frustrated by our lack of control of our lives, we older folks must not attempt to control the young or vainly try to live vicariously through them by dominating their lives. We must step aside, trusting that God will lead a new generation in the church.

Grandparent as a Vocation

Of those sixty-five and older, 80 percent have grandchildren. One-third of these older Christians say that grandparenting is the most satisfying aspect of their lives.[37] And yet grandparenting has its challenges. Successful grandparenting typically depends on parents who value having grandparents in their children's lives. In my last church, the major task being faced by many older members was caring for grandchildren who, for various reasons, had been handed off to the grandparents to raise.

Grandparents can provide a constant, reliable safety net for grandchildren, giving them much-needed emotional support in their negoti-

ations and tensions with their parents, teachers, and peers. Grandparents also give children a sense of security and stability when dealing with divorce, parental substance abuse, or parental illness or death.

Grandparents are quite naturally called to be storytellers. As teachers and mentors, grandparents are a link with a family's past, giving children a wider picture of the world and its meaning, and a richer array of life options, than may be available through parents. Deuteronomy praises the truths that grandparents can teach their progeny:

> Remember the days long past;
>   consider the years long gone.
> Ask your father, he will tell you about it;
>   ask your elders, they will give you the details. (32:7)

In the early days of my ministry a young woman tearfully told of her discovery of her husband's infidelity that occurred at a business convention. "I'm leaving him, of course, even though he says he's sorry and will never do it again. I can't trust him. First I'm going to tell my sainted grandmother. This will just break her heart." Two days later the she was back in my office. She surprised me when she told me, "Well, I've decided to try to forgive Jim and see if we can pick up and move on from here."

"What led you to change your mind?" I asked. And she told me this story:

> I told my grandmother, "I've got something to tell you that will be a shock. Jim has committed adultery." Grandmother said, "Not a shock to me. Many men go crazy at Jim's age. Is he repentant? Has this happened before?"
>
> "Grandmother!" I said. "I never would have thought that you would justify infidelity."
>
> "Didn't say I justified it," she said. "Just said that if Jim's repentant, if you think you can find a way to forgive him, then maybe you should. Men can be much better husbands after this sort of thing."
>
> I told her that I was surprised she would even suggest that I take Jim back. That's when she said, "I took your grandfather back twice after he had played the fool. Sometimes marriages are better after this sort of thing. Ours sure was."
>
> "*Grandfather!*"

Some of the wisdom that grandparents have to teach is unpleasant for the young to hear. There are times when the elderly, without even trying, pronounce prophetic judgment on the superficial values of our society, its infatuation with youth, its denial of death, its ethos of self-help, its idolization of stuff, its elevation of individualism, and its myths of self-sufficiency. Elders have a nasty habit of putting uncomfortable questions to the young: What's the point of your life? Will accumulation of all this stuff really lead to happiness? Amid the ravages of time and mortality, what are you giving your life to that will last?

Above all, grandparents have a responsibility, by virtue of their baptism, to pass on their Christian faith to their grandchildren. If it is true that many elders have a heightened spiritual sense in their later years and that many middle-aged persons are so consumed with careers and other life projects that they withdraw from religious activity, then it is especially important for the elderly to instruct their grandchildren in the faith. As a college chaplain, I noted that the majority of college students who identified themselves as Christians testified that those most responsible for bringing them into the faith were their grandparents.

Sinners as we are, even a great good like grandparenting can be perverted if it stands between us and God or distracts us from the rest of our Christian vocation. Some of the elderly are living diminished lives because they feel no concern for anyone but their grandchildren. To the dear person who brags, "I would do anything for my grandchildren," the church must say, "That's not good enough."

The rite of baptism is upfront in proclaiming that progeny is not limited to biological heirs. In most services of baptism, members of the congregation present candidates, and the entire congregation pledges to take responsibility for the newly baptized in this strange, countercultural family called church. Grandparenting can be a vocation that goes beyond biology.

I once served a congregation in which the majority of members were over sixty-five. We set out to attract younger adults who were moving into our changing neighborhood.

"Do you miss your grandparents?" I would ask as I visited the young adults in the apartment building near the church. "We've got grandparents to spare."

Our church was pleasantly surprised that a number of young adults gravitated toward our congregation, saying, in effect, "Growing up is too tough without some help from those with gray hair." We began asking young adult visitors to Sunday dinner. Those meals proved to be one of the most important doorways into our church and a major means of evangelism.

In that same congregation, I asked the evangelism committee, "Who are the people in this town who need us?" One of our older members answered, "Young couples with babies." She explained, "Young couples are having babies, and they know so little about babies. They also don't have grandparents nearby, so there's nobody to adore the babies."

After much discussion, we selected a couple in their seventies to be our baby visitors, and they called on every baby who was born in a mile radius of our church. When a baby was brought home, within a week or two, this couple would show up on the doorstep, saying, "We understand that your lives have been turned upside down by God's gift." Then after admiring the newborn, they would say, "Our church makes young children a priority. Here's a Bible storybook. It's never too soon to read Bible stories to your baby. Here's a brochure about what our church is doing. We want you to know that our church is here to help you be the parents this adorable child deserves."

The baby visitors were our most successful evangelistic program. At least twenty young couples joined our church as fruit of this ministry. Half of the couples were unmarried. A fourth of the babies were being raised by single parents. That program reminded us and our neighborhood that Christian baptism is a sign of our responsibility for one another, the first step into the church's countercultural family.

In a church in North Carolina, the pastor invited those who were to be baptized to come to the front of the sanctuary. A mother and two little girls came forward. "This is Alicia and her daughters, Juanita and Loris," said the pastor. "We met them through our migrant hospitality ministry." As the mother gave her testimony, the pastor translated into English: "When we came to America, we realized that people didn't want us here. We heard what the president said on TV. But the Methodists welcomed us. Back home, we had never heard of

Methodists. John and Mary got me a great job in town. Elizabeth even helped me get a car to go to work. Alice's grandchildren got the kids settled in their new school. We couldn't have made it without you."

The pastor said, "I'd like to ask everyone who brought this dear family to us to come down and join us at the baptistery." Eighteen people—all of them older adults—surrounded the family. Grandparenting had become a vocation.

Elder-Friendly Churches

Here are some appropriate questions (gleaned from James Houston and Michael Parker) that churches should ask themselves:

- What are the demographics of our congregation?
- What specific programs are offered for seniors?
- Have we partnered with other community agencies for senior care?
- Do we have a system for supporting senior caregivers?
- Are we using technology to keep in close contact with our seniors?
- Is our church truly accessible for those with mobility issues?
- Do we have multiple ways of encouraging intergenerational interaction?
- Do we have nutrition programs for seniors?
- Do we have a sound system for the hearing impaired?[38]

What if your church had a trained and vetted ombudsman for the aging? People who are moving through the health care system need advocates, interpreters, those who can support them in an often impersonal system.[39] A well-informed congregational advocate for the elderly who is knowledgeable about care options and who has established relationships with care facilities, including hospice, in the community can reassure older persons and support their caregivers.

A study in the 1980s showed that 39 percent of Americans with serious problems are apt to seek help from a member of the clergy;

clergy are the major mental health counselors.[40] Older women are more likely than either older men or younger people to turn to clergy for help with personal problems.[41] It therefore behooves every pastor to be knowledgeable about the predictable crises of the aging. Even more important than knowing when and how to help is realizing when and how to refer people to other professional caregivers such as counselors, psychologists, psychiatrists, physicians, and social workers.[42]

Because older adults often feel vulnerable and fearful, and therefore concerned about their safety, the security of church spaces is an important concern. We expect churches to be safe sanctuaries for our children; how about for the elderly? The AARP website has practical ideas for improving the safety of older adults (www.aarp.org).

Many older adults suffer from dementia. To make the church more elder-friendly, churches should seek education on how to work with people with dementia. Fortunately, the National Institute on Aging has a helpful website with concise information about Alzheimer's disease and how to make a church friendly and safe for those with dementia diagnoses (www.nia.nih.gov).

Many congregations lack a compelling sense of mission. The presence of elderly members or the elderly in the community near the church offers a great opportunity for congregational revitalization and engagement in mission. Here are some other ways to make a church elder-friendly.

- Designate a trained coordinator of older adult ministry to organize and deploy people of all ages in ministry to and with older adults.
- Recognize and affirm caregivers for the elderly in a congregational worship service.
- Start a caregiver support group. Keep an active list of caregivers and offer them periodic relief from their work as well as resources and ideas to help them with the burdens of care they have assumed.
- Conduct a survey of those in the congregation and the neighborhood who may benefit from Meals on Wheels and other support from the congregation.

- Have regular luncheons for older adults and their caregivers.
- Offer transportation for older adults for every church function, and establish a vetted team of informed volunteers who are available to provide transportation, oversight, help with medical visits, and friendly conversation to the elderly.
- Offer help; don't wait for elders to ask.

Worship and the Elderly

Much of the church's worship, like the second half of life, is a time for reflection and assessment. That is one reason the elderly have a high level of church attendance. Many older adults enjoy the opportunities that worship affords for fellowship and for contemplation and review. So many of Jesus's parables are stories of judgment when the master asks simply, "What have you done with what you have been given?" (see Matt. 25:14–30). Aging can be a time of reflection and solitude, a time of looking back on one's life and taking stock, which is not always a wholly pleasant undertaking. And yet, with the perspective of time, some of the things that caused anguish in an earlier stage of life can be seen as relatively unimportant. Some of the good fortune that was hardly noticed is now assessed to have greater significance.

Guilt for things done and left undone can plague older adults. Some look on the behavior of adult children and second-guess their parenting. Others regret the accumulated mistakes they have made.

Regular use of prayers of corporate confession and assurances of pardon and forgiveness is a sign to the elderly that the church is there to relieve one encumbrance of old age: burdensome regret.

Christian worship not only expresses our deepest beliefs and most ardent aspirations. As we are busy praising God, we are also being formed and reformed by God in our worship. Some of our perfectly normal, natural reactions can be disciplined in worship by the formative power of the Holy Spirit and the Word of God. Even though we tend to be self-centered, it is possible to be changed, to some degree, by allowing the Holy Spirit to work in our lives and by submitting ourselves to Scripture.

"You can't teach an old dog new tricks," libel often applied to older people, is challenged by the Christian faith and its views of conversion and sanctification. God's transformative work in us does not end at sixty-five. Nor does aging mean that we are unable to learn new patterns and assume new habits. One of those habits may be the habit of altruism. It is possible for a person who has been greedy and self-centered to see, in later years, the true worth of things and become more giving. The person who has felt financially insecure and therefore has been relentlessly acquisitive may come to realize that now they have fewer pressing commitments and are free to be more generous, to invest in causes that benefit others, to increase their range of commitments, to rise above fixation with personal needs, and to feel the pain of others as vividly as their own.

In sermons, preachers should take care not to use words that demean or stereotype the aging. Much of Protestant worship is dominated by words, so those who are incapable of using words well are at a disadvantage in worship. It is not surprising then that the Eucharist—full of actions too deep for words—is important in nursing homes or that patients who are verbally dysfunctional suddenly join in when "Amazing Grace" is sung or Psalm 23 is recited. They are drawing deep from the well within, showing habits of faith that were accrued over a lifetime.

Music takes us deeper than the verbal, drawing us out of our loneliness as we join with others in singing the same words and notes. A service in which all the music is exclusively of one generation to the neglect of others falls short of the wonderfully intergenerational quality of Christian worship at its best.

"Do you love and miss your grandparents?" I used to ask students at Duke University Chapel. "Well, here at the chapel we'll introduce you to your great-great-grandparents! This morning we will enjoy one of Isaac Watts's greatest hits and submit ourselves to the wisdom of dead people who can deepen your prayer life."

When a church I once served installed a drop-down screen in the sanctuary for the display of the words to our songs and other acts of worship, I expected pushback from some of our older members.

"For the first time in a long time I can actually see the words to the hymns!" a vision-impaired octogenarian said as she gave encouragement to the church's reach toward a new generation.

SEVEN

Ending in God

Before we end, let's talk about the end, eschatology, last things, our future with God. We use "the end" in at least two ways. *End* means "final"—the last chapter of the story, when the game is over, the last breath, *finis*. *End* can also mean *telos*, "purpose"—the result of our work, the meaning of the story, the goal of our efforts, the point of it all, our ultimate destination. The Westminster Confession asks new Christians, "What is the chief end of humanity?" What's our purpose, the meaning of our lives? The Christian is taught to answer, "To glorify God and to enjoy God forever." We are here on this earth for no better reason than the glorification and enjoyment of God, in all life's ups and downs, so that one day, by God's grace, we may enjoy God forever.

Our Last, Best Hope

We older adults have an advantage over younger cohorts when it comes to pondering matters of the end. Death denial is widespread; our rituals for dying are in disarray. The traditional Christian Service of Death and Resurrection is replaced with a bouncy, upbeat Celebration of Life where we are urged to laugh about the foibles of the deceased, an exercise that all too easily degenerates into corporate make-believe that death has not really occurred.

157

Youth infatuation and cosmetic surgical intervention to cover the physical effects of aging indicate that we find it difficult to think about aging's most daunting task—dying. We ask, "How can creatures so wonderful as we be finite?" Eat this food, follow these principles, live by this regimen twice daily, take this pill, work out, endow an institution—live forever. Even with our culture's pervasive denial, those of us past sixty-five have fewer means of evading the reality toward which we are moving. We know in our more truthful moments that over even well-lived lives, the most faithful friendships, our greatest artistic and cultural achievements, the most abstemious of diets, and the institutions that we've built and supported hovers a solemn warning: *this too shall pass.*

The satanic promise to Adam and Eve in the garden ("You will be like God" [Gen. 3:5]) is the lie of immortality. I'm sorry, but there is no path to godlike immortality. Only God is eternal. Surely, this is a truth that's more comprehensible to the old, whose myriad of little losses culminate in the big loss: *thanatos.*

Too bleak? To Christians are given the resources to be honest about mortality. As Paul says, "We always carry Jesus' death around in our bodies so that Jesus' life can also be seen in our bodies" (2 Cor. 4:10). Our lives are not our own. We live each day not for ourselves, and we die on our last day not unto ourselves. Christians are able to be so brutally honest about death, utterly realistic about the lethal human situation, because we are so optimistic about the power of God in Christ. We have confidence in the promise of God's steadfast love, which overcomes death and the forces of evil. God is life and light, and in the resurrection of crucified Jesus Christ, our final foe is defeated: *Thanatos* vanquished by *Christos.*

The Christian faith has its origins in a cemetery and the jolt of God's surprise move—the resurrection of the body of crucified Jesus. The church originates in the shock of Jesus Christ returning to the same disciples who deserted him and fled into the darkness. They left Jesus's body at what they thought was the end; he bodily returned to them that they might begin again and become his body in motion, his church. It's not over with us and God until God says it's over. If we are to have life beyond the limits of this passing, earthly life, our hope is that the God who raised Jesus will bring us along with

him into eternity. Our hope is that Jesus Christ not only is raised to everlasting life but also, in an amazing act of love, reaches out to us in our mortality and takes us along for the ride. Jesus Christ refused to be raised alone. As John Calvin put it, "Christ rose that he might have us as companions in the life to come."[1]

Eternal life means being welcomed by God into God's existence, being subsumed into God's story, taking our place in God's reign, and being adopted into the communion of saints. This enlistment into God's story begins whenever we join in God's work in the world. Our days with God in this life are a foretaste of our end.

Revelation comes at the end of the Bible and the beginning of the church. The Revelation to John seems to be a vision of a person whose world was coming apart, whose horizon was ending. And yet as so often happens with human history in the hands of redemptive God, the pain of the present moment is radically transformed by God's intervention. The Lamb—slaughtered, crucified, and bloody—reigns at the center of heaven, ruling from the throne.

> Then I saw a new heaven and a new earth, for the former heaven and the former earth had passed away, and the sea was no more. I saw the holy city, New Jerusalem, coming down out of heaven from God, made ready as a bride beautifully dressed for her husband. I heard a loud voice from the throne say, "Look! God's dwelling is here with humankind. He will dwell with them, and they will be his peoples. God himself will be with them as their God. He will wipe away every tear from their eyes. Death will be no more. There will be no mourning, crying, or pain anymore, for the former things have passed away." Then the one seated on the throne said, "Look! I'm making all things new." (Rev. 21:1–5)

In the Revelation, John gives us a poetic, visionary celebration that makes a strong theological claim: God has triumphed. At last God has what God wants when "every knee should bend . . . and every tongue should confess that Jesus Christ is Lord" (Phil. 2:10–11 NRSV). The One whom the world pushed out of the world on a cross has risen and returned in order to transform the world. The creation that God began in Genesis is brought to its fulfillment. The glorification and enjoyment of God, for which we were created, glimpsed

only momentarily here, will there be our full-time job. We will forever whoop it up in the choir with no more pressing business than praise (Rev. 19).

In my pastoral experience, people don't think much about the end or eternal life or heaven until they must. Perhaps this is as it should be. Jesus urged us not to overly concern ourselves with tomorrow but rather to focus on the blessings and the work that God gives us today (Matt. 6:25–34). People in power, people who are in good health, those who are young and have an expansive future ahead of them need not think much about finitude or spend much time pondering what's next. However, for people over sixty-five, thinking about our end is not an optional activity. Our bodies, the deaths of our friends and family, and the sense that the world we inhabited is slipping away speak to us of our finale.

Earlier we discussed the vocation of older adults to witness and to give testimony. Matters of the end, mortality, and the hope of eternal life may be the distinctive content of elders' unique witness. We older adults can be salt and light in a death-denying culture as we testify that life after life is not simply a future expectation; it can be a present reality.

Eschatological hope for God's great victory at the end empowers us now. This life is preparation and training for whatever life is to come, though the resurrection of the body and eternal life are gifts of God. All along life's way we can experience the redemptive, resurrecting work of the One who raised crucified Jesus from the dead. There is no situation at any time in our lives so bleak and tragic as to be immune from God's saving work, no tragedy so frightful that it is beyond the reach of a redemptive God. Though full emancipation takes place only after we have departed this life, this life, here and now, can be transformed by knowing our end in God.

I asked the director of an inner-city ministry that cares for the bodily and the spiritual needs of deeply impoverished older adults how she has kept going against all odds, performing this demanding work for decades. She replied, "I try to take the long view. We're in a battle here, but I know who will finally win the war. God isn't forever mocked. I'm giving my people a foretaste of what God has in store for them. That keeps me going."

As Jesus said, "I came so that they could have life" (John 10:10). Because we anticipate that time, that place when "the kingdom of the world has become the kingdom of our Lord and his Christ, and he will rule forever and always" (Rev. 11:15), we don't lose hope. Affirmation of God's ultimate triumph is among the most politically charged and economically relevant of Christian doctrines, especially for those over sixty-five. People who are dealing with unfinished business, unrealized expectations, and worry over the current state of affairs need to hear the evangelical word that the last chapter will be written by the God who raised crucified Jesus from the dead.

Jesus defeated death, triumphed, and, in an amazing act of grace, takes us along through this veil of tears all the way to whatever realm God has in store for us in eternity. Our belief is not based on some naive fantasy about the future but on the solid evidence of God's love that we've experienced here. Because God in Christ has gone to such extraordinary lengths to get to us in this life, we cannot believe that God will fail to reach out to us in death.

> I believe that the present suffering is nothing compared to the coming glory that is going to be revealed to us. The whole creation waits breathless with anticipation for the revelation of God's sons and daughters. Creation was subjected to frustration, not by its own choice—it was the choice of the one who subjected it—but in the hope that the creation itself will be set free from slavery to decay and brought into the glorious freedom of God's children. We know that the whole creation is groaning together and suffering labor pains up until now. And it's not only the creation. We ourselves who have the Spirit as the first crop of the harvest also groan inside as we wait to be adopted and for our bodies to be set free. We were saved in hope. If we see what we hope for, that isn't hope. Who hopes for what they already see? But if we hope for what we don't see, we wait for it with patience. (Rom. 8:18–25)

When it comes to our ultimate destiny, our fates are in the hands of a merciful God who is God of the just and the unjust, who makes his sun to shine on the undeserving heads of both the righteous and the unrighteous (Matt. 5:45), whose Son came to save sinners, only sinners. In death, we are forced to fall back on the everlasting arms,

compelled to admit just how little we are able to control our lives. If the elderly are closer to their end, if their daily lives give them a foretaste of their contingency and mortality, then it can truly be said of them that they are turning and becoming as little children, not too far from the kingdom (18:3).

Revelation says that in paradise, when the kingdom of heaven comes on the earth in its fullness, there will be no church (21:22). Why? Presumably, we won't need the church to train us to be at peace with God and our neighbors. We won't have to content ourselves with glimpses of eternity in Sunday worship. We will have arrived. The people of God will shine like the sun. We will see God, not as through a mirror dimly but face-to-face (1 Cor. 13:12). The veil of mortality will be lifted, and our always aging, wasting bodies will be made whole. That stunning, glorious light who is God Almighty and the Lamb will effusively shine on us (Rev. 21:22). We will then see God fully and see ourselves as we have been created from the beginning to be. We will be home.

Until then, we who are aging (that's all of us) can see our lives with God in this present moment, in whatever circumstance we find ourselves, as preparation to be with God forever.

The Christian Funeral

Recently, I attended the funeral of a longtime friend. He was active in his church and was a vibrant, though not unquestioning, believer. The preacher at his funeral seemed unaware—or unconcerned—about my deceased friend's relationship with Christ or his commitment to God's work. She went on at length about my friend's personal charm and his cooking ability.

"And best of all, he was a grandfather who truly loved his grandchildren." Wow, what a remarkable achievement. Take that all you unaffectionate grandfathers!

It was an unfortunate funeral sermon, not only because it was poorly delivered and badly constructed but also because it lacked theological interest or substance. Furthermore, all my friend's virtues and vices are quite beside the point at the end. The sermon implied that our hope in life, in death, in any life beyond death is in our charm,

good cooking, and affectionate grandparenting. Jesus Christ failed to win even a cameo role in the sermon, and everybody left the service with the impression that the Christian faith has nothing to say at the time of death than what the world already knows.

We must recover the funeral as a multigenerational, church-wide event, not as a private service for the family. Everyone who attends a funeral either is in the acute crisis of grief or is preparing for grief, so a funeral is for the whole church, an opportunity for the church to say to itself and the world what it believes about God. A funeral is a service of corporate Christian worship, a time for education and testimony, and also a prophetic witness to a world that denies death or settles for sentimental bromides and superficial banalities.

In funerals, we give back to God one whom God gave to us. Funerals are a time of memory and gratitude for a life, but our most grateful remembering should not be about the alleged achievements of the deceased. Funerals should stress the ways that we are cherished and owned by God. "If we live, we live for the Lord, and if we die, we die for the Lord. Therefore, whether we live or die, we belong to God" (Rom. 14:8). In life, in death, and in life beyond death, we are claimed, named, cherished, and commissioned by God.

Carole Bailey Stoneking says that what we most need in assessing successful aging is not "optimism, but hope."[2] Our hope is not found in what we can remember and recall about the deceased but rather in God's remembering of us all. Throughout the Scriptures, God is said to remember individuals and Israel (Gen. 9:16; 19:29; Lev. 26:42–43; Ps. 105:42). To say that God remembers is to praise God's fidelity. Humanity forgets; God remembers. Whether in life or in death, we are not forgotten.

Thomas Long and Thomas Lynch, our best contemporary interpreters of Christian funerals, say that the purpose of funeral rites is "to get the dead where they need to be and the living where they need to be."[3] The body is lovingly carried to its final resting place, and the mourners return to life without the bodily presence of the deceased. The funeral is an affirmation not only that in grief we need others to help us deal with our grieving but also that the person who died was a member of the Body of Christ, a social being who had a claim on us and on whom we were dependent. By God's grace alone, the funeral

is not only a service of death but also a service of resurrection, an affirmation that whether we live or die, we are God's.

"Remember your creator in the days of your youth," counsels Ecclesiastes 12:1 (NRSV). It's also important to remember God in your last days when so much is forgotten. Let us remember God in our last quarter of life as we ponder the theological significance of our aging, because there is no one to lift the heaviest burdens of aging but God. As I admitted at the beginning of this book, when all is said and done (sooner rather than later for this septuagenarian), there is no cure for the ills of mortality and finitude but God. In our ending, as in our beginning, may we live in such a way that in our coming and going, in our living and dying, we are able to join the church in proclaiming, "Thanks be to God!"

Notes

Introduction

1. Will Willimon, *Accidental Preacher: A Memoir* (Grand Rapids: Eerdmans, 2019), 201–2.

2. T. S. Eliot, *Love Song of J. Alfred Prufrock*, in *The Complete Poems and Plays: 1909–1950* (New York: Harcourt, Brace, 1952), 7.

3. Dylan Thomas, "Do Not Go Gentle into That Good Night," Poets.org, February 1, 2015, https://www.poets.org/poetsorg/poem/do-not-go-gentle-good-night.

4. Marc Freedman, "The Boomers, Good Work, and the Next Stage of Life," in *MetLife Foundation/Civic Ventures New Face of Work Survey* (San Francisco: Civic Ventures, 2005), 4, http://www.encore.org/files/new_face_of_work[1].pdf.

5. Cited in Lloyd R. Bailey, *Biblical Perspectives on Death* (Philadelphia: Fortress, 1979), ix. See also Augustine, "Sermon 51," in *St. Augustine: Essential Sermons*, trans. Edmund Hill, ed. Boniface Ramsey (Hyde Park, NY: New City Press, 2007), 63–75.

6. David S. Potter, *The Roman Empire at Bay: AD 180–395* (New York: Routledge, 2004), 18.

7. Data from the US Bureau of the Census 1984 as interpreted in Sheldon S. Tobin, James W. Ellor, and Susan M. Anderson-Ray, *Enabling the Elderly: Religious Institutions within the Community Service System* (Albany: State University of New York Press, 1986), 5–6.

Chapter 1: Aging with Scripture

1. Robert Browning, "Rabbi Ben Ezra," Poetry Foundation, https://www.poetry foundation.org/poems/43775/rabbi-ben-ezra.

2. Billy Graham, *Nearing Home: Life, Faith, and Finishing Well* (Nashville: Nelson, 2011).

3. Graham, *Nearing Home*, 8.

4. Richard B. Hays and Judith C. Hays, "The Christian Practice of Growing Old: The Witness of Scripture," in *Growing Old in Christ*, ed. Stanley Hauerwas, Carole

Bailey Stoneking, Keith G. Meador, and David Cloutier (Grand Rapids: Eerdmans, 2003), 11.

5. Hays and Hays, "Christian Practice of Growing Old," 11.

6. Martha C. Nussbaum and Saul Levmore, *Aging Thoughtfully: Conversations about Retirement, Romance, Wrinkles, and Regret* (New York: Oxford University Press, 2017), 10.

7. Mike Featherstone and Mike Hepworth, "Images of Ageing in Social Gerontology," in *The Cambridge Handbook of Age and Ageing* (Cambridge: Cambridge University Press, 2005), http://www.credoreference.com/entry/cupage/images_of_ageing in social gerontology.

8. John Calvin, *Institutes of the Christian Religion*, ed. John T. McNeill, trans. Ford Lewis Battles, LCC (Philadelphia: Westminster, 1960), book 1, chap. 6, §1.

Chapter 2: The Storm of Aging

1. William Shakespeare, *As You Like It*, act 2, scene 7, lines 140–65.

2. David Wright, "Lines on Retirement after Reading Lear," in *In a Fine Frenzy: Poets Respond to Shakespeare*, ed. David Starkey and Paul Willis (Des Moines: University of Iowa Press, 2005), 211.

3. William Shakespeare, *King Lear*, act 1, scene 1, line 90.

4. Shakespeare, *King Lear*, act 1, scene 1, line 40.

5. Shakespeare, *King Lear*, act 1, scene 1, line 297.

6. Shakespeare, *King Lear*, act 4, scene 7, lines 58–59.

7. Shakespeare, *King Lear*, act 1, scene 1, lines 313–16, 317–18.

8. Shakespeare, *King Lear*, act 3, scene 3, line 22.

9. Shakespeare, *King Lear*, act 5, scene 3, lines 394–95.

10. Martha C. Nussbaum and Saul Levmore, *Aging Thoughtfully: Conversations about Retirement, Romance, Wrinkles, and Regret* (New York: Oxford University Press, 2017), 17.

11. Nussbaum and Levmore, *Aging Thoughtfully*, 11.

12. Shakespeare, *King Lear*, act 1, scene 4, line 158.

13. "A person's characteristics tend to become more accentuated as his life goes on." Paul Tournier, *Learn to Grow Old*, trans. Edwin Hudson (Louisville: Westminster John Knox, 1991), 118.

14. Stanley M. Hauerwas, *A Community of Character: Toward a Constructive Christian Social Ethic* (Notre Dame: Notre Dame University Press, 1981).

Chapter 3: Retiring with God

1. Richard Rohr, *Falling Upward: A Spirituality for the Two Halves of Life* (San Francisco: Jossey-Bass, 2011), xii.

2. Rohr, *Falling Upward*, 26.

3. Rohr, *Falling Upward*, xiii–xiv.

4. Rohr, *Falling Upward*, 45.

5. Rohr, *Falling Upward*, 48.

6. Oliver O'Donovan, "The Practice of Being Old," in *Church, Society, and the Christian Common Good: Essays in Conversation with Philip Turner*, ed. Ephraim Radnor (Eugene, OR: Cascade, 2017), 208.

7. Rohr, *Falling Upward*, 138. Using James Fowler and Richard Rohr (rather uncritically), Terry Nyhuis urges congregations to move from being closed, limited, and divisive "First Half Churches" to being more open, accepting, and embracing "Second Half Churches." Terry L. Nyhuis, "Aging Baby Boomers, Churches, and the Second Half of Life (Challenges for Boomers and Their Churches)" (DMin diss., George Fox University, Newberg, Oregon, 2016), 65–77, 81–87, http://digitalcommons.georgefox.edu/dmin/136.

8. "Suicide," National Institute of Mental Health, last updated April 2019, https://www.nimh.nih.gov/health/statistics/suicide.shtml.

9. PK, "Average Retirement Age in the United States," *DQYDJ* (blog), September 27, 2019, https://dqydj.com/average-retirement-age-in-the-united-states.

10. PK, "Average Retirement Age."

11. James Hollis, *Finding Meaning in the Second Half of Life: How to Finally, Really Grow Up* (New York: Gotham Books, 2005), 260.

12. Hollis, *Finding Meaning*, 14–15.

13. Hollis, *Finding Meaning*, 149–50.

14. "Wealth Inequality in the United States," Inequality.org, Institute for Policy Studies, https://inequality.org/facts/wealth-inequality.

15. Social Security Administration Fact Sheet, https://www.ssa.gov/news/press/factsheets/basicfact-alt.pdf.

16. Martha C. Nussbaum and Saul Levmore, *Aging Thoughtfully: Conversations about Retirement, Romance, Wrinkles, and Regret* (New York: Oxford University Press, 2017), 182–83.

17. Nussbaum and Levmore, *Aging Thoughtfully*, 182–83.

18. "Topic No. 751 Social Security and Medicare Withholding Rates," IRS.gov, last updated August 23, 2019, https://www.irs.gov/taxtopics/tc751#targetText=Social%20Security%20and%20Medicare%20Withholding,employee%2C%20or%202.9%25%20total.

19. Robert S. Pfeiffer, "Entitlement Spending," February 17, 2019, federalsafetynet.com/entitlement-spending.html.

20. Kenneth Calhoun, "Nightblooming," *Paris Review* 189 (Summer 2009), https://www.theparisreview.org/fiction/5930/nightblooming-kenneth-calhoun.

21. Barbara Boxer, "A Segment of Former U.S. Senator Barbara Boxer's Retirement Speech," *LA Times*, February 3, 2017, video, https://www.latimes.com/politics/92496452-132.html.

22. See my proposed "Liturgy for Retirement" in John H. Westerhoff III and William H. Willimon, eds., *Liturgy and Learning through the Life Cycle*, rev. ed. (Akron, OH: OSL, 1994), chap. 12, pp. 149–52.

23. Preached in Duke University Chapel, July 13, 1997.

24. Shakespeare, *Macbeth*, act 5, scene 5, lines 30–31.

25. Reynolds Price, *A Whole New Life: An Illness and a Healing* (New York: Atheneum, 1994).

26. Price, *Whole New Life*, 183.

27. Price, *Whole New Life*, 183.

28. Erdman Palmore, *The Honorable Elders: A Cross-Cultural Analysis of Aging in Japan* (Durham, NC: Duke University Press, 1975).

29. Thomas Naylor and William H. Willimon, *The Search for Meaning* (Nashville: Abingdon, 1994).

Chapter 4: Successful Aging

1. James O'Neill, *The Third Pill*, BBC, August 31, 2018, https://www.bbc.co.uk/programmes/b0bgmxh3.

2. Christiane Northrup, "Goddesses Never Age: Your Best Years Are Ahead," Christiane Northrup, MD, October 6, 2016, https://www.drnorthrup.com/goddesses-never-age-best-years-ahead/.

3. Cicero, "Cato Maior de Senectute," 35–36, quoted in Martha C. Nussbaum and Saul Levmore, *Aging Thoughtfully: Conversations about Retirement, Romance, Wrinkles, and Regret* (New York: Oxford University Press, 2017), 77.

4. James Woodward, *Valuing Age: Pastoral Ministry with Older People* (London: SPCK, 2008), 137–38.

5. J. W. Rowe and R. L. Kahn, *Successful Aging* (New York: Pantheon Books, 1998), 122–24.

6. Rowe and Kahn, *Successful Aging*, 144.

7. James M. Houston and Michael Parker, *A Vision for the Aging Church: Renewing Ministry for and by Seniors* (Downers Grove, IL: IVP Academic, 2011), 143–44.

8. Carole Bailey Stoneking, "Modernity: The Social Construction of Aging," in *Growing Old in Christ*, ed. Stanley Hauerwas, Carole Bailey Stoneking, Keith G. Meador, and David Cloutier (Grand Rapids: Eerdmans, 2003), 63–89.

9. Arthur Frank, *The Wounded Storyteller: Body, Illness, and Ethics* (Chicago: University of Chicago Press, 1995), 25.

10. A. R. Ammons, "In View of the Fact," in *Bosh and Flapdoodle* (New York: Norton, 2005), 49.

11. Donald Hall, "Affirmation," Poets.org, May 4, 2016, https://www.poets.org/poetsorg/poem/affirmation.

12. Carl G. Jung, *The Portable Jung*, ed. Joseph Campbell (New York: Penguin, 1976), 17.

13. It's interesting to see fifty-year-olds urged to do some of the adventuring that I'm advocating for sixty-five-year-olds. See Marianne Williamson, "Keep a Sense of Adventure," in *50 Things to Do When You Turn 50: 50 Experts on the Subject of Turning 50*, ed. Ronnie Sellers, 34–38 (Portland, ME: Sellers, 2005).

14. Woodward, *Valuing Age*, 12.

15. Woodward, *Valuing Age*, 53.

16. W. Daniel Hale, Richard G. Bennett, and Panagis Galiatsatos, *Building Healthy Communities through Medical-Religious Partnerships*, 3rd ed. (Baltimore: Johns Hopkins University Press, 2018), 128.

17. Woodward, *Valuing Age*, 112.

18. Woodward, *Valuing Age*, 98.

19. George E. Vaillant, *Triumphs of Experience: The Men of the Harvard Grant Study* (Cambridge: Harvard University Press, 2012), 225.

20. Vaillant, *Triumphs of Experience*, 147–48.

21. Woodward, *Valuing Age*, 205–6.

22. Roland D. Martinson interviewed fifty elders, most of whom were Christians, and assembled a revealing array of testimonies in his book *Elders Rising: The Promise and Peril of Aging* (Minneapolis: Fortress, 2018).

23. Richard Rohr, *Falling Upward: A Spirituality for the Two Halves of Life* (San Francisco: Jossey-Bass, 2011), 24.

24. Undue cheerfulness about aging pervades Richard Bimler's handbook, *Joyfully Aging: A Christian's Guide* (St. Louis: Concordia, 2012).

25. May Sarton, *As We Are Now* (New York: Norton, 1992), 1.

26. Vaillant, *Triumphs of Experience*. Vaillant assembled and summarized some of his insights derived from the Grant Study in *Aging Well: Surprising Guideposts to a Happier Life from the Landmark Harvard Study of Adult Development* (New York: Little, Brown, 2003).

27. Vaillant, *Triumphs of Experience*, 188.

28. Quoted in R. Paul Stevens, *Aging Matters: Finding Your Calling for the Rest of Your Life* (Grand Rapids: Eerdmans, 2016), 143.

29. Vaillant, *Triumphs of Experience*, 332.

30. Vaillant, *Triumphs of Experience*, 338.

31. Vaillant, *Triumphs of Experience*, 252–55.

32. Vaillant, *Triumphs of Experience*, 256–57.

33. Vaillant, *Triumphs of Experience*, 213.

34. Cf. Pope John Paul II, "Encyclical Letter *Evangelium Vitae*," March 25, 1999, para. 65, w2.vatican.va/content/john-paul-ii/en/encyclicals/documents/hf_jp-ii_enc _25031995_evangelium-vitae.html.

35. Pope John Paul II, "Encyclical Letter of His Holiness Pope to the Elderly," 1999, http://w2.vatican.va/content/john-paul-ii/en/letters/1999/documents/hf_jp-ii _let_01101999_elderly.html.

36. Thomas Moore, *Ageless Soul: The Lifelong Journey toward Meaning and Joy* (New York: St. Martin's, 2017), 3.

37. George Vaillant, *The Wisdom of the Ego* (Cambridge: Harvard University Press, 1993).

38. T. S. Eliot, "Little Gidding," in *The Complete Poems and Plays: 1909–1950* (New York: Harcourt, Brace, 1962), 142.

39. Quoted in Martinson, *Elders Rising*, 219.

40. John Stuart Mill, *Autobiography* (New York: Penguin, 1989), 115–16.

41. T. S. Eliot, "Eastcoker," in *Complete Poems and Plays*, 129.

42. William F. May, *The Patient's Ordeal* (Indianapolis: University of Indiana Press, 1991), 143.

43. Plato, *The Republic*, book 1, 329c.

44. Careen Yarnal and Xinyi Qian, "Older-Adult Playfulness: An Innovative Construct and Measurement for Healthy Aging Research," *American Journal of Play* 4, no. 1 (Summer 2011): 52–79.

45. Tom Robbins, *Still Life with Woodpecker* (New York: Bantam Books, 1980), 89.

46. Lu Yu, "Written in a Carefree Mood," trans. Burton Watson, March 2, 2009, https://poetrymala.blogspot.com/2009/03/written-in-carefree-mood.html.

47. Somerset Maugham, *The Summing Up* (New York: Doubleday & Doran, 1938), 290.

48. Mary Pipher, *Another Country: Navigating the Emotional Terrain of Our Elders* (New York: Riverhead Books, 1999), 15.

49. Malcolm Muggeridge, *The Chronicles of Wasted Time* (Vancouver: Regent College Publishing, 1999), quoted in Woodward, *Valuing Age*, 197–98.

50. William Shakespeare, *Hamlet*, act 3, scene 1, line 80.

51. On the exaggerated fears of some older adults see Will Willimon, *Fear of the Other: No Fear in Love* (Nashville: Abingdon, 2016), 21–26.

52. Willimon, *Fear of the Other*, 26.

53. Cited in Allen Lane, *Adam Smith: An Enlightened Life* (New York: Penguin, 2010), 187.

Chapter 5: With God in the Last Quarter of Life

1. Eugene C. Bianchi, *Aging as a Spiritual Journey* (Eugene, OR: Wipf & Stock, 2011), 190.

2. George E. Vaillant, *Triumphs of Experience: The Men of the Harvard Grant Study* (Cambridge: Harvard University Press, 2012), 53, 119.

3. Dan Buettner, "The Fountain of Youth," *TED Radio Hour*, May 11, 2018.

4. Vaillant, *Triumphs of Experience*, 218.

5. John Wesley, Sermon 24, "Upon Our Lord's Sermon On The Mount: Discourse Four," §I.1.

6. Simone Weil, *Waiting for God* (New York: Putnam's Sons, 1951), 31.

7. Martha C. Nussbaum and Saul Levmore, *Aging Thoughtfully: Conversations about Retirement, Romance, Wrinkles, and Regret* (New York: Oxford University Press, 2017), 17.

8. Erik H. Erikson, *Identity and the Life Cycle* (New York: Norton, 1959), 180.

9. Nussbaum and Levmore, *Aging Thoughtfully*, 25.

10. Martin Luther, *Lectures on Romans*, ed. Hilton C. Oswald, vol. 25 in *Luther's Works*, American ed. (St. Louis: Concordia, 1972), 291.

11. Christian B. Miller, *The Character Gap: How Good Are We?* (Oxford: Oxford University Press, 2017), 98.

12. Thomas Moore has a helpful discussion of anger with and among the aging in chapter 8 of Thomas Moore, *Ageless Soul: The Lifelong Journey toward Meaning and Joy* (New York: St. Martin's, 2017).

13. Dick Van Dyke, *Keep Moving: And Other Tips and Truths about Living Well Longer* (New York: Point Productions, 2015).

14. Neal M. Krause, *Aging in the Church: How Social Relationships Affect Health* (Philadelphia: Templeton Foundation Press, 2008), 145.

15. G. W. F. Hegel, *The Philosophy of Right*, trans. S. W. Dyde (Kitchener, Ontario: Batoche Books, 2001), 21.

16. "2019 Alzheimer's Disease Facts and Figures," Alzheimer's Association, https://www.alz.org/media/Documents/alzheimers-facts-and-figures-2019-r.pdf, 17.

17. James Woodward, *Valuing Age: Pastoral Ministry with Older People* (London: SPCK, 2008), 97.

18. Refrain from, "I Am Thine, O Lord," #419, *The United Methodist Hymnal* (Nashville, TN: United Methodist Publishing House, 1989).

19. Keith Meador and Shaun C. Henson, "Growing Old in a Therapeutic Culture," in *Growing Old in Christ*, ed. Stanley Hauerwas, Carole Bailey Stoneking, Keith G. Meador, and David Cloutier (Grand Rapids: Eerdmans, 2003), 90–111.

20. Mary Pipher, *Another Country: Navigating the Emotional Terrain of Our Elders* (New York: Riverhead Books, 1999), 8.

21. Woodward, *Valuing Age*, 16.

22. Richard Rohr, *Falling Upward: A Spirituality for the Two Halves of Life* (San Francisco: Jossey-Bass, 2011), 94, 110.

23. Thomas Moore has a thoughtful chapter on sexuality among the aging. See chapter 6 of Moore, *Ageless Soul*.

24. "Widowhood," Medicine Encyclopedia, 1998, https://medicine.jrank.org/pages /1840/Widowhood-demography-widowhood.html.

25. Woodward, *Valuing Age*, 121.

26. Steven Sapp, *Light on a Grey Area: American Public Policy on Aging* (Nashville: Abingdon, 1992), 49.

27. Krause, *Aging in the Church*, 207.

28. Pew Forum on Religion and Public Life, "'Nones' on the Rise: One-in-Five Adults Have No Religious Affiliation," Pew Research Center, October 9, 2012, https:// www.pewforum.org/Unaffiliated/nones-on-the-rise.aspx.

29. Cited in Krause, *Aging in the Church*, 139–60.

30. Helen Rose Ebaugh, ed., *Handbook of Religion and Social Institutions* (New York: Springer, 2006), 140.

31. Vaillant, *Triumphs of Experience*, 431.

32. Vaillant, *Triumphs of Experience*, 433.

33. Vaillant, *Triumphs of Experience*, 343.

34. Vaillant, *Triumphs of Experience*, 346.

35. Harold G. Koenig and Douglas M. Lawson, *Faith in the Future: Health Care, Aging, and the Role of Religion* (Philadelphia: Templeton Foundation Press, 2004), 10.

36. Koenig and Lawson, *Faith in the Future*, 11.

37. Krause, *Aging in the Church*, 134.

38. George Barna, *The State of the Church 2002* (Ventura, CA: ISS AC AJR Resources, 2002), 79.

39. Krause, *Aging in the Church*, 16.

40. Krause, *Aging in the Church*, 153.

41. James M. Houston and Michael Parker, *A Vision for the Aging Church: Renewing Ministry for and by Seniors* (Downers Grove, IL: IVP Academic, 2011), 10. For a dramatic presentation of the horror of being both poor and old during a time of stress, see Sheri Fink, *Five Days at Memorial: Life and Death at a Storm Ravaged Hospital* (New York: Random House, 2013).

42. Vaillant, *Triumphs of Experience*, 357.

43. Preached in Duke University Chapel, December 3, 2000 (the First Sunday of Advent).

44. This sermon was dependent upon (dependency is a good thing!) a classic article by the Christian theologian Gilbert Meilaender: "I Want to Burden My Loved Ones," *First Things* (October 1991): 12–14.

45. Nussbaum and Levmore, *Aging Thoughtfully*, 120. Vaillant says that "the keys to successful aging often lie more in the realm of secular relationships" than in the religious community, though he doesn't offer any evidence for that claim. Vaillant, *Triumphs of Experience*, 278.

46. Richard B. Hays and Judith C. Hays, "The Christian Practice of Growing Old," in *Growing Old in Christ*, 15.

47. Philip Roth, quoted in David Remnick, "Philip Roth," *New Yorker*, June 4 and 11, 2018, 44.

48. Cicero, *De Senectute*, sec. 8, line 26.

49. Kafka, quoted in Remnick, "Philip Roth," 44.

50. Plato, *The Republic*, book 1, 328e.

51. Vaillant, *Triumphs of Experience*, 252.

52. Vaillant, *Triumphs of Experience*, 254.

53. Quoted in Vaillant, *Triumphs of Experience*, 249.

54. Lovett H. Weems Jr., *Church Leadership: Vision, Team, Culture, Integrity*, rev. ed. (Nashville: Abingdon, 2010), 26.

55. See the learned smackdown of the idea of progress in John Gray, *Seven Types of Atheism* (New York: Farrar, Straus & Giroux, 2018), 54–70.

56. David Matzko McCarthy, "Generational Conflict: Continuity and Change," in *Growing Old in Christ*, 226–46.

57. McCarthy, "Generational Conflict," 227.

Chapter 6: Growing Old in Church

1. André Resner Jr. says in his commentary on this passage, "I believe that Jesus's words here are to be taken as lament." André Resner Jr., *The Lectionary Commentary: Theological Exegesis for Sunday's Texts*, ed. Roger E. Van Harn (Grand Rapids: Eerdmans, 2001), 274.

2. Rowan A. Greer, "Special Gift and Special Burden: Views of Old Age in the Early Church," in *Growing Old in Christ*, ed. Stanley Hauerwas, Carole Bailey Stoneking, Keith G. Meador, and David Cloutier (Grand Rapids: Eerdmans, 2003), 37.

3. Neal M. Krause, *Aging in the Church: How Social Relationships Affect Health* (Philadelphia: Templeton Foundation Press, 2008), 148.

4. Krause, *Aging in the Church*, 146.

5. See Jimmy Carter, *The Virtues of Aging* (New York: Random House, 1998).

6. Krause, *Aging in the Church*, 147.

7. Krause, *Aging in the Church*, 152.

8. Krause, *Aging in the Church*, 156.

9. Krause, *Aging in the Church*, 172.

10. "Size and Demographics of Aging Populations," delivered at Institute of Medicine Food Forum, published in *Providing Healthy and Safe Foods as We Age: Workshop Summary* (Washington, DC: National Academies Press, 2010), https://www.ncbi.nlm.nih.gov/books/NBK51841.

11. Quoted in David Matzko McCarthy, "Generational Conflict: Continuity and Change," in *Growing Old in Christ*, 230–31.

12. Erik H. Erikson, *Identity and the Life Cycle* (New York: Norton, 1959), 211.

13. George E. Vaillant, *Triumphs of Experience: The Men of the Harvard Grant Study* (Cambridge: Harvard University Press), 135.

14. Augustine, "Sermon 161," in *St. Augustine: Essential Sermons*, trans. Edmund Hill, ed. Boniface Ramsey (Hyde Park, NY: New City Press, 2007), 221–22.

15. Will Willimon, *Making Disciples: Confirmation Through Mentoring* (Nashville: Abingdon, 2018).

16. Cited in Krause, *Aging in the Church*, 102.

17. Mary Pipher, *Another Country: Navigating the Emotional Terrain of Our Elders* (New York: Riverhead Books, 1999), 16.

18. Henri Nouwen and Walter J. Gaffney, *Aging, The Fulfillment of Life* (New York: Image Books/Doubleday, 1990), 87.

19. Pipher, *Another Country*, 15.

20. Nouwen and Gaffney, *Aging, The Fulfillment of Life*, 89.

21. The classic, Christian testimonial to the challenges of being a caregiver for someone we love who is dying is Madeleine L'Engle, *Summer of the Great Grandmother* (San Francisco: HarperOne, 1986).

22. Joan Chittister, *The Gift of Years: Growing Older Gracefully* (Katonah, NY: Bluebridge, 2008), 9.

23. A good resource for a preretirement study is R. Paul Stevens, *Aging Matters: Finding Your Calling for the Rest of Your Life* (Grand Rapids: Eerdmans, 2016).

24. Zalman Schachter-Shalomi, *From Age-ing to Sage-ing: A Profound New Vision of Growing Older* (New York: Grand Central, 1995).

25. George E. Vaillant, *Aging Well: Surprising Guideposts to a Happier Life from the Landmark Harvard Study of Adult Development* (New York: Little, Brown, 2003), 144.

26. John Wesley, "The Use of Money," quoted in *On Moral Business: Classical and Contemporary Resources for Ethics in Economic Life*, ed. Max L. Stackhouse (Grand Rapids: Eerdmans, 1995), 194–97.

27. Plato, *Symposium*, sec. 208a.

28. Eugene Bianchi, *Aging as a Spiritual Journey* (Eugene, OR: Wipf & Stock, 1987), 169.

29. Karl Barth, *Church Dogmatics*, vol. III, 4 (Edinburgh: T&T Clark, 1961), 607–8.

30. Hermann Hesse, *The Glass Bead Game*, trans. Richard Winston and Clara Winston (New York: Holt, Rinehart & Winston, 1969), 58.

31. See my more extended treatment of Christian vocation in Will Willimon, *Accidental Preacher: A Memoir* (Grand Rapids: Eerdmans, 2019), 97–116.

32. Kathleen A. Cahalan and Bonnie J. Miller-McLemore, ed., *Calling All Years Good: Christian Vocation throughout Life's Seasons* (Grand Rapids: Eerdmans, 2017), 121–22.

33. John Wesley, *Arminian Magazine* 3 (1782): 128.

34. Find this painting at https://www.theguardian.com/artanddesign/2018/jul /13/rembrandt-an-old-woman-reading.

35. Krause, *Aging in the Church*, 147.

36. Oliver O'Donovan, "The Practice of Being Old," in *Church, Society, and the Christian Common Good: Essays in Conversation with Philip Turner*, ed. Ephraim Radnor (Eugene, OR: Cascade, 2017), 214.

37. Vaillant, *Triumphs of Experience*, 60.

38. James M. Houston and Michael Parker, *A Vision for the Aging Church: Renewing Ministry for and by Seniors* (Downers Grove, IL: IVP Academic, 2011), appendix B.

39. Dr. Louise Aronson's book, *Elderhood*, begins by noting that over half of all the elderly who require hospital stays are sent there because of debilitatingly negative interactions with drugs. Her book is an impassioned plea for doctors to do a better job with the treatment of the elderly, both in prescribing medication and in directing treatment. Louise Aronson, *Elderhood: Redefining Aging, Transforming Medicine, Reimagining Life* (New York: Bloomsbury, 2019), 24, 131.

40. Krause, *Aging in the Church*, 115.

41. Krause, *Aging in the Church*, 183.

42. A congregation who wants to be active in ministering to the health needs of older adults will find informed, practical help in the standard guide to the subject,

W. Daniel Hale, Richard G. Bennett, and Panagis Galiatsatos, *Building Healthy Communities through Medical-Religious Partnerships*, 3rd ed. (Baltimore: Johns Hopkins University Press, 2018).

Chapter 7: Ending in God

1. John Calvin, *Institutes of the Christian Religion*, ed. John T. McNeill, trans. Ford Lewis Battles, LCC (Philadelphia: Westminster, 1960), book 3, chap. 25, §3.

2. Carole Bailey Stoneking, "Modernity: The Social Construction of Aging," in *Growing Old in Christ*, ed. Stanley Hauerwas, Carole Bailey Stoneking, Keith G. Meador, and David Cloutier (Grand Rapids: Eerdmans, 2003), 84.

3. Thomas G. Long and Thomas Lynch, *The Good Funeral* (Louisville: Westminster John Knox, 2013), 18.

Name Index

Scripture Index

Contents

For my sister, Harriet, and my brother, Bud,
as they approach ninety with vitality

Published by Baker Academic
a division of Baker Publishing Group
PO Box 6287, Grand Rapids, MI 49516-6287
www.bakeracademic.com

Printed in the United States of America

Library of Congress Cataloging-in-Publication Data
Names: Willimon, William H., author.
Title: Aging: growing old in church / Will Willimon.
Description: Grand Rapids : Baker Academic, a division of Baker Publishing Group,
    2020. | Series: Pastoring for life: theological wisdom for ministering well | Includes
    index.
Identifiers: LCCN 2019031878 | ISBN 9781540960818 (paperback)
Subjects: LCSH: Older persons—Religious life. | Aging—Religious
    aspects—Christianity.
Classification: LCC BV4580.W525 2020 | DDC 248.8/5—dc23
LC record available at https://lccn.loc.gov/2019031878

ISBN 9781540962744 (casebound)

20   21   22   23   24   25   26   7   6   5   4   3   2   1

AGING

GROWING OLD
IN CHURCH

WILL WILLIMON

Baker Academic

a division of Baker Publishing Group
Grand Rapids, Michigan

PASTORING FOR LIFE

Theological Wisdom for Ministering Well

Jason Byassee, Series Editor

Aging: Growing Old in Church
by Will Willimon

Friendship: The Heart of Being Human
by Victor Lee Austin

*Recovering: From Brokenness and Addiction to
Blessedness and Community*
by Aaron White

Other Books by the Author

Calling and Character: Virtues of the Ordained Life

*Pastor: The Theology and Practice of Ordained
Ministry*

Accidental Preacher: A Memoir

*Who Lynched Willie Earle? Preaching to Confront
Racism*

Fear of the Other: No Fear in Love

"Will Willimon is sui generis on the American religious scene. He has a distinctive ability to cover a host of urgent issues while remaining grounded in the transformative truth of the gospel. His writing is marked by wisdom, good humor, passion, and common sense. In this book he looks aging full in the face, understanding that it is, most predictably, a season of loss. But Willimon also knows that, for the Christian, aging permits honesty, gratitude, and most of all a durable sense of agency that is rooted in an embrace of vocation. I am glad, in my aging, that I have been instructed by this book. Many other readers—those aging and those who love an aging person—will welcome this book."

—**Walter Brueggemann**, Columbia Theological Seminary

"Will Willimon has written many wise books, but this may be his wisest. He gently teaches us how growing old in faith is so dramatically different from simply growing old. He shows how aging calls us to relinquish our grip on some tasks and roles, to strengthen our grasp on abiding treasures, and to open our arms to new blessings we are being given. For those of us at the end of our days, this is more than a book; it's a companion along the way."

—**Thomas G. Long**, Candler School of Theology, Emory University

"I live in the eschatological tension between the already and the not yet: already in my sixties and not yet retired, and, more to the point, already in the final third of my life and not yet entirely reconciled to that fact. In short, I am one for whom Will Willimon wrote *Aging*, and I am grateful that he did. The book is remarkably honest, without a whiff of sentimentality or denial, and yet sincerely and substantively hopeful. It offers wise guidance and concrete advice for both individuals and churches. It is at once provoking, challenging, and inspiring, just as I would expect from Willimon's writing."

—**Craig C. Hill**, Perkins School of Theology, Southern Methodist University

"For Christians who want to grow old faithfully and truthfully, Willimon offers an experienced voice. He never pretends that aging is simply a cheerful matter; instead he offers practical and biblical reflections for those who want their last years to draw them more deeply into the life of the church—reflections that in different ways may be just as helpful for those who are (for now) young."

—**Gilbert Meilaender**, Valparaiso University

"I will," I shouted as I clattered back down the stairs.

What had become of him? He was much in demand but nowhere to be seen backstage. True, Reader; there were plenty of places to hide if you knew your way around, but Pedro had never been here before as far as I knew, and in any case, why would he be hiding? He seemed too serious a character to indulge in such childish play, particularly when no one else was in the game. It was a puzzle.

I sat on the bottom step for a moment, thinking. If he wasn't hiding and he wasn't backstage or front of house, then he must have gone outside. Yes, that was it. The brass-belcher's remarks must have upset him more than I had realized. Pedro had deserved praise, not insults for doing what he did. He had probably gone outside to get away from us all.

I ran to the stage door. It stood open, but there was no sign of Caleb. This was unusual, for if Caleb were called away for any reason, he would not leave the door like that. This confirmed my theory. I emerged into the little courtyard that led onto Russell Street. It too was deserted. Where would he have gone? Left toward Covent Garden, or right toward Drury Lane? I stood indecisively, trying to see the place as he would have seen it. He probably had not meant to go far. Perhaps he just wanted some air? Well, if he wanted open spaces, he would have headed for the market. There, despite the constant din of the fruit and vegetable sellers crying out the latest bargains, the wagons passing to and fro, not to mention the clucking of the poultry on the butcher's block, the only uninterrupted view of the sky in this part of town opened up. I felt a sudden stab of concern for him. A boy in fine livery would stick out like a sore thumb among the tough apprentices of the market—I should know, for most of them were my friends.

I had a bad time negotiating the busy crossing on Bow Street. It was packed with people going about their business. A bailiff hurried by with his men, loaded down with goods they must have just seized from some poor debtor. A hawker of ballads stood on the corner crying out his latest wares.

"You 'eard it 'ere first, ladies and gents: the dying speech of John Jeffreys, traitor, thief, and murderer. "'Ot off the press! 'Ear 'ow 'e laments 'is wicked crimes afore 'e took the drop at Newgate last week."

I gave the ballad maker a wide berth, having no taste for such grisly songs. In any case, they were all pure invention: the unfortunate Jeffreys would have had no time for long versified speeches before the trap opened, and certainly no time afterward unless he revived on the table before the anatomy men dissected his body.

My attempt to steer a path through the crowd gathered around the ballad seller had the unfortunate consequence of bringing my feet plumb into the middle of some freshly dropped horse manure. I cursed. To add insult to injury, a black coach and four with a ducal crest rattled by, spraying me with the icy water from a puddle outside the Magistrates' Court. I hopped back too late, colliding with one of the Bow Street runners, our local law enforcers. He pushed me roughly away.

"Watch where you're going, you idiot!" he bellowed, brushing down his uniform.

"That goes double for you, you old fogrum!" I replied, and dashed across the road before he could box my ears.

(I should perhaps explain here for the more delicate among my readers that a different deportment is required on the streets of London than is usually taught to young ladies and gentlemen. Believe me when I assure you that I would not have survived long in my present situation if I had not learned this early on. I hope you are not unduly shocked, for there is much more of the like to come.)

I ran as fast as I could out onto the piazza and dodged under one of the arches of the houses flanking the marketplace. I shook out my skirt and scraped my shoes on a piece of old sacking lying in the corner. Thankfully, the cold weather had quelled some of the riper odors of the street: the refuse, piss, and dung that gave our streets their distinctive odor were noticeably less overwhelming this morning. This was just as well as I was now carrying most of it on my shoes and skirt. But the cold had another consequence: having neglected to put on a shawl over my woolen dress, I was already shivering. Time to find the violinist and get back into the warm.

I looked around the piazza. It was a crisp winter's day—the painted houses stood out gaily against the bright blue sky, each roof ridge, each chimney pot sharp and distinct. At first I saw nothing unusual; just the normal collection of servants making purchases, stallholders waylaying the naive with rotten fruits hidden under their most gleaming articles for sale, apprentice boys lounging outside the inns finishing a late breakfast, gentlemen passing in and out of the coffeehouses.

Then I spotted him. I had not seen him at first because he was, as I had feared, surrounded by a crowd of some of the roughest boys of the market, pushed up against the stone monument in the center of the square. Foremost among them was a tall, thin youth of about seventeen with a close-cropped head of dark hair. It was Billy Shepherd, the leader of one of the gangs that vie for control of the market underworld. I've known Billy ever since I first played on the streets: he was a bully then and shows no signs of improvement as he gets older. Of course, he is by no means the only tyrant in Covent Garden. The thing that makes Billy different, that has thrust him to the head of his gang, is that he is clever. He links a total absence of moral scruples with the cunning of a fox. Let me put it this way: if the Devil challenged him to a sinning match, and they were taking bets, I'd put my money on Billy to win. You don't believe me? Well, here's my shilling, Reader: put yours down on the table and we'll see who's the richer at the end of the adventure.

Knowing Billy as I do, I looked anxiously around, wondering if Syd's gang was anywhere in sight. Syd was Billy's rival for mastery of the square. Though a gentle giant, Syd had a mean pair of fists when roused to defend his territory. If I could persuade him to take Pedro under his wing, he would look after him. Unfortunately, I could see neither hide nor hair of my friend. I was on my own if I wanted to return Pedro to the theater in one piece. And I had better act quickly, for Billy now advanced on Pedro and grabbed him by the jacket. Pedro stared back at him in disbelief, confused by the attack he had done nothing to provoke. He didn't understand that Billy needed no excuse.

"'Oi! Billy!" I shouted, running over the cobbles to reach them. "Leave him! He's with me!"

Billy leaned coolly against a pillar, pinning Pedro by the throat. A couple of his burly mates chuckled as I came sliding to a stop at the bottom of the steps to the monument.

"Found yourself a beau, 'ave you, Cat?" he sneered. "Scraping the barrel with this one, ain't you? What's wrong with one of us?" His eyes, pieces of ice in his pasty face, sparkled maliciously as he looked down at me.

"Oh, hold your tongue!" I snapped back, annoyed to feel that I was blushing. "He's not my beau. I met him only this morning but he saved my neck at the theater just now."

"Saved your pretty white neck, did he?" said Billy. "Well, ain't that nice to 'ear. I tell you what, if you give me a kiss, I'll let him go." He puckered up his ugly fat lips and waited. His gang all laughed as if Billy was the sharpest wit in London.

"Kiss my arse, you toad! I'll smack you in the face if you don't let him go this instant!"

"Ooo! I am scared!" Billy said in a mock whine. "The little cat will get out her claws, will she? 'Elp, boys, I'm terrified."

His cronies sniggered again. One with a sharp nose like the snout of a ferret made a meowing sound behind me, plunging them into fresh paroxysms of mirth.

"I'm warning you!" I said, taking a step toward Billy. I did not know what I was going to do, but anger was driving me recklessly on, like a runaway horse pulling a carriage downhill.

But at least my rage produced one good effect: Billy released his hold on Pedro and swaggered toward me as if he owned the whole market and everything in it—including me. "Or what? Are you askin' for a beatin'? 'Cause I'll give you one, even though you are a girl. Mind you, you're no lady, so it don't count." He gave me an evil grin, displaying his row of blackened teeth. "You're just a daggle-tail 'oo can speak like a duchess when it suits but can't wash off the stink of the gutter no matter 'ow you pretend to your fine friends in the theater."

"A daggle-tail cat!" repeated Ferret-Features with an appreciative chuckle.

I was searching for a suitably tart response when Pedro, his fists raised, scrambled in to stand between me and Billy.

"Don't you dare touch her!" he challenged.

Even I had to admit, my champion's threat was not very impressive. He looked as if one stout blow would knock him to kingdom come. But I appreciated his courage all the same.

"Or what, Blackie?" jeered Billy. "You want a gob-full of claret too, eh?"

"Leave him out of this!" I said angrily.

Billy flicked a contemptuous look at Pedro. "Wot ya think, boys? Our Cat 'ere 'as fallen for 'is dusky charms." Billy pushed Pedro aside and tucked me under his sweaty armpit. "We can't 'ave our English girls messin' with no African slave boys, can we now?"

I struggled to free myself from his arm, but he continued to tow me away. If I didn't do something quickly, he would bring his boys in against Pedro in a lynch mob. There was nothing the London youth liked better than a bit of foreigner-bashing. I had to think of something to draw their fire away from him.

But the African wasn't helping. "I'm no slave!" declared Pedro proudly, standing up erect.

"Let me go, you fathead!" I protested, punching Billy ineffectually in the ribs to get him to release me. "Back off, Billy *Boil*!"

Billy winced. He did indeed have the misfortune to have a large inflamed spot on the end of his nose. I had not realized that he was so sensitive about it—if I had, I would have employed the insult sooner. He shoved me roughly away, onto the cobbles, and called me a name that you do not hear in polite company. He then aimed a kick at me.

"Run!" I yelled at Pedro as I picked myself up and made a dash for home. I did not even look around to see if he was following. I had done my best by distracting Billy; Pedro would have to rely on his own wits for the rest. At least in part the trick had worked, for I could hear the thunder of footsteps on my heels: Billy and his boys were after me. I leapfrogged over a grocer's stall, knocking over a crate of apples as I passed through. A boy cursed behind me as he fell to the ground, feet forced from under him by the green ammunition I had let loose.

"Come back 'ere, you vandal!" shouted the unfortunate owner of the stall, but I was not fool enough to obey him.

Out of the corner of my eye, I saw Pedro running parallel, chased by two of Billy's thugs. He was outstripping them easily and appeared to stand a better chance of getting home in one piece than I did. I could hear the panting breath of someone hot on my heels. If I didn't get out of sight, it was all up for me. I took a sharp right, dodging out of view of my pursuers for a few precious seconds, and dived under the cheesemonger's stall. Mrs. Peters was minding the shop—a lucky thing for me, for she was known to be a kindhearted woman.

"Hide me, please!" I hissed to her plump ankles.

"Lawd love us, Cat!" she muttered. "What scrape 'ave you got into now?"

I had no time to reply, for Billy Shepherd had arrived at her stall. I shrank close to a churn, hoping he would not think to look under the table. My hiding place had the sour smell of milk about to spoil, but in my present situation I could not afford to be too particular.

"'Oi, missus! Which way she go?" asked Billy, panting hard.

"'Oo's that?" Mrs. Peters replied with forced cheerfulness, though I could see her knuckles were white as she clenched a cloth by her side. All of the stallholders had reason to fear Billy Shepherd. He was a nasty piece of work who would not think twice about wrecking their business if it suited him. They had been appealing to Syd to do something about Billy, and we all knew a confrontation was brewing.

"Don't be clever with me," growled Billy. "Cat—that red-'aired girl from the theater. 'Oo else d'you think I mean?"

"Oh, 'er," said Mrs. Peters as if the daylight of understanding was just dawning in her benighted mind. "I saw 'er run off down Russell Street as if the devil 'imself were after 'er."

Billy swore. "I don't believe you, you old cow. She couldn't get so far so fast."

"If you don't believe me, search my stall then—and 'is—and 'ers." She waved her cloth at the other stallholders. This was a high-risk strategy on her part. I slid as close as I could to the churn, feeling the metal cold on my cheek. "I've got nuffink to 'ide from the likes of you."

"Watch it, woman, or my boys will be paying you a call one of these nights."

Mrs. Peters fell silent. Would Billy take up her invitation to search the stall? If he did, I was dead. But perhaps the thought of poking around through the highly smelling cheeses deterred him. He hesitated just long enough for one of his boys to come running back to him.

"Billy, Blackie's been spotted. Over 'ere!"

The hobnailed boots thundered off across the cobbles on the scent of a new quarry. I waited till the din had died away completely and then scrambled out of my hiding place.

"Thanks, Mrs. Peters," I said gratefully, gulping breaths of fresh air.

"Don't you do that to me again, Cat!" she said, venting her fury by hacking at a round cheese the size of a cartwheel axle.

"Sorry. I didn't mean to get you into trouble."

She wiped her forehead with the back of her hand and stood looking at me, her hands on her hips. "I know, dearie, but you stay out of 'is way, won't you? Or you'll be found in the gutter one mornin' with your throat slit like wot 'appened to poor Nat Perkins." She looked around the edge of her stall, checking that the coast was clear. "You'd better get out of 'ere while you can."

I nodded and headed off southward, intending to circle around and enter the theater from the Drury Lane side. I just hoped that Pedro had managed to get away too.

I found him leaning over a water fountain near the stage door. His fine livery was in tatters and he had a bloodied nose and black eye. He looked up as I approached and gave me a nod, his white teeth stained with blood from a cut to his mouth.

"You got away too then?" he asked.

"Better than you, by the looks of it."

He shrugged. "I took a wrong turn but there was only one of them by the time he caught up with me—the small one. I soon sorted him out and got away before the others arrived."

"Sorted him out?" I asked incredulously. I'd not put Pedro down as a street fighter.

"I can look after myself, you know."

"So you didn't need my help then?" I asked sarcastically. "I wish you'd told me, for I'd've spared myself a lot of trouble. I s'pose you'd've beaten them all single-handed, would you?"

"Well, I have to admit that it wasn't looking promising until you showed up." He shook the water off his face and dusted down his ruined clothes. "Shall we go in?"

He didn't seem to realize just how close we had come to serious injury. "You may have dealt out one beating this morning," I told him grumpily, 'but we both face another when they see what a state you're in."

"Beatings are nothing new. Thank you for coming to help me, Miss Cat." He gave me a mocking bow.

I could not help but smile at his flamboyant flourish. He had bowed as if I were a duchess.

"It's just Cat, Pedro. You saved me from the balloon; I rescued you from the Boil. So, we're even then?"

"Yes, we're quits."

It was only as we reached the safety of the theater that it really struck me that we hadn't heard the last of this morning's escapade. I had made myself a very formidable enemy in Billy "Boil" Shepherd—and his enemies had the unfortunate habit of meeting sudden ends down dark alleyways. Not a pleasant thought.

SCENE 3—A TRIUMPH

As I had predicted, we were both soundly beaten for arriving back at the theater covered in mud and, in Pedro's case, blood. No one wanted to hear our explanations. As far as Signor Angelini was concerned, the only thing that mattered was that Pedro had missed an hour of rehearsal time and returned having spoiled both his clothes and appearance. As for me, Mrs. Reid did not look kindly upon my mud-spattered skirts nor on the part she assumed I had played in ruining her Mogul Prince.

"It's all very well for you to cry, missee," she scolded as I nursed my hands, raw from the blows she had just inflicted, "but you should have thought first before you led the boy off into the streets. If you want to stay at Drury Lane, you have to start acting like a lady, not like a street beggar's brat."

"I didn't lead him anywhere!" I protested, outraged by the unfairness of her accusations.

"I was saving him from being mobbed by the market gangs!"

"Well, you didn't do a very good job, did you?" she replied, stabbing a pin into Pedro's costume as he stood patiently waiting for her to finish. He had been thrashed by Signor Angelini but I will not tell you where. Suffice to say that the beating will not interfere with his violin playing nor be visible to the public. He winced as she tugged on a red silk sash but then, seeing that I was watching, he gave me a wink when her back was turned.

Sarah Bowers entered carrying an enormous confection on a tray. I looked again: it wasn't a dessert as I had at first thought but a lavishly decorated turban of pale pink.

"'Ere you go," said Sarah, ramming the hat on Pedro's head so that it covered the cut on his right temple. "I've gone to town with the jools—they should take eyes off that there black 'un of yours."

Indeed the twinkling gemstones were dazzling even in the pale light of the Sparrow's Nest; it was not hard to imagine them in their full splendor under the chandeliers. But Sarah's talk of jewels reminded me of another subject I had almost forgotten in today's adventures.

"Are those real?" I asked, stretching up to tap on the big ruby set in the center of the turban. A white ostrich feather bobbed over Pedro's head like a swan's neck dipping into a silken stream.

"I certainly hope so," said Pedro, squinting at himself in the mirror, "because then I'll be on the first boat to France and will live off my riches for the rest of my days."

Mellowing a little as she admired the effect of the costume over which she had slaved so hard, Mrs. Reid laughed. "You won't get far with those, my lad; they are all paste. Gimcrack rubbish the lot of them. The feather's worth more than they are put together—all the way from Africa, would you believe it! So mind you see that no harm comes to it if you don't want a second beating!" Her nearsighted eyes glared a warning at him in the mirror as she fixed a single pearl earring in his lobe.

Pedro nodded, sending the ostrich feather into a swaying dance.

"Mind you, you rarely see the real thing, Cat," added Sarah, arranging the folds of the turban. "When the ladies sit in the boxes with ropes of pearls and diamonds around their necks, you know they're mostly fake. There's many a duchess with her jools laid up in lavender, if the rumors be true."

"Laid up in lavender?" I asked.

"At the pawnbrokers, dear," explained Mrs. Reid, "to pay gambling debts usually. So think about that if ever you are tempted to try your luck at the card table." She gave Sarah and me a cautionary look over the top of her glasses.

I was very unlikely to face that temptation. No one could possibly think I had money to lose in a card game, let alone jewels. But perhaps Mrs. Reid could help me with the mystery of Mr. Sheridan's diamond.

"Mrs. Reid," I began, passing her the tape measure that had fallen to the floor, "if you had a real jewel, where would you keep it for safety?"

"Locked in a big iron chest in the Tower of London, guards on the door day and night," she chuckled. "If only . . ."

"Forget the chest," said Sarah, throwing a shovelful of coal onto the fire. "Just give me the guards, six foot tall and 'andsome as can be." She stood up and mimed flouncing across the hearth rug like a fine lady, swinging a jewel on the end of a chain around her neck.

"You bold madam!" laughed Mrs. Reid. "You'll come to no good, you will, if you carry on like that. Now, young man, take off your finery, and Cat can show you where to get something to eat before the show starts. You've not got long."

Grabbing some small beer, cold meat, bread, and sweet wrinkled apples from the table laid out in the green room, Pedro and I made our picnic in my favorite hideaway of the manager's box. Already the early arrivals were taking their seats in the pit, and a number of servants were lounging in the galleries, saving places for their masters and mistresses. The stage was empty—the balloon (now repaired) was well hidden in the flies so that it could descend unheralded to the amazement of the crowd. Pedro had a lot to play against if he was to make his mark tonight.

"I'll watch you from here if Mr. Sheridan lets me," I told him. He had gone very quiet, and I suspected that nerves were beginning to have an effect on him. "Are you nervous?"

Pedro shook his head, the pearl earring that he had not taken off glinting in the candlelight. "No, I'm not nervous. I was just thinking about all the other theaters I've performed in. This one is undoubtedly the grandest." He looked about him, taking in the raked seating capable of accommodating thousands of London's finest citizens—as well as some of her worst. "You really live here?"

"All my life," I replied simply. "And you?"

He shrugged. "I don't remember much about the early years except . . ." He paused, thinking back, ". . . friendly faces and a hot sun."

"So how did you get to drizzly, cold London?" I asked, encouraging this new mood for shared confidences.

Pedro's face took on a hardened, embittered expression.

"When I was still an infant, my people were sold by our enemies to the slavers. We were split up. I got lucky, I suppose you would say, for on the voyage to the colonies I caught the eye of a gentleman, a Mr. Hawkins. He saw me playing on a sailor's pipe one day—I'd managed to get out of the hell belowdecks by entertaining the crew. He bought me and spent a few years training me up as a violinist. Then he got some of his money back by sending me on tour in the southwest, performing in theaters and private houses. That lasted for a couple of seasons and then I was sold on to Signor Angelini last month."

"Sold? So you are a slave then?" I asked curiously.

Pedro flashed me a dangerous look. "I am no such thing. I am an apprentice musician under articles to Signor Angelini. Once on the shores of your country, I became free—as free as you are."

"Sorry," I mumbled, realizing I had offended him. "So you can leave when you like? You can go home?"

He gave a hollow laugh. "Home? Where is that, pray? My family were all sold for slaves. If they are still alive, how could I ever find them? I can't even remember my proper name." He looked at me angrily, as if I was somehow partly to blame for his misfortune. He wasn't to know that, though describing a very different life, it sounded to me as if Pedro and I shared much in common: we had both been thrown out into the world at an early age and were now cut off from our origins. I had often wondered what name my mother had given me. I had vague memories of a woman caring for me—I sometimes dreamed of her but no image remained in my waking mind. But at least I knew exactly why I had ended up as Cat.

"So why are you called Pedro?" I asked.

"That was the name of my first master's dog— you see how highly he valued me," Pedro replied with an ironic smile. "My second name is Hawkins, after him. But I'm going to make my own name now. I won't be anyone's performing monkey any longer. Now I've reached London, I'm going to make my name as the best musician in Europe." He held his head proudly, glaring down at the audience below as if challenging them to refuse his claim.

"I can believe it," I replied.

He raised his mug of beer to acknowledge my remark and took a swig. Wiping his mouth, he then asked:

"And what about you? What are you going to do when you are too old to live here?"

I was taken aback. I had never considered a life when I was not living backstage at Drury Lane. But he was right: a day would come when I could no longer bed down on the costumes in the Sparrow's Nest. I did not want him to think that I was completely without talent, unable to take care of myself.

"I'm going to be a writer," I said on impulse. "I'll write for the stage." Pedro gave me a skeptical look. "I've been taught to read and write by the old prompter. He always told me that there was no better education to be had anywhere in the world. Shakespeare, Dryden, Johnson—I've read them all. I speak French with the ballerinas—and I can read it too."

"But you're a girl," he said dismissively. He clearly didn't think very much of my talents.

It was my turn to get angry. "So? Women can make a lot of money from writing. Look at Mrs. Radcliffe and Mrs. Inchbald."

He snorted. "And what have you got to write about? Have you traveled the world? Have you been to the Indies and the Americas? Have you moved in high society like I have?"

"No, but at least I wasn't carrying a tray of drinks at the time!" I answered angrily.

He laughed. "Touché."

"What do you mean by that?"

"Touché—a hit. It's from fencing—a hobby of my old master."

"Oh." I was feeling quite out of spirits now. Compared to the worldly Pedro, learned in the gentlemanly arts of music and swordplay, I knew nothing. But I still refused to accept defeat. "For your information, I've got plenty to write about. Like Mr. Sheridan's diamond, for example."

"Diamond?" It was his turn to look impressed, but even so I instantly regretted that I'd even mentioned it.

"I shouldn't have told you that. Forget it."

"Of course I can't forget it! You'd better tell me now—or I'll ask Mr. Sheridan himself."

"You wouldn't!"

"Would!" His face was determined, ruthless even. I believed him capable of anything at that moment.

"I'll tell you if you promise to keep it a secret." He nodded, giving me a solemn bow, hand on heart. "Well, Mr. Sheridan has hidden a treasure in the theater and I'm looking after it for him."

"Where is it?" he asked eagerly.

I then remembered what Pedro said about running away to France with the jewels from his turban and was therefore thankful to be able to deny all knowledge of its exact location.

"I don't know. But I'm to tell him if anyone comes sneaking around to look for it."

He gave me a queer look, perhaps wondering if I meant him. "I'll help you," he said. "It sounds exciting. Perhaps we'll get a reward if we catch someone who's after it."

I shrugged. "Maybe." I looked away to the auditorium and saw that it was almost full. "Hadn't you better get changed? The performance is about to start."

Pedro brushed the crumbs off his lap and bowed again.

"Tonight I will play for you, Cat," he said gallantly as he left the box.

As I watched him go, I wondered about my new friend, for I supposed that was what he was after all we had been through today. Pedro was the most unusual boy I'd ever met and I wasn't talking about his skin color. I couldn't forget the music that poured from his violin that morning: he seemed to be in touch with something much greater than anything I knew, something almost holy. That was it, I thought with a smile as I realized what image I was feeling my way toward: he was like a priest, a priest of music, superior to the rest of us who had never gone beyond the veil into the Holy of Holies. That was until you mentioned money to him—that brought him straight back to earth among the rest of us. I wouldn't be encouraging him to think any more about the diamond—that had been a big mistake.

Mr. Sheridan had not yet arrived, though I expected him to come for the first night of the balloon farce, *The Mogul's Tale,* after the main play. This meant I had the delicious luxury of the box to myself. I sat in his chair and played with the opera glasses. I trained them on the pit, picking out the men on the seats below as they chewed on handfuls of nuts and oranges. Jonas Miller, the clerk from across the road, a pinched-nose youth with straggly fair hair and a poor complexion, was here again, sitting at the end of the bench just under my box. He must spend all his wages on tickets. Jonas was a fanatic about the theater and was famous for his devotion to Miss Stageldoir, sending her weekly offerings of nosegays and other tokens of his affection. She ignored him, of course, saying that he was only a clerk with ideas above his station. I could have added that he was a louse who never missed an opportunity to insult those below him. As I was somewhere near the bottom of life's pile, that meant he treated me cruelly when our paths crossed, either directing some foul remark in my direction or pushing me roughly out of his way.

Jonas was at present sitting next to a dark-suited young man, both with eyes trained on a pamphlet in their laps. Deciding to have my revenge by abusing my position of power, I focused the glasses to spy on the paper they were looking at. It was only a caricature—some crude picture lampooning the government or the royal family. I bent closer to the edge of the box to listen to what they were saying.

"Captain Sparkler's been at it again," cried Jonas. "Look at what he's done to the king. He looks like a sack of Norfolk potatoes. What's this? He's only gone and drawn him squatting on 'the dung heap of history.' Ouch! That's a bit bold, ain't it?"

"The French king doesn't look very happy though," said the other. "I'm not sure French liberty is to his liking."

"I'm all for a bit of French revolutionary spirit here, aren't you, Reuben? Shake up the old orders—give us young men a chance. After all, *we* are the future of this country, not that old German fart, the king."

Reuben looked about him nervously. "Ssh!" he hissed. "Someone might hear you! They've got people out looking for troublemakers. You know you could be carted off to the Tower for insulting the king? Not to mention being hanged, drawn, and quartered for treason."

"They wouldn't dare," bragged Jonas, though I noticed he had dropped his voice despite his bold words. "They're too scared of us—afraid we'll do to them what the Frenchies have done to their king, making him come at their beck and call. And we might." Jonas tried to swell impressively, but to my eye he just looked like a bullfrog, croaking out empty threats.

He was wasting his breath. The mob would never treat King George as the French had their Louis. And as for putting him on the dung heap, that was impossible! Britain without a king was as inconceivable as London without its theaters. Hadn't we tried it with Cromwell and decided we rather liked royalty after all? It was just a shame Jonas's concern for the underclasses did not stretch to those under him, I thought, turning my attention to the more interesting events on the stage. The orchestra filed in. It had gone six-thirty: the performance was starting at last.

I had a long wait to see both Pedro and the balloon as I first had to sit through *The Haunted Tower*, a dark Gothic opera that I did not rate much higher than the productions of Mr. Salter's pen, but at least the audience seemed to like it. Mr. Kemble made sure there was plenty of fake blood and screaming to keep them happy.

A door opened behind me in the fifth act, and I had to scramble out of my chair to make way for Mr. Sheridan. He was accompanied by a gentleman and two young people, a boy and a girl a few years older than me, both finely dressed. As I ducked out of the way, I caught a glimpse of the sky blue silk of the girl's lace-edged gown and felt a pang of envy. I had never owned anything so beautiful in my entire life.

"Keeping my seat warm for me, were you, Cat?" joked Mr. Sheridan.

"Yes, sir." I bobbed a curtsy, knowing better than to presume upon his kindness in the presence of outsiders. The boy was staring at me with undisguised curiosity, as if I was something intriguing in a cage in the zoological garden.

"Run along then," Mr. Sheridan said, shooing me away. "Make room for Lord Francis and Lady Elizabeth."

Not needing to be told twice, I quit the box. The rich masters had come to throw out the servant. With no revolution here to change the old ways in my favor, I would have to find another vantage point from which to watch Pedro.

Sneaking downstairs, I crept through the door into the pit. Respectable girls did not usually come down here, so I grabbed a pile of theater bills from Sally Hubbard, the doorkeeper, and stood by the entrance, pretending to be there to sell them.

Things were not going well for me if I was to get my wish of seeing Pedro and the balloon. It was now so crowded (standing room only) that I could barely see the stage, being several feet shorter than the men surrounding me. One portly gentleman standing at the very back noticed my predicament as I hopped from foot to foot. He offered his assistance in a most gentlemanlike manner and lifted me up onto a pillar by the entrance, where I could hang on by the candle bracket. I now had a superb view over everyone's heads to the stage. I smiled my thanks to him and he tipped his hat most courteously to me.

At last the curtain rose. The stage was empty. On realizing this, the men in the pit began to mutter angrily to each other. They had been promised a spectacle such as they had never seen before in the theater, and now it looked as though they had been duped. I smiled to myself, knowing they were about to witness something that would rival the feats of the most daring rope walkers at Bartholomew Fair.

The orchestra struck up an Eastern tune, evoking an exotic Asia, a land of moguls and tigers, diamonds and spices. The grumbling died away. Then, from the very roof of the stage, a long rope tumbled down, a small anchor at its end. It fell on the stage with a clatter. Next came a creaking of ropes and shouts of "Ware below!" and the basket of the balloon appeared suspended above the stage, swaying slightly. The crowd gasped. Slowly, without a hitch, the basket came down, Mr. Andrews, its sole passenger, saluting the audience as it inched to the floor. I held my breath: had Mr. Bishop really solved the problem with the ropes? I wondered. Now the silken canopy came into sight, and the crowd cheered and began to applaud wildly, standing on the benches to whistle their approval.

"Capital!" bellowed my kind gentleman, mopping his forehead with his handkerchief. The heat of the audience's enthusiasm was making the pit quite sultry.

The basket touched down and Mr. Andrews, a tall man famed for his comic roles, leaped out and bowed. Everyone whistled and clapped.

"Encore! Again!" cried many voices around me.

Mr. Andrews held up his hand for silence. The hubbub was quickly stilled.

"I am one John Smith, a poor English balloonist. I earn an honest living by offering rides in my craft in Green Park in that greatest of cities, London." (A cheer from the partisan London audience.) "But one day, as I mounted in my balloon, I was blown by a sudden wind to the east. I wonder to what fair country I have been carried? I shall explore before *I return*." He gave the last words special emphasis and winked at the front rows, in effect promising them another balloon ride at the end of the piece. Placated, the gentlemen resumed their seats and gave him their attention.

The farce was absurd and simple: John Smith has landed in the harem of the Great Mogul and is caught by the palace guards. Threatened with death, his only hope is to persuade the Great Mogul himself to spare him. The mogul, played by Mr. Kemble, turns out to be not a monstrous tyrant but a man of learning and mercy. He frees John Smith in return for a balloon ride. Straightforward enough stuff, providing plenty of opportunities for the ballet and musicians to show off their prowess at the exotic style now much in vogue. But where was Pedro? I wondered as the minutes ticked by. The play was nearing its end and he had still not done his turn.

"And now," declared the mogul, interrupting my thoughts, "I will show you the greatest wonder of my kingdom. My son and heir will entertain you before you depart." He clapped his hands and two pantalooned slaves entered, carrying a chest built on poles to resemble the bulbous towers of an Eastern potentate's palace.

What an introduction! Pedro had been pitched against the balloon. If he wanted to make his mark, he would have to produce something to rival that silken ball of hot air. I clenched my fingernails into my palm, my heart pounding for him.

The slaves lifted the lid of the casket, and there was a blinding flash as two firework fountains burst into flame, spilling glowing white sparks onto the stage. With great agility, Pedro leaped over the trail of hissing embers and landed neatly center stage. The silks and satins of his robe gleamed richly and the jewels in his turban flashed with fire to match the scintillating sparks of the fireworks. With the same swiftness I had seen him use that morning, he produced his violin as if from thin air and tucked it under his chin. He then began to play, a new piece full of such haunting melodies and strange harmonies that I was at once transported to the

India of my imagination: a land of palaces, unimaginable riches, heavily laden merchant ships at anchor, a beating sun. I cannot have been the only one so transfixed, for the audience was absolutely silent, hanging on every note that issued from his instrument like a stream of liquid gold sound.

Pedro finished and there was a pause. Had I misjudged the audience's reaction? Then the house erupted into tumultuous applause, stamping, cheering, and whistling, crying for an encore. Pedro was ready. He launched himself into a new melody, spinning faster and faster as the tune gathered pace. The audience cheered and clapped in time to the beat until it got too fast for them to keep up. The music and Pedro's wild spinning came to a stop at the same triumphant moment, and applause rang out once more.

It took some minutes before the play was able to resume. When the noise had simmered down, Mr. Andrews gave his farewell speech and climbed into the basket.

"Farewell! See you in Green Park!" he shouted, waving cheerfully to the audience. They waved back and then waited. We all waited. It became clear something was wrong with the pulley system once more. The play was about to end with a flop.

Suddenly, Pedro leapt into action. Abandoning his violin in the hands of a startled Mr. Kemble, he jumped into the basket and shinnied his way up the nearest rope. The audience began to murmur, wondering if this was all part of the act. Mr. Kemble seized the moment.

"Look, my son goes to ask the gods to allow the balloon of the Christian barbarian to return to his damp island," the Great Mogul declaimed, waving the violin bow at the ceiling.

The crowd laughed and cheered the Mogul Prince as he climbed up and disappeared under the silken canopy. Then the slack ropes of the grounded balloon began to shake. I guessed that Pedro was adjusting them in the tackle above. Only a minute or so had passed, and Pedro reemerged, sliding rapidly down the rope to spring to the floor.

"Are the gods content to let this heathenish contraption rise again?" asked the mogul.

Pedro gave a nod, his ostrich feather agreeing with him vigorously over his head.

"Then, farewell, stranger!" cried the mogul. He clapped his hands twice, Mr. Andrews gave a slightly nervous wave to the spectators, and the balloon creaked once more into action. As it disappeared up into the roof, the actors and audience all tilted their heads to watch and the curtain fell.

"Amazing!" cried my gentleman, clapping and cheering with the best of them despite his advanced years. "In all my days, I've never seen the like! Did you enjoy it, my dear?"

"It was wonderful!" I said sincerely, accepting his hand to jump down from my vantage point. "And Pedro was brilliant."

"Pedro?" he asked, his eyebrow cocked with interest.

"The little prince—Pedro Hawkins."

The man straightened up and started to chant, "Bravo Pedro! Bravo the prince!"

Those near us took up his call and soon the whole theater was ringing with Pedro's name. As the curtain rose again, he was ushered forward by Mr. Kemble to take his own bow.

Pedro Hawkins had made a name for himself.

Act II - In which the world is turned upside down at a boxing match between the Bow Street Butcher and the Camden Crusher...

ACT II

SCENE 1—THE DUKE'S CHILDREN

I ran as quickly as I could to the green room so I would be the first to congratulate Pedro on his London debut. In the end, I need not have hurried, because I had a long wait—the crowd must have demanded a further encore. Finally, the performers piled into the room, talking loudly in their exhilaration at being in a hit. Mr. Andrews and Mr. Kemble had their arms around each other's shoulders, faces glowing with high spirits. Mr. Andrews was mimicking his companion's extemporized lines about calling on the gods for permission, making the actor-manager roar with laughter.

I looked in vain for Pedro. He had not come in with the others. The green room was already stifling with the heat of so many bodies crushed together, the clink of wine glasses being raised to toast the success, the odors of greasepaint and perspiration. I wormed my way to the door, ducking through the crowd of Eastern beauties and slaves in curling slippers. There, on the threshold, was Pedro. He was having his hand shaken by each of the stage crew in turn. Long Tom thrust a mug of foaming beer into his hand, and Mr. Bishop slapped him on the back as he made to drink it, slopping beer everywhere. The stage crew howled with exuberant laughter. Pedro smiled uncertainly, wondering if they were mocking him or merely having a lark. But the friendly smiles on their faces told him that they now considered him initiated as one of the boys, so he grinned and downed the rest in a gulp.

I hovered shyly to one side, waiting for my opportunity to congratulate him, but before I could get a word in, Mr. Kemble had come forward and steered Pedro into the thick of things, shouting out to the crowd, "Here is the man of the moment! What a performance!"

"Indeed," agreed Mr. Andrews. "Without your quick thinking the crowd might have hanged us all from that damned balloon."

Pedro accepted the adulation with dignity, bowing to those who came up to compliment him. I still could not reach him—so thick was the press—but I noticed that he was looking around, perhaps trying to spot me in the forest of grown-ups.

"Pedro!" I shouted from the corner I had been backed into. Peter Dodsley was embracing Pedro with great emotion. "Pedro, over here!"

My voice must have carried to his sharp ears for he turned and waved. He broke away from the first violinist and began to duck and weave his way through the crowd until finally we were together again.

"Did you watch?" he asked eagerly. "I played to your box but I couldn't spot you."

"No, you wouldn't've. Mr. Sheridan arrived with guests and threw me out." Pedro's face fell. "But I watched from the pit. I had a splendid view. And you were magnificent!"

Pedro's face cracked into a wide smile. "So no one noticed my black eye then?"

I laughed and shook my head. "Absolutely not."

There was a loud call for silence at the door. We turned to look and saw Mr. Sheridan standing framed in the doorway, flanked by his three smart guests who had ousted me from the box.

"Ladies and gentlemen," Mr. Sheridan called. A hush spread from the front of the room to the back like a wave rippling over a peaceful lake. "I have the great honor of presenting a very special visitor to you. The Duke of Avon expressed the desire of personally conveying his appreciation of tonight's performance to you all."

The Duke of Avon, a stately gentleman with white locks brushed forward from a receding hairline, stepped into the room and cleared his throat.

"As my honorable friend here says, I thought you excelled yourselves tonight—none more so than our little African. Where is he? My children in particular would like to meet him."

"Go on," I hissed, pushing Pedro forward.

Arriving before the duke, he gave an elegant bow.

"An unforgettable debut!" declared the peer. "Well done!"

Mr. Sheridan then steered Pedro to one side to meet Lady Elizabeth and Lord Francis.

Conversation in the green room picked up again as the private interview commenced, but I stayed close to the door, watching the fictitious prince meet some of our country's highest nobility. Lord Francis looked younger than his sister; I guessed he was probably only a few years older than me. He had a head of unruly dark brown curls and vivid blue eyes. I noticed that he could not stand still; he fidgeted from foot to foot with barely suppressed excitement, looking at everyone and everything that passed. By contrast, his sister stood serenely and listened to Pedro as he recounted what he had done to save the balloon flight. I liked her expression: at once intelligent and gentle. She did not seem to think it beneath her to spend time giving her attention to a mere player.

Lord Francis then spotted me. He nudged Lady Elizabeth.

"Look, it's Sheridan's Cat, Lizzie," he said, grinning over at me. "I wondered what had become of her."

I would have slipped away, but Pedro strode over and hooked me by the arm. "Allow me to introduce you to her."

He dragged me over. "You say, my lord, that you want to know about the theater; well, here is our resident expert." He waved his hand toward me in a flourish like a conjuror producing a white rabbit from a hat.

I blushed at the introduction and curtsied.

"So, Miss . . . ?" began Lady Elizabeth tentatively.

"Miss Catherine Royal," I supplied, thinking it the moment to use my full title.

"Miss Royal, what do you do at the theater?" she asked.

"Do you sing?" asked Lord Francis eagerly. "Do you play?"

I hesitated. Message-runner did not sound very impressive faced with the cream of English society who expected me to dazzle them as Pedro had done.

"She writes," said Pedro quickly. "Oh yes, the first production of her pen will soon be on all good bookstands—a story of mystery and intrigue from a child prodigy. She is the bookseller's dream, a gift to the journals!"

I gaped. Fortunately no one noticed as they were now discussing my forthcoming work eagerly.

"Well, I am impressed!" exclaimed Lady Elizabeth. "Will it be full of banditi and haunted castles?"

"Or highwaymen and thief catchers?" asked Lord Francis.

They both turned expectantly to me. I could not help smiling at the absurd tale Pedro had spun, but I was not going to let the theater—or myself—down in front of them. I would prove that I was worthy of their respect.

"Oh no, nothing like that," I said with a superior air. "It is set here, in Drury Lane, and will go from the lowest ranks of society to the highest, from the gangs and barrow boys to the baronets and beauties. My themes will be—" (I cast around for some suitably Shakespearean language to impress them, not having in truth a clue what I was talking about) "the wickedness of treason, the sting of revenge, and the noble disinterestedness of love, all set behind the scenes."

"Excellent!" said Lord Francis, clapping his hands with enthusiasm. "And what's it to be called?"

I went blank for a moment, floundering around

for a title appropriate to the medley of themes I had just described.

"*The Diamond of Drury Lane*," Pedro extemporized quickly.

I vowed to kick him later for his recklessness. I had much rather he had not mentioned the diamond. Neither of us seemed to be doing very well in keeping Mr. Sheridan's secret. If Pedro had his way, it would be splashed all over the bookstalls and magazines.

"That sounds wonderful," said Lady Elizabeth, addressing herself to me. "Perhaps you and Mr. Hawkins would accept an engagement to entertain a gathering of our friends next Friday—if you can be spared from your other duties, that is?"

"What kind of engagement?" I asked hesitantly.

"Mr. Hawkins to play, of course, and you to read us a chapter of your most interesting work."

"Capital idea," said Lord Francis.

"Yes, we will," answered Pedro before I could think up an excuse.

"Then we will expect you around six," said Lady Elizabeth, making a note in a small notebook with a tiny pencil that she had taken from her reticule.

"But . . ." I began.

Pedro interrupted, stepping on my toes to stop me saying any more. "What Miss Royal means to say is, 'Thank you, but where exactly should we come?'"

"Grosvenor Square," said Lord Francis, stifling a yawn as if the very thought of home was wearisome to him. "South side. You can't miss it."

Grosvenor Square! This was sounding more and more daunting. Grosvenor Square was the most desirable address in the West End. Only the very best families lived there. If you did not have some kind of title, you need not even think of presuming to pollute this hallowed turf with your presence. The families even had their own private garden square in the center—a rare luxury in the crammed streets of London—which was barricaded from the riffraff by railings. I remember once, when an errand took me into that part of town, how I stood gazing longingly into the forbidden garden, watching the rich children playing on the unsullied green lawn—that was before I was rudely moved on by a footman.

"We most willingly accept your gracious invitation," said Pedro with a bow.

Lady Elizabeth clearly considered the matter settled and turned to look for her father. He arrived, reeling a little unsteadily, flushed-faced and happy. I suspected he had been partaking of the champagne Mr. Sheridan had ordered in.

"Come along, my dears, time you were in your beds," he said, offering his arm to his daughter. "Did you get what you want, Lizzie?" he asked, chucking her under her chin.

Lady Elizabeth nodded, her blue eyes sparkling up at him. "Indeed, Papa, more. Miss Royal has also agreed to entertain us."

The Duke of Avon gave me a skeptical look, which took in my patched dress and tumbled appearance.

"She writes the most wonderful stories, sir," said Lord Francis quickly.

"Oh? A writer, is she? How extraordinary for a girl of her class!" the duke exclaimed. Once again I had the impression that this noble family thought I was a curiosity, like the two-headed calf, to be put on show at the fair. "I will be very interested to hear more about this. Perhaps you need a patron to get published, young lady? I am all for encouraging the lower orders to rise above the disadvantages of their station in life—as long as it is consistent with womanly virtues, of course," he added as an afterthought.

Pedro was not slow to pick up on the offer of monetary support. "I can vouch for Miss Royal, your grace. I expect it can be arranged for her to leave a sample of her work when we come on Friday so that you may peruse it at your leisure."

"Excellent," he said. "Till Friday then."

With a slight nod of dismissal, the duke swept off to return to his carriage, taking his children with him, Lady Elizabeth on his arm, Lord Francis lagging behind, still enraptured by the world behind the scenes.

As soon as they were out of earshot, I turned to my friend. "Pedro! What were you thinking of?"

"Your future, Cat," he grinned, "and mine. Offers like that don't come by every day, believe me."

"But I haven't written anything suitable for a duke's eyes, nor the ears of his children!"

"Oh, that's no problem. They don't want to hear about people like them; they want a bit of the rough and raw world of the common people. It's like a voyage to a foreign country for them."

"But I haven't got anything ready for Friday!"

"Then you'd better start burning the midnight oil, Cat. I don't want to hear any more excuses. You'll never realize your ambition to be a writer if you don't put pen to paper. Besides, I'm counting on you to support my first private engagement in London. You won't let me down, will you?" He gave me an appraising look that suggested he still had his doubts about me. Well, I'd show him!

"Oh," I sighed irritably, "all right. I'll do my best."

"You'd better get started then," he said, pushing me in the direction of the Sparrow's Nest. "I'll expect to see at least four pages by tomorrow. Good night."

"Good night, slave driver," I muttered under my breath.

SCENE 2—HIGH SOCIETY

When Mrs. Reid heard about my invitation to Lady Elizabeth's tea party, she was almost as thrilled for me as if she were going herself. Appointed by my patron to keep an eye on me, she took her duties seriously, chastising me for wrongdoing, seeing to my food and clothes. She usually acted toward me like a strict mistress to a servant, so I was particularly touched when she promised to make me a dress suitable for the occasion.

"You'll be representing the theater, mind," she said to excuse her softheartedness. "We can't have you letting the side down."

Johnny also thought it a splendid opportunity. I told him all about it the next morning as we sorted through the old scripts for Mr. Kemble. Johnny bent over the table, a pen tucked behind his ear, no jacket on, the sleeves of his fine linen shirt rolled up to his elbows, displaying his ink-stained fingers.

That made me wonder if he was an aspiring author too.

"Johnny, do you write?"

He laughed. "Not *write* in the sense you mean, Catkin. But if you want to show me what you're doing, I'll be able to help with grammar, spelling, and so on."

"So why do you have ink stains on your fingers?"

He looked down at his hands, turning them over to contemplate them. "You are a sharp one. The Bow Street magistrate could do with your help. No villain would escape your beady eye."

"Oh, he doesn't stir out of doors," I said matter-of-factly. "If you want anything solved around here—stolen property returned, revenge for assault, runaway wives tracked down—you have to go to one of the gangs. They know everything that's happening on their turf."

"Hmm," said Johnny skeptically. "I suspect they mete out a rather rough justice, that lot."

"Some do," I agreed. "Billy Shepherd's boys, for example, are a bad bunch, more likely to be the cause of the problem than a help. And if you do something that makes them lose face, then you're in trouble. They have a keen sense of honor. . . ." I faltered, remembering what I had done the day before.

"Honor? That's a strange word to use about a bunch of thugs."

"It's not just gentlemen that fight if they think they've been insulted, Johnny," I explained. I had to put him straight for he wouldn't last long on our streets if he didn't know about the code of honor that prevailed out there. "But not all gangs are like Shepherd's. Thankfully, there's my friend Syd and his lads. They help keep Shepherd's lot in check. If you need help, go to Syd: he's always fair. And remember, it's Billy Shepherd you have to watch. He'll steal a blind man's stick if it takes his fancy— and kick him into the gutter in the bargain." Having delivered my little lesson, I realized Johnny had successfully diverted me from asking about his inky fingers. "So, tell me."

"Tell you what?"

His air of innocence as he rifled through the papers did not fool me.

"Tell me what you've been up to."

He looked about him. "I don't suppose it will do any harm to let you in on the secret," he said. "I draw."

"Draw? What, likenesses? Could you draw me, for example?"

He nodded. "Though I doubt I could do justice to your freckled nose and scruffy long curls." I hit him. "Ouch!"

"Will you illustrate my manuscript for me? I'm sure the duke's children would love to see more about what life is like backstage."

He looked at me for a moment, considering my request. "Of course I will," he said at length. "Avon is a decent fellow, I believe. The son also. And Lady Elizabeth is . . . is everything a lady should be. No, I don't mind entertaining her friends."

It seemed a strange way to put it, but at least I now had something new I could offer on Friday.

Hopefully, the young lords and ladies would excuse the writing if they were diverted by the pictures.

Pedro was able to escape from his rehearsal at noon so I decided it was high time to introduce him to Syd Fletcher. He needed the protection of Syd's gang now that he had had his meeting with Shepherd. I also wanted to tell Syd about our good fortune. Syd was bound to be very impressed: his father, a butcher, could only dream of supplying the likes of the Avon household, whereas Pedro and I were actually invited indoors! Perhaps this would at long last make Syd change his refusal and let me in as a member of his gang.

Two of Syd's boys were watching the street outside the back entrance to the Fletchers' butcher shop, lounging in the wintry sunshine. Nick was spitting wads of tobacco at the wall while Joe practiced a flamboyant shuffle of his pack of cards, letting them arch from one hand to the other.

"'Ello, Cat," said Nick in a friendly tone, eyeing my companion with interest. "Come to see the big man, I s'pose?"

"Of course. Why do you ask?"

"I's 'opin' that you might've come to call on me and Joe, that's all," he laughed. "Well, you can go on in—'e's almost done for the day."

They waved us through into the gang's inner sanctum: the slaughterhouse at the back of the shop. We found Syd washing down the bloody block where many a creature met a sudden end, his blond hair flopping over his face as he scrubbed hard with a bristle brush. As all parts of the animal were put to use, the room was full of red-stained buckets containing every organ and cut known to man—from ox tongue to tail, as Syd would put it, guffawing loudly at his own wit. The place had that curious odor of sawdust mixed with the surprisingly sweet smell of carnage, a scent that hung around Syd even when he was away from home. He looked up and smiled when he saw me.

"Well, if it ain't our little ray of sunshine! How's tricks, Cat?"

"Good, Syd, thanks." I always felt comfortable with Syd—I'd known him so long that he was like the older brother I'd never had. Even as very little children playing in the streets, he'd looked out for me and taught me so many things.

I introduced my companion. Syd wiped his palms on his blood-stained apron before shaking Pedro's hand, dwarfing the musician with his six feet of muscular body.

"I 'ear you were quite the sensation last night, Prince," said Syd admiringly. "The 'ole market's abuzz with it."

Pedro shrugged, but I could tell this was pleasant news for him.

"And there's more," I said quickly. "We have both been invited to a duke's house!"

"Whatever for?" asked Syd, shooting me a concerned look. "You're not going for scullery maid, are you, Cat?"

"Of course not, you oaf!" I snapped. I am the only one Syd allows to talk to him so irreverently. "We are to entertain Lady Elizabeth and Lord Francis."

Syd gave a snort of laughter. This was far from the awed expression of amazement I had been anticipating. He moved across to a sack of sawdust that hung suspended from the ceiling and gave it a punch with his calloused knuckles. "I can see what the boy can do, Cat, but what about you? Are you goin' to give 'em a bit of your sharp tongue and show 'em 'ow to fight like a wildcat?" He gave the sack a quick double jab. "That's all you're good for, ain't it?"

This fairly took the wind out of my sails. "I'm going to read to them—read a story I've written," I said quietly.

Syd could see that he had offended me. He gave an appreciative whistle, hugging the sack to still its pendulum motion. "Now ain't that just grand: a girl that can 'old 'er own in the market place 'oo can also read and write like a fine lady. I never knew you 'ad it in you, Cat. You'll knock 'em dead, you will."

"Thanks, Syd," I said in a gloomy tone.

Pedro could tell I was beginning to worry again about our visit to Grosvenor Square, so he changed the subject.

"Tell me, Syd, how do things work around here?" he asked, picking his way like a peacock across the sawdust in his shiny buckled shoes. "I met Billy Boil yesterday, but it seems I would have been better off meeting some of your boys."

"Billy *Boil*?" Syd gave a loud guffaw of laughter, which attracted Nick and Joe in from outside. "You 'ear that? The prince has met Billy *Boil*!"

"That's what Cat called him to his face," Pedro continued.

"I like it!" said Syd appreciatively, turning in my direction. "You called 'im that, did you, Cat? I bet 'e weren't pleased."

"No, he tried to beat her up but she escaped him," Pedro explained.

I would have made Pedro shut up if I could, but it was too late. I had had no intention of confiding in Syd, knowing the likely consequences.

"'E threatened my Cat, did 'e?" asked Syd, his blue eyes now cold with anger. "'E'll regret that, 'e will."

"I don't want any trouble on my account," I said quickly. "He was after Pedro really."

"Was 'e now?" Syd strode over to Pedro and gave him a long, searching stare, gauging his uses.

"Well, you can tell Boil next time you see 'im that the prince's in," said Syd.

"He's what?" I asked.

"Prince's in the gang. One of us."

"What!" I protested. "I've been asking to join for months and months, and you let him in not five minutes after meeting him. That's not fair!"

Nick and Joe began to laugh until Syd gave them a stern look.

"I don't 'ave girls in my gang, Cat, as I keep tellin' you."

"But you have African violinists?"

Pedro gave me a glare that implied I'd insulted his origins. I hadn't meant it like that—it was the violinist bit that I'd really meant to draw Syd's attention to.

"Yeah, 'e's a boy, in case you ain't noticed."

"Of course I've noticed!" I said stamping my foot with anger. "But I'm as good as any of you!"

"No, you're better, Cat," said Syd with a wink, "which is why I don't want you in my gang."

"Pedro, tell him! Tell him how I saw the Boil off for you!"

Pedro shrugged. "You ran away quick enough, that's true."

The rat! I'd done far more than that and he knew it! His words served to confirm Syd in his decision that I was not fit to number among his boys. I was sure Nick and Joe were laughing at me. I felt hot with embarrassment and anger, but Syd had dismissed my request and turned his thoughts to other matters.

"As for Billy Boil," he continued, perching on the block, swinging a cleaver absentmindedly in his right hand, "'E's planning a big fight for Monday night, and now I've got a new reason for wanting to beat 'im to a pulp. The gang's meeting at the Rose at ten. Will you be there?" he looked at his newest gang member.

"Of course," agreed Pedro at once.

I moved quickly to dissuade him. "But Pedro, you'll get in trouble again. You don't know how nasty these fights can get!"

"I'll see 'e doesn't come to grief," promised Syd. "'E's our lucky mascot, 'e is. No other gang 'as the star of the stage in their ranks, do they now?"

"No," I said shortly, "because all the other stars are too sensible to get involved."

Pedro gave me a dig in the ribs. "Don't fret. I'm not afraid of a beating. And if you make sure everyone sees that you are safely tucked up in bed, then you'll not be held to blame for whatever happens."

"Perhaps," I grumbled resentfully, "but I wouldn't put it past Mrs. Reid to find some way of making it my fault."

Syd chuckled. "Well, I'll 'ave a word with 'er then." He swung the cleaver in a menacing fashion. "Make 'er see sense."

"Oh, you're both hopeless!" I exclaimed as Pedro, Nick, and Joe fell about laughing.

Syd, who I knew would be the last person to threaten a lady, threw the cleaver aside with a clatter and stood up. "I must go. I 'ave my trainin' this afternoon. You'll come and see me in my boxin' match, won't you, Cat?"

I nodded, though feeling very reluctant. I was not eager to watch two grown boys beating each other up for money, particularly when one was my good friend. "Sunday morning, isn't it?'

"That's right, in Marylebone Fields. You'll 'ave to dress as a boy, like last time."

"Can I come?" asked Pedro eagerly.

"Of course, Prince. All the gang's goin' to be there. You can look after Cat for me."

As if I couldn't look after myself!

"Who are you fighting?" I asked, trying not to show them how angry I still was. They'd only put it down to me being a moody girl if I did and laugh about it when I'd gone.

A worried frown passed across Syd's face for a moment. "The Camden Crusher."

"Is he good?"

"Not as good as me," Syd said proudly, flexing his muscles and rolling his bull-sized neck to warm up. "I'll set 'im to rights, you'll see." He rocked lightly from foot to foot, making a few practice punches at the air.

"I hope so, Syd. Better that than having the surgeon set you to rights afterward."

"Should we knock at the front door or use the tradesman's entrance?" I asked Pedro nervously, clutching my manuscript under my arm.

We both looked up at the tall sandstone house rising four floors above us. The large windows were all lit, shining out into the cold January evening in an opulent display, telling the world that money was no object as far as candles were concerned. An imposing flight of six marble stairs ran up to the black front door. The knocker—a brass dragon's head—gleamed balefully at us. To our right, partially hidden by the spiked iron railing, was a mean, narrow staircase that ran down to the lower floors: the tradesman's entrance.

Pedro looked back at the front door. "We're not bidden to the kitchen; we're here to see the family." He mounted the steps before his courage failed, seized the knocker, and thumped it twice. Almost immediately, the door swung open, and a white-wigged, liveried servant stood there, looking down his long nose at us.

"Yes?" he said dubiously, holding out his hand for a message.

"We're from Drury Lane. Lady Elizabeth is expecting us," said Pedro, ignoring the out-stretched hand and making to step inside.

"I doubt that very much," said the footman with a sardonic smile, blocking his way.

"We're here for the tea party," I added boldly, annoyed by the man's supercilious attitude. "If you don't believe us, why don't you ask her?"

Perhaps our confidence made him think better of shutting the door in our faces. "Wait here," he ordered. He turned to another footman standing in the hall. "Watch them," he told his colleague. "See that they don't touch anything." He then strode swiftly up the red-carpeted stairs.

We stood under the hawkish gaze of the second servant, waiting for our fate to be decided. Before long, the footman returned and reluctantly opened the door wide enough to allow us in.

"Apparently, you are expected," he said with ill grace. "Would you like to leave your cloak here, miss?"

I took off my hood and handed over my old black cloak, revealing underneath the white muslin dress with a green silk sash Mrs. Reid had made for me from one of the ripped ballet dresses she had stashed away. The footman's manner instantly became more respectful.

"Step this way, miss," he said, bowing me up the stairs.

I winked at Pedro, who was staring at me as if seeing me properly for the first time.

"You look—well, you look different, Cat," he muttered on the way upstairs. "I didn't know you washed up so well."

I grinned. "But I'm still the same Cat underneath, even if my hair is neat for once."

Sarah had spent hours that day taming my red mop into a series of ringlets tied back with a matching green bow. I felt I looked good enough for the company we were about to meet, and that gave me the confidence to continue up the stairs.

The footman stopped by a door on the floor above. Inside we could hear the tinkle of the piano and the laughter of young voices.

"Who shall I say is here?" he asked me.

"Miss Royal and Mr. Hawkins, if you please," I said with dignity.

He opened the door and gave a cough.

"Lady Elizabeth, your visitors have arrived: Miss Royal and Mr. Hawkins."

He ushered us forward and then closed the door behind us.

My first impression was of a sea of pink faces turned curiously in our direction. Then I took in the fine muslin petticoats that seemed so light as if made of nothing but spun sugar, the smart breeches and jackets of the boys, the elaborately arranged hair of the girls. Suddenly my own outfit seemed very tawdry.

"Miss Royal, Mr. Hawkins, we are delighted to see you both," said Lady Elizabeth, rising from a cherry-red silk sofa to greet us.

Lord Francis bounded over, abandoning a group of three sour-faced young people. "Just when we needed livening up!" he said enthusiastically. "Who's to go first, eh?"

Pedro bowed. "I am to have that pleasure."

I nearly giggled. It seemed so funny to hear Pedro putting on a refined act in front of this audience—it was like we were all playing at being lords and ladies for the day. I had to remind myself that we were probably the only ones in the room without a title.

As might have been expected, Pedro's concert was a great success. He played the piece by Mozart I had first heard him perform, and it had the same mesmerizing effect in the duke's drawing room as it had at Drury Lane. The music transported us all. Pedro seemed able to conduct our emotions, using his bow as a baton, making us smile or weep by turns. When he stopped, I knew that he had succeeded in claiming his place in this room as an equal by virtue of his talent alone. Indeed, there was something in his gift that put him beyond our reach. He was loudly applauded. Even the sour-faced trio were impressed.

"Now, Miss Royal, it is your turn," said Lord Francis, taking my hand and leading me to a chair. "We are most eager to hear from you."

My heart was thumping so hard I was surprised he could not hear it. I felt most unwilling to read after the virtuoso display we had all just witnessed—it was like bringing the ballet chorus girl on after the principal dancer. "If you wish, sir," I said, unfolding my papers and giving a nervous cough to clear my throat of the frog that had taken up residence there. I took a deep breath.

"Reader, you are set to embark on an adventure told by an ignorant and prejudiced author—me." I sneaked a look over the top of my papers. Lord Francis and the boy beside him were laughing; Lady Elizabeth smiled. They gave me the courage to continue. *"'Much harm done, Tom?' I asked as I clambered over the upturned benches to reach the stagehand as he cleared away the debris from last night's riot. . . ."*

Ten minutes later, I came to the end of my recital and waited. The room was quiet. In that instant, I was convinced I had failed—I had shocked, possibly scandalized them, and they were just struggling to find the words to tell me so. I had been so stupid even to think that I could pass myself off as an author in this discerning gathering. My hopes of launching myself on a new career with ducal patronage plummeted to the ground as rapidly as had the balloon in the extract I had just finished reading them.

"Heavens!" said a pale girl with long brown ringlets like the sausages in Syd's shop. "To think that people really live like this! Fighting in the streets—can you believe it!"

I could sense all their eyes were fixed on me. I felt like a cadaver on the surgeon's table being anatomized before the gaze of curious students.

"I think it's grand," said Lord Francis, thumping his fist playfully into his neighbor's stomach. "Come on, Charlie, how about it?"

Pedro gave me an amused look over Lord Francis's head: though I had changed a few details to protect the identities of my subjects, any astute listener would have been able to identify him as the boy who ended up with a black eye after outrunning the gang.

"Frank!" scolded Lady Elizabeth, her eyebrow raised in warning.

Lord Francis gave her an apologetic look and helped the winded Charles to a seat.

"Well, it certainly was unorthodox," said a sweet-looking girl with a heart-shaped face. "Though perhaps the subject matter is a little unbecoming for a lady. I would have expected Miss Royal to begin with some witty general observation, a wryly expressed universal truth, for example, on love and courtship—the usual themes for the female pen."

"Oh, Jane!" protested Lord Francis. "How can you be so dull? We don't want none of that girly stuff. Straight into the action, that's what we like and that's what Miss Royal gave us. And I thought the pictures were capital."

The sour-looking fellow, with a face like a weasel and sleek silver-blond hair, piped up from his corner: "The pictures did indeed display an uncommon talent but I'm not sure if Miss What's-Her-Name's outpourings are respectable enough for my sisters to hear, Lady Elizabeth."

Our hostess now looked worried.

"Rubbish, Marchmont!" exclaimed Lord Francis.

Marchmont! The name struck a chord with me. I turned to take a closer look at my critic, wondering if I could trace any family likeness to the dark-cloaked man who had threatened me at the stage door.

"It's stuff like that which leads to anarchy. We see it daily in France; I hope to God we do not see it here," the Marchmont boy continued, like some little politician on the hustings. Tension crackled between him and his host. I had the impression that they were old sparring partners between whom there was no love lost.

"Parroting your favorite Pittite phrases, are you?" said Lord Francis. "You'd better not let your father find out. As a friend of liberty, he wouldn't like to hear that his son's a dyed-in-the-wool reactionary."

"Francis!" said Lady Elizabeth, scandalized.

"I think we had better go," said Marchmont, rising and leading his sisters to the door. "Thank you for a lovely evening, Lady Elizabeth. The *music* was superb."

The Marchmonts' departure was taken as the signal for the party to break up. Pedro and I lingered in a corner, wondering if we should slip out or wait to be dismissed. We had been expecting to receive something for our trouble. I hoped that my audacity in reading my poor stuff to the duke's children had not lost us our bounty. Pedro would never let me hear the end of it if it had.

When the last person had left, Lady Elizabeth turned to her brother.

"Frank, do you have to be so rude to my guests?"

He shrugged. "I don't know why you invited them, Lizzie. Just because Father's friendly with his father, it doesn't mean we have to endure them. You know I think Marchmont a prig. You are too polite to say what you really think of his sisters, but I know you don't like them."

"Yes, but to attack him in our own drawing room—that's very bad manners!"

"And criticizing your brother in front of strangers isn't?" he said with a nod at Pedro and me.

Lady Elizabeth blushed. "I'm sorry. I did not realize you were still here." She nudged her brother. "Go on," she hissed, "pay them!"

Lord Francis strode over to us and bowed. "A token of our sincere appreciation of your talents," he said, dropping a promisingly heavy purse into Pedro's hand.

"Thank you, sir," said Pedro.

Lord Francis turned to me. "I hope our ill-mannered guest did not offend you, Miss Royal? You did splendidly. Tell me: does all this really happen as you describe it?"

I nodded and smiled into his friendly eyes, thinking how much I liked him. "Yes, sir."

"It's even better than she writes it," Pedro butted in, trying to impress the young nobleman. "We have parties and music, boxing and battles."

"Boxing!" Lord Francis grabbed at the word eagerly. "My great passion is the ring! I want to learn how to box, but Father won't let me."

"Well," said Pedro leaning forward confidentially, "Cat here—I mean Miss Royal—just so happens to be best friends with Covent Garden's boxing champion. We are watching him in a match on Sunday. For a small consideration," he chinked the purse suggestively, "we might be able to take you along."

"Pedro!" I whispered in warning. This really did not sound like a good idea.

"Will you? . . . Yes, I might be able to get away," said Lord Francis, thinking aloud. He stole a look over his shoulder at his sister, who was now running her fingers over the piano keyboard in a melancholy love song, lost deep in thought. "Lizzie's a bit absentminded at the moment, mooning over one of her suitors who ran off late last night. She's not as sharp as normal. If I pretend to be ill and get out of church, I should be able to do it."

"We'll meet you on the corner of Grosvenor Square then," said Pedro quickly. "At ten."

"At ten," agreed Lord Francis.

"*If* you are coming," I said sullenly, glaring at Pedro, "you'd better dress down a bit, sir."

"Right you are, Cat—I mean Miss Royal," grinned Lord Francis.

SCENE 3—BOW STREET BUTCHER
V. CAMDEN CRUSHER

I was not looking forward to the prospect of trying to smuggle his lordship into the boxing match. It was bad enough that I had to pretend to be a boy to pass unnoticed, but bringing along someone who would have no idea how to blend in seemed pure recklessness. I could imagine what fun the lads would have if they found out that one of their lords and masters was mingling with them. Lord Francis would be very lucky to get home in one piece. Pedro didn't have a clue what he was doing.

I confided my fears to Johnny the next morning over lessons. Having heard from Mrs. Reid how Old Carver had undertaken my education, Johnny had insisted on carrying this on. His choice of reading matter was very different from Mr. Carver's solid diet of English greats: Johnny was improving my French so that I could read

Rousseau in the original, and his idea of English composition revolved around the cream of the crop of the latest political tracts. It was not all hard work, however: at my insistence, he was also giving me lessons in drawing.

We were sketching a bust we had found in one of the airy club rooms on the first floor of the theater when I raised the subject of the match.

"I agree: it doesn't sound like a good idea," said Johnny, lifting his pencil to measure the space between Roman nose and weak Roman chin of Julius Caesar. "But neither do I think it a good idea for you to gad about town dressed as a boy, Catkin."

I scribbled a big proboscis on my drawing, which made the emperor look as if he had a beak. "What were you saying earlier about men and women being equal? How else am I to enjoy equal freedom if I don't disguise myself?"

He looked down awkwardly at his sketch, for he knew that all his counterarguments ran against his own principles. "You've lived too long in the theater, Cat. All these breeches roles for actresses must have gone to your head."

"Don't worry about me, Johnny. I do it all the time. It's Lord Francis you should worry about." I was then struck by what I considered a brilliant idea. "I know, why don't you come with us? If you were there, you could help us look after him."

"I can't do that, Catkin." He gave a vicious twist to Caesar's thin-lipped mouth.

"Why ever not? It's your day off, isn't it?"

"Yes, but I don't want to be seen just now." He sighed.

Now, the only reason I knew for a grown man to hide himself was to avoid those to whom he owed money; many a man lives in fear of hearing the bailiff's knock on the door coming to cart him off to debtor's prison.

"But even if you are hiding from the bailiffs," I said, assuming my guess was correct, "you're free to go out on a Sunday, aren't you? I thought they couldn't arrest people on the Sabbath?"

Johnny laughed and flicked his pencil deftly into the air, catching it as it spun to the floor. "So you think I'm on the run from the bailiffs, do you? It's a likely enough tale. Still, you would agree,

Catkin, that it would not be wise to allow anyone to see me, follow me, and thus find out where I have concealed myself?"

I shrugged. "I suppose not. But is that likely at a boxing match?"

"You'd be surprised," said Johnny, putting the sketch away in his portfolio. "Many gentlemen of my acquaintance are bound to be there for the gambling. I can't risk it. Now, let's see what you have done."

I showed him my drawing.

He chuckled. "You have made the old villain look like one of those anteaters from the Americas. A very good start if you want a career as the first female cartoonist, Cat."

On Sunday morning, Pedro and I waited at the corner of Grosvenor Square for Lord Francis. We appeared to have arrived at rush hour: carriage after carriage was drawing up at the front doors, taking the inhabitants off to the church service of their choice. Only a few families were brave enough to expose their expensive attire to the streets by walking the short distance to the parish church.

I spotted the duke and Lady Elizabeth emerging from their house shortly before ten. Pulling Pedro out of sight behind a carriage waiting on the corner, I watched them walk arm in arm in the opposite direction.

"'Ere, what you playin' at?" protested the coachman, flicking his long whip in our direction. "Get away from my carriage."

Enjoying my breeches role (as Johnny put it), I couldn't resist the temptation to indulge in a bit of unladylike shouting.

"What's your problem, mate? We haven't scratched your precious paintwork." I then stuck my tongue out at him.

"Come on, Cat," said Pedro, grabbing the back of my jacket and towing me into Charles Street, away from the anger of the coachman and the reach of his whip. "You're enjoying this too much."

I laughed. "I can't tell you how good it feels to get out of petticoats! I feel quite a different person."

"I can see that." Pedro looked about him as the church clocks began to chime the hour across London. "Where is he?"

There was a shrill whistle behind us, and a clod of earth hit Pedro on the back of his head. He turned around to shout a protest as out of the alley bolted a tall, scruffy boy, his face blackened with soot like a chimney sweep. He ran straight up to us and presented himself for our inspection, arms thrown wide.

"Lord Francis!" I exclaimed. "I'd never've recognized you!"

Lord Francis the chimney sweep looked me up and down. "Nor I you, Miss Royal."

"Forget Miss Royal," I replied, stuffing a stray strand of hair deeper into my cap. "Call me Cat."

"And you'd both better drop that lord business," said Lord Francis, digging his hands into his breeches pockets. "How about calling me Frank?"

"As you wish, sir," said Pedro.

"Frank," Lord Francis said as he cast an eye across the square to see that his father was out of sight.

"Frank," said Pedro uncertainly.

"Come on, we'd better hurry!" I said, setting off toward Oxford Street. "We don't want to miss it."

As we ran through the streets, dodging the carriages, jumping the puddles, jostling the families occupying the pavement as they walked to church, I felt a great bubble of happiness inside me. Despite my fears, I was looking forward to the adventure ahead. If only I didn't have to watch Syd take a beating!

There was a light drizzle in the air as a cold rain shower tried to dampen the holiday mood. Mixing with the swirling smoke from thousands of chimney pots, the rain settled on the day like a damp blanket, forcing the light to work hard to break through the clouds. Yet despite the gray, dank weather, there was no sign of anyone being deterred—crowds began to thicken with people heading for the boxing match as we drew nearer to Marylebone. You could tell at a glance which ones they were: groups of shouting boys, loud-voiced men from Camden or Covent Garden, crafty bookmakers eyeing the punters to spot the

gullible—very different from the respectable families bound for the morning service.

We arrived at the very edge of town. Just
beyond Oxford Street the buildings give way to
villages, fields, and woods, though every year more
acreage is covered with houses as London creeps
ever farther north like the tide rising to cover the
mudflats in the Thames. Today, as we escaped
the bricks and mortar of the city, we were also
escaping our everyday drudgery, hoping to be
thrilled by the primitive pleasure of watching a
trial of strength. Man against man, fighting in an
arena where neither education nor money gave
you the edge: it was brute force and quick reactions
that counted.

"Place your bets, gents!" called out one
bookmaker, waving his notebook in the air as he wove
through the crowds. "Two to one for the Camden
Crusher to beat the Butcher with a knockout!"

"That doesn't sound too good for your friend,
does it?" said Lord Francis, looking longingly after
the bookmaker. "Shall I place a bet on him
winning?" He chinked some coins in his pocket.

"No!" I said quickly, pulling him back. "Just how do you think a chimney sweep could afford to bet gold? You'll be found out in one second flat."

"I suppose you are right," said Lord Francis gloomily, withdrawing his hand from his pocket. "And Father's always forbidden me to bet."

"He's a sensible man," said Pedro, gazing after the toffee-apple seller, a large woman with a tray of glistening wares who was following the crowd through the gates onto the field. Lord Francis saw where he was looking.

"I did take the precaution of putting a few pennies in among my guineas," he whispered, pressing some into Pedro's hand. "Why don't you buy us all one?"

"Thank you very much, sir," said Pedro as he hastened off to catch up with her.

"Not 'sir'—Frank!" I hissed as a man at my elbow turned to look at us curiously.

"Thanks, Frank," Pedro corrected himself and scrambled through the press to the toffee-apple seller. He returned bearing four sticks aloft in triumph.

"Four!" said Lord Francis. "Why four?"

"One for luck," mumbled Pedro through a mouthful of toffee. He swallowed. "She'd seen me at the theater, she said, so gave me one for nothing."

It was then that I realized I had wasted my time worrying about Lord Francis drawing attention to us. Having Pedro was sufficient to make most people turn in our direction. I pulled my hat lower on my brow and said dryly, "Come on. Let's find ourselves a spot before we get mobbed by Pedro's admirers."

The crowd was dividing in two around the raised platform. The arena was surrounded by rails and had a three-foot square—the scratch—marked out in chalk at the center. A number of gentlemen sat on benches at the ringside; the rest of us found the best spot we could at ground level. Diving under arms and through narrow gaps, we managed to push our way through to the front.

Syd was sitting in his corner with his second—his father—listening intently to his advice. He had not yet stripped to the waist but was flexing his bare hands thoughtfully. On the other side of the chalk square sat the Camden Crusher—a lad of sixteen, built like an ox, with a small head and powerful shoulders. He had already stripped and his second, a dandified gentleman in a bottle-green jacket with a sharp face like a fox, was oiling his back for him—and, believe me, there was a lot of him to oil.

Nick, the lookout we had met outside Syd's shop, sidled up to us.

"'Ello, prince, Cat. 'Oo's the soot?"

"Frank," said Pedro, handing Nick the spare toffee apple. "He's new."

Nick gave Lord Francis a curious look. "'E's a bit big for the chimneys, ain't 'e? I thought they only liked nippers of eight 'n' under."

"My master specializes in big chimneys, big houses," said Lord Francis quickly. "My younger brother does the small ones."

"Oh," said Nick, losing interest. "Right you are." He nudged me and nodded over at the Crusher. "Looks bad, don't it, Cat? But Syd'll be glad you came. You're 'is lucky mascot. Oi, Syd! Cat's 'ere!" he shouted.

Syd turned around to look down on us. He gave me a wink. "All right, Cat?" he called over. Seeing him standing up there made me think of him as the victim on the scaffold but, as I would not for any money let him see my concern, I gave him my broadest smile.

"Yes," I called up. "Good luck!"

He gave me a nod and then returned to his preparations.

When I turned to speak to Pedro, I found him and Lord Francis sniggering over a piece of paper Nick was showing them.

"What's that?" I asked, making a grab for the pamphlet. I could see it was a cartoon.

"Nuffink," said Nick, hiding it behind his back.

"Don't give me that!" I said, trying to wrestle it from him. "Let me see!"

"Er, Cat," said Lord Francis in an undertone, "I don't think it's suitable for a lady's eyes."

"Stuff that!" I said, determined not to be left out. "Give it here!"

By tickling Nick in the ribs, I succeeded in making him surrender the paper. Perhaps I should not have done so, for as soon as I looked at it, I felt my cheeks go scarlet. It was a very crude representation of a member of the government squatting on a chamberpot marked "The Oppressed Masses."

"The word is," said Nick, covering for my embarrassment, "old Captain Sparkler's gone too far this time. The beak's after him."

"Beak?" asked Lord Francis.

"Gawd, Frank, wot country 'ave you been livin' in? Beak: ma-gi-strate. Got it?"

"Oh," said Lord Francis quickly. "Of course."

"'E's to be made han heg-sample of, they say. Government's got the wind up. 'E's to be done for treason—'anged or transported most like."

"No!" I exclaimed. "All because he poked some fun at a few people! That's not fair!"

"Wot's fair got to do with it? It's powerful people 'e's takin' on, Cat. They don't like to be made to look like fools. They 'ate 'im for makin' fun of 'em. 'E can draw as many bare bums as 'e likes, but you watch, they'll get 'im for attackin' the king. 'Is last cartoon was plain treason, it was. Banned, I 'ear, so sales 'ave gone sky 'igh as you'd expect."

"So, have they caught him yet?" asked Pedro.

"Not likely," said Nick with evident pleasure. "'E's too clever for 'em, is Captain Sparkler. 'E loves to drive 'em wild by flauntin' these pictures in front of 'em as 'e dances out of their reach. The word is 'e's stowed away on a ship for France."

"So how is the pertinacious captain able to draw a cartoon referring to a political scandal that broke last week?" asked Lord Francis, sounding exactly like the nobleman he was rather than the chimney sweep he was pretending to be.

"Lawd, Frankie boy, you swallered a dictionary or somethink?" marveled Nick. Lord Francis now flushed and began to stammer an excuse. "No, don't you apologize. Nuffink wrong with a bit of learnin'. You be proud of it, mate! Look at our Cat here: 'oo'd think she 'ad all that stuff packed away in 'er pretty little 'ead? Syd's always 'olding 'er up as a model to the rest of us 'alfwits!" Nick began to laugh at the very idea of him and the gang learning to read and write like gentlemen.

I did not quell Nick's overloud comments, as I was still thinking about Lord Francis's question. Yes, how was a man, rumored to be in France, able to be so up-to-the-minute with his cartoons? The obvious answer was that he had never left. He must be in hiding, and I had a shrewd suspicion where.

So pleased was I by my own powers of deduction that I was eager to share my guess with Pedro to impress him with my cleverness. Unfortunately, there were too many people around at the moment: it would have to wait.

"Gentlemen!" The referee stood forward and held up his hand for silence. "I present our fighters to you: the reigning champion—the Camden Crusher!"

The Camden Crusher lumbered to his feet and raised his glistening arms to acknowledge the cheers and whistles of his supporters.

"And our challenger: the Bow Street Butcher!"

Rather more nimbly, Syd stripped off his shirt, bounced to his feet, and bowed to acknowledge the applause. His hair looked very pale against his flushed cheeks.

"Go for him, Crusher!" yelled a man on the far side.

"Let's hear it for the brave butcher!" shouted another.

The crowd cheered Syd again, but rather, I felt, as a crowd for a public execution would comfort a popular criminal with their voices. Everyone was expecting him to be well and truly crushed by the boy from Camden.

"You can do it, Syd!" I cried.

Hearing my high voice over the others, Syd turned in my direction to give me a special smile and a nod.

"Now, you know the rules, gents," said the referee in a voice that commanded silence. "Nothing below the belt. If you're down, you have half a minute to return to set-to at the scratch. If you fail to come up to scratch, then your opponent wins. Are you ready, gents?"

Syd grunted his agreement and raised his fists to chest height. The Crusher nodded, giving Syd a mocking smile.

"You're dead," he mouthed.

"Then . . ." said the referee, moving back, "set to!"

The fight began. The Crusher piled forward and grabbed Syd in a wrestling hold, pushing him back against the rails. Syd took small, quick jabs at his opponent's stomach—one, two, three, four, five—until he collided painfully with the wooden bar. There they stayed, the Crusher grinding down Syd's resistance with a flurry of punches that left great red welts on his skin. Once it was clear that the pair were caught on the rails, the referee rushed forward with the seconds to part the fighters. The seconds led their boys back to the scratch, both hissing encouragement and advice. The boxers set to again, this time exchanging body blows. Head down, arms pumping like pistons, Syd grazed his knuckles as his fist caught the side of the Crusher's ribs. Blood dripped from the Crusher's nose as a second jab caught him in the face. When the fighters circled around, I could see that Syd too was bleeding, in his case from a cut to his temple. Blows rained down fast and furious, bone smacking into flesh, red sweat dripping down their backs. I could hardly bear to watch and was reduced to covering my eyes with my hands. The more bloody and vicious the fight became, the more the crowd cheered. Peeking through my fingers, I could see money changing hands as the gentlemen at the ringside placed new bets. Syd was holding his own. I guessed the odds on him were shortening.

Then disaster struck: the Crusher landed a powerful blow to Syd's jaw, knocking him backward to the floor. Syd rolled over with a groan, his eyes now at a level with our heads only a few feet away.

"One! Two! Three . . . !" chanted the crowd.

Syd's dad rushed over to help him to his feet, but he was not moving.

"Come on, son!" he bellowed. "Get up!"

"Fifteen! Sixteen! Seventeen . . .!"

"Come on, Syd!" I screamed above the jeers and hoots. "Keep going!"

Perhaps Syd heard me, for his eyes locked on mine and, through the trickles of blood running down his face, I thought I could see him smile. Slowly, he heaved himself to his knees, then to his feet. Swaying like a drunken man, he let his father lead him to the chalk square.

"Twenty-eight! Twenty-nine . . .!"

He had come up to scratch just in time.

"Set to!" shouted the referee.

Some in the crowd groaned—an easy victory snatched from the Crusher's grasp. Those of us backing the outsider cheered lustily.

Battle recommenced, now slower as the toll of all those blows began to tell on the combatants. Syd was moving heavily as if he had weights tied to his legs, but the Crusher seemed barely to be moving at all as he stood defending himself in the middle of the scratch. I began to think that maybe, just maybe, Syd could win this one. I stopped peeking through my fingers and joined in with the chant of "Butcher! Butcher!" that Pedro and Nick had started. Next to me Lord Francis was hopping up and down, yelling his encouragement.

"At him, man! Go for him, sir!" he shouted, failing miserably to keep in character. Fortunately, everyone was too engrossed in the fight to notice.

With sweat pouring from his brow, the Crusher struck out with another of the right hooks for which he was famed, but Syd leaped back, out of harm's way. The Crusher lost his balance and, before he could right himself, Syd came in with a blow to his jaw that sent the champion staggering. The Crusher collapsed to his knees, hands on the floor, breathing hard.

"One! Two! Three!" the crowd began to chant again.

"Get up, you lazy oaf!" screamed the Crusher's second. "Get up, you good-for-nothing girl!"

But the Crusher swayed and then fell forward, the side of his face pressed against the floor, eyes glassy, a dribble of saliva trailing from his half-open mouth. He didn't move. The second kicked him with his foot, trying to make him stir.

"Twenty-eight! Twenty-nine! Thirty!" bellowed the crowd.

The Crusher hadn't moved.

A huge cheer went up. Even those who had lost their bets threw their hats in the air to applaud the plucky newcomer. Nick, Pedro, Lord Francis, and I jumped up and down together and cheered with the best of them. Syd, bowing to each corner in turn, gave us a two-handed victory signal when he faced us. The Crusher's second was not looking after his man. He was in a huddle with Syd's father at the side of the stage. As they broke apart, he thrust a purse into the butcher's fist and they gave each other a businesslike nod. Behind them, some friends of the Crusher had rushed into the ring to help the defeated boy to his feet. He did not look badly injured, but he missed his stool completely when he went to sit down, ending up on the floor again.

The referee bounded over the prostrate body of the Crusher and raised Syd's fist in the air.

"Gents, we have a new champion. I give you the Bow Street Butcher!"

SCENE 4—BILLY "BOIL" SHEPHERD

"Come on, let's go and congratulate Syd," said Pedro eagerly as he launched himself against the tide of people now flowing away from the boxing ring.

Nick and Lord Francis ran after him. Being the last in line, I tried to follow, but a party of gentlemen jumped from the ringside into my path, blocking my way.

"Splendid fight!" enthused a man in a black silk hat as he leaped heavily down, practically flattening me as he did so.

"A rare talent, that butcher," commented his friend. "Perhaps I should ask cook to get the meat from him in future—show some support."

"Or perhaps not," said the other, already laughing in anticipation of his own witticism. "You don't know what he does with the ones he knocks out cold. Chop, chop! Meat pies, sir?"

The gentlemen both laughed raucously. I

glared at them and tried to push past, annoyed that they could imply anything so cruel about Syd. The gray-haired man must have noticed me trying to squeeze between them for he looked down and automatically clapped his hand to his watch chain.

"We'd better get back to the club," he murmured to his companion. "This place is rife with pickpockets, they say."

The pair pushed past me, knocking me backward into another bystander. I had no time to be offended, for I now found myself buffeted to the ground by the person I had been thrown against.

"Watch where you're goin', Tiddler," he jeered.

I knew that voice. I kept my head down, eyes trained on the steel caps of his boots, hoping he wouldn't notice. Unfortunately for me, some of my hair had escaped from the back of my cap.

"'Ere, wot's this?" he crowed with delight. I was seized by the shoulder and pulled to my feet. "Well, well, a little pussycat pretendin' to be a tom."

A hand snatched the cap from my head, letting my hair tumble over my face. I pushed it out of my eyes and looked furiously up into the face of Billy

Boil. He was not looking at me now: he stood in the middle of a group of his followers, twirling my cap nonchalantly on an index finger, gazing about him to see if I was under anyone's protection.

"'Ere on your own? That's very brave of you, ain't it? Come to see lover boy fight?"

"Give me that!" I said in a fury, making a grab for my cap.

"Oops!" said Billy with a taunting smile as he sent the hat sailing over my head to a pox-faced boy on the other side. Pox-Face dangled the cap just out of reach, pulling it away each time I jumped to snatch it back. Billy's gang, simple minds all, hooted with laughter. I, however, was not amused. I felt hot with humiliation and was annoyed that I teetered so perilously close to tears.

"Aw, look, boys! The little pussycat doesn't like playing with us!" jeered Billy when his sharp eye spotted me wiping away a tear of anger.

Sick of their teasing, I tried to make a run for it, determined to abandon my hat if this was the only way of escape, but Billy stepped forward to catch me by the back of my jacket. Reluctant though I am to admit this, Reader, I have to say that Billy does have his boys well trained, for his gang quickly formed a ring around me, shutting me in as well as hiding me from any friends who might be looking for me.

"Such a shame she don't like playing with us, for I 'eard Little Miss Cat wanted to be in a gang." Billy pulled me toward him. "I'd even 'eard that the blockhead butcher didn't want 'er, so I thought to myself, I thought, why not let 'er join me gang? Add a bit of class, she would." Billy grabbed my cap from Pox-Face and presented it to me with a bow. "Wot you say to that?"

I took the hat suspiciously, expecting him to whip it away again at the last moment, but he didn't. I quickly stuffed it back on my head and made a dash to escape. He gave another tug on my jacket, bringing me back like a fish on a line.

"Not so fast. You ain't given me your answer."

"Answer?" I asked warily, feeling like a sheep surrounded by a pack of wolves.

"Yeah. Do you want to join my gang?"

I stopped pulling away from him.

"You're joking."

"I'm not."

I gazed up into Billy's hard green eyes but saw no mockery in them, only cold calculation. "Why me?"

He looked away and winked at his followers. "Gawd, girl, I'm not askin' you to marry me nor nuffink! Why not you? You're as good as many a boy I know—and better than some."

Despite myself, I felt a rush of pleasure to hear this compliment from Billy Shepherd, of all people. He was offering me a chance to really belong in Covent Garden, to move from the sidelines where Syd had put me and join in with the boys' adventures, to be party to the secret signs and passwords of a gang. I was tempted, sorely tempted. If only the offer had come from Syd, whom I admired and trusted, and not from his devious rival! I would have to refuse, of course, but . . . I looked around the ring of faces, hard-bitten, tough characters all. What would they do to me when I said no?

"That's very decent of you, Billy," I began, backing away from him, looking for an escape route, a weak spot in the wall. Perhaps if I ducked under the biggest boy's legs? "But you don't want a girl like me in your gang."

He gave me a broad grin and tipped his hat back on his head. He smirked at his boys. "See, I told you I'd 'ave to woo 'er!" He turned back to me. "You're wrong, girl. That's just what I want."

"But I'm useless at fighting—I'd let you down."

His grin, if anything, got wider. It was like looking into the jaws of a Nile crocodile waiting to swallow me up. "Don't believe it, Cat. You're a terror when your blood's up—a real little wildcat with 'er claws out. Anyway, I want other talents in my gang than fightin'. I've got Meatpie Matt 'ere to do the punchin'." He gestured toward a burly lad not much smaller than Syd but with none of Syd's blond good looks to recommend him. "Nah, I need you for somethink else."

I had backed up as far as I could go without actually bumping into the ferret-featured boy with carrot-red hair on my side of the circle.

"What's that?" I asked, curious despite myself to know what had prompted Billy to make so astonishing an offer. I could see how he might derive a twisted pleasure from taking one of Syd's friends away from him, but it still seemed a very unlikely proposition.

"It's obvious, ain't it?" said Billy, rocking on his heels casually, though his eyes were still fixed on me. "Brains, Cat, brains. I want you for what you know—though, as you're bein' so slow on the old uptake, perhaps your reputation for wit and learnin' is a case of *misrepresentation?*" He said the last word proudly, as he rarely indulged in words with more than two syllables.

I was flattered. I had not known that I was so highly spoken of in the market. But his praise did not change the essentials of my position: I would have to rely on some of the brains for which I was famed to extricate myself from this circle. But how?

Suddenly, a sooty boy burst through the outer guard into the middle of the circle.

"There you are, Cat!" exclaimed Lord Francis. "We wondered what had happened to you! I was very perturbed to find that you had not followed us."

"Per-what?" guffawed Billy, grabbing Lord Francis by the lapels of his filthy jacket. "Oo do you think you are, Sootie? A dook or somethink?"

It was an alarmingly accurate guess. I could tell from the look on Lord Francis's good-natured face that he had only just twigged he had walked in on a dangerous situation. He opened and shut his mouth like a fish landed at Billingsgate, but made no comprehensible sound.

"Queer fellas you're making friends with, Cat," said Billy, discarding Lord Francis by pushing him to one side into Meatpie Matt. Meatpie threw the peer of the realm to the ground like a rag doll. "That'll 'ave to stop, you understand? Can't 'ave a girl in my gang mixin' with the wrong sort."

"Er, Billy," I began, my eyes on the crumpled body of Lord Francis.

"Yeah, Pussycat?"

"I haven't actually given you my answer yet."

Lord Francis started to scramble to his feet. Billy absentmindedly kicked him to the floor again and stood with his hobnailed boot on the neck of the duke's son.

"Wot was that you were sayin'?" he said, his eyes sparkling maliciously. We both knew that if I refused to join him, the pressure of his boot would increase.

"Can I think about your offer?" I asked lamely, though I knew what his answer was likely to be.

"Sadly not. For a number of pressin' reasons." He made Lord Francis gasp as he placed more weight on his neck, "I need an immediate acceptance."

My choices were not attractive. Refuse and face the consequences of being the reason why a member of the nobility is kicked to a pulp; accept and find myself under Billy's leadership. I'd prefer to put *my* neck under his boot than to do that. At least I could try to help Lord Francis, not least because his face was now an unbecoming shade of purple.

"Billy, really it's very decent of you—but no!"

Even as I spoke, I put my head down and ran full pelt at him, taking him quite by surprise. I charged into his stomach, knocking us both to the floor, in the process achieving my aim of getting him away from Lord Francis. In the confusion that followed, Lord Francis scrambled to his feet and had the sense to run for it. I tried to do the same but found my ankle seized by Billy. I froze. There was no kind Mrs. Peters to hide me today.

"Wot you make of that, Billy?" laughed Ferret-Features. "Not a wildcat—a miniature bull, that's wot she is!"

The gang were all now roaring with laughter at the ridiculous sight of their great leader floored by a girl half his size—all except Billy, that is. He did not appreciate the joke. I could feel his hand shaking with anger, but he had to make light of it or risk losing their respect. I knew then I was in deep trouble.

"Look, lads!" he exclaimed, pulling on my ankle. "You saw that: she fair threw 'erself at me, she did. Couldn't resist me!"

"Let go, you beast!" I shouted, kicking at him to release his grip, squirming and twisting on the muddy ground.

Without looking at me, Billy tightened his hold and got to his feet, in effect dragging me up upside down so I was left dangling powerlessly. My ankle hurt hellishly in his fist and I could feel all the blood rush to my head. Billy was now pretending not to hear my protests, play-acting as if I did not exist. This his gang found even funnier.

"Anyone 'ear that cat meowin'?" he asked his gang loudly, cupping his free hand to his ear. "Sounds in a bad way. Perhaps someone should put it out of its misery."

The boys bellowed with laughter; Ferret-Features doubled up with mirth. Then, suddenly, the laughter stopped. I felt the grip on my leg give way as I was dropped hurriedly to the floor. Next a pair of strong hands lifted me to my feet and clumsily brushed me off.

"What you doing to Cat?" asked Syd from behind me, his voice laced with menace.

Billy's grin had frozen on his face. He looked pale, tensing for a fight.

"We were just playin', weren't we, Cat?" said Billy. "'Avin' a laugh." His right hand was feeling for something in his pocket. I caught a glimpse of a blade in his palm.

"I didn't see her laughing," said Pedro, pushing his way forward to stand beside me, Lord Francis with him.

Billy shot Pedro a poisonous look, and I could feel Syd's bandaged hands tighten on my shoulders as he prepared himself for another battle. Panic fluttered in my stomach: I didn't want to be the reason that more blood was spilled.

"It was nothing, Syd. Let's go," I muttered, turning away.

Syd looked down at my upturned face with a strange expression in his eyes: part pity, part understanding. I knew then he'd seen the knife too and was concerned for what would happen to me if this confrontation developed into a brawl. He addressed himself to Billy again. "I've 'ad enough fightin' for one day, Boil, but I'll take you all on if I find you touchin' Cat again. Understand this: no one, but no one, messes with my Cat and gets away with it."

Billy slipped his hand in his pocket for a second, then raised his hands, palms open, as if to say something placatory to his rival, but Syd ignored him, steered me around, and marched me through the silent ranks of Billy's gang. Having just seen him fell the Camden Crusher, no one wanted to chance their arm against him now.

Once we had reached the safety of Syd's party of supporters, I felt relieved but also ashamed of myself. I should not have come to the match. I had run straight into trouble and almost come to grief. Syd's father, a ruddy-faced man with fists like hams, gave me a disapproving stare as he watched his son usher me over to a stool at the ringside.

"Let's see that ankle, Cat," Syd said tenderly, taking off the rough woolen stocking on my right leg. Lord Francis, whom I suspected I had to thank for raising the alarm, hovered behind Syd, looking both embarrassed and anxious. Indeed my ankle was not a pretty sight: you could see the marks made by Billy's fingers now blooming into red and blue bruises.

Syd's frown deepened. "I should've punched his stupid face in 'ad I known 'e'd done this."

"It's nothing, Syd," I said quickly, not wanting him to think I was bothered by so slight an injury. "As he said, he was just teasing."

"Teasing!" exploded Pedro. "He had you upside down. That's torture, not teasing. You shouldn't play his game, Cat!"

"I didn't exactly ask to be treated like that!" I answered, channeling the pain into anger at

Pedro's remark. "If you hadn't all run off so quick, I wouldn't have been left alone and he wouldn't've dared pick on me!" I stood up, intending to make a dignified exit, stamping off back home, but collapsed again as a stabbing pain shot up my leg.

"Cat is right," said Lord Francis, looking abject. "We were most remiss to leave a lady on her own."

"We were what?" asked Nick.

"You shouldn't've run off," I translated, "leaving me with that dung-ball Billy Shepherd."

"So that was Billy 'Boil' Shepherd?" asked Lord Francis eagerly.

The knowledge that he had just been wrestling with one of London's most infamous gang leaders seemed to restore his spirits, which had been depressed by Billy's boot.

"Let me make some amends for our lamentable neglect by paying for a chair to carry you home," he said, pulling out a guinea from his well-filled purse.

Nick and Syd stared at him in amazement.

"Where'd you get that?" asked Syd. "I'll not 'ave you friends with no thief, Cat." He rounded on me, assuming that Lord Francis's wealth must be ill-gotten.

"Nothing to worry about, Syd," said Pedro, "it's his. He's not what he seems."

Syd gave the blackened face of Lord Francis a hard stare. He may not be quick, but given time, Syd can usually see his way through a brick wall. "You a gent?"

Lord Francis glanced at Pedro anxiously. He now knew to fear the gang leaders of Covent Garden. He wasn't to know that the mountain of muscle in front of him had a much sweeter nature—few people did.

"He is," said Pedro.

"What d'you mean bringin' 'im along, Cat?" Syd said angrily, immediately assuming it was all my fault. "Didn't you stop to think what might 'appen to 'im if 'e was found out?"

"It was my idea," said Pedro, but he could not draw Syd's fire like that. Syd had got it fixed in his head that I must be responsible for the whole affair.

"So why didn't you stop it?" he continued, still berating me. "You know Pedro's green—'e don't know nuffink yet about the streets, but you do, Cat! I thought you were clever!"

It might have been a good moment to employ one of those moves that Richardson's heroines use in his novels—a good faint or tears might have reminded Syd he was supposed to be feeling sorry for me. But it was beneath my dignity to indulge in such foolishness.

"You're right, Syd, I should've stopped him," I said, feeling quite defeated by the day. "If you don't mind, I'd like to accept Lord Francis's offer and go home." I stood up. Lord Francis offered me his arm and I began to hobble over to the gate.

My avowal of being in the wrong had taken the heat out of Syd's anger.

"You can't walk like that all the way to Oxford Street, you daft kitten. I'll carry you," he said, picking me up as if I weighed no more than a doll. "Come on, your lordship, if you must," he added grudgingly over his shoulder to Lord Francis. "I ain't got the gold for a chair—you'll 'ave to foot that bill."

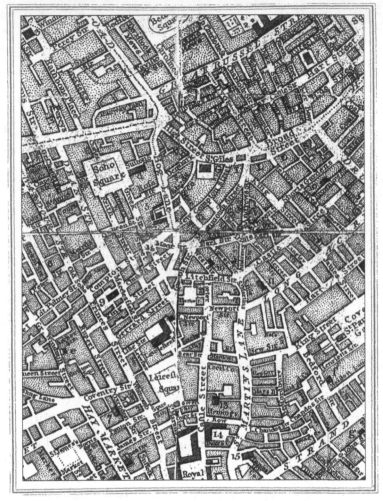

Act III - In which two of our characters have very close shaves . . .

ACT III

SCENE 1—A REWARD

I have to confess that I was in a very bad mood for the rest of that day and did not want to see anyone. I hid in the Sparrow's Nest with my ankle wrapped in a cold cloth, feeling sorry for myself. Covent Garden, my home, had become a dangerous place for me. Now that Billy and his gang bore me a grudge for turning them down, I could no longer take my freedom to roam for granted. What was worse, I had fallen out with Johnny. As I half-expected, I met little sympathy for my injury when he spotted me alighting from the sedan chair. He had gallantly rushed out to check that I had enough money to pay for my ride (the Irish chairmen would not think twice about thumping a passenger who turned out to not have the means to pay for the luxury of being carried across London). Leaning on his arm to hobble inside, I told him about the disastrous turn of my outing.

"If you want to run with the hounds, Cat, you shouldn't be surprised if you get a few nips," he said, helping me through the stage door.

That was rich coming from a wanted man skulking in hiding.

"And I suppose that if you want your wit to *sparkle* brightly, Captain," I said boldly, "you have to take cover under the skirts of Drury Lane to escape the pack baying for your blood?" I enjoyed the quiet revenge of seeing his face drain of color as my words hit home.

The pleasure was short-lived. He tightened his grip on my arm and dragged me around so he could look into my face.

"Who told you?" he hissed, his eyes glinting with anger as he gave me a shake. I felt suddenly scared: here was a Johnny I had not yet seen, determined and dangerous. It was the first time my mild teacher had so much as laid a finger on me.

"No one. I guessed," I explained hurriedly. "Don't worry, no one else knows."

He gave me a searching stare and then let go of my arm. He seemed cold and unfamiliar, not the same man who had spent so many hours with me that week.

"They'd better not hear about it from you, Cat, or you'll be the death of me," he hissed. Turning his back, he strode away, heading for the prompter's office, which he had made his temporary home.

"Johnny! I'm sorry!" I called softly after him, glancing around to check no one was in earshot. "Of course I won't say anything. You can trust me."

He gave a shrug without turning to look at me.

"Can I, Cat?" he said and banged the door closed behind him.

So, Reader, you can understand why I had retreated to my nest in a sullen mood. It was now ten o'clock. The theater was quiet but the streets outside were alive with revelers as the taverns did a roaring Sunday trade. Even from my attic, I could hear voices calling out the name of the Bow Street Butcher. Syd was the local hero and was doubtless being feted by his gang somewhere nearby, glorying in his triumph. All his boys would be around him. Pedro was probably there, leading the singing, perhaps playing for him, spending the money Lord Francis had given him for taking him along on his adventure. Of everyone, I felt most angry with Pedro. He was like the cuckoo coming to throw the chick from her nest: he'd taken the place that should've been mine in Syd's gang. And it was his stupidity that brought Lord Francis to the match in the first place, causing me to argue with Syd! And as for my ankle—well, if I could've thought of a way to blame Pedro, I would have.

After an hour of such dismal complaints, I'd had enough.

"Come on, Cat," I told the darkness, "stop feeling sorry for yourself." I realized I was both hungry and thirsty. If I stopped sulking and did something about this, I'd begin to feel happier. This proved to be the case for, standing up, I found that my ankle was much better. Heartened, I picked up my candle and went downstairs in search of company and some food. There would be few people around this late on a Sunday, but I might be able to make it up with Johnny and have supper with him; failing that, perhaps Caleb, the night porter, might have something to eat.

Backstage was silent and very dark. I didn't like it like this: a theater should be full of people and life. Empty, it echoed with ghosts of past performances and dead actors. My candle cast long, misshapen shadows where it caught on the ropes strung like spiderwebs from the roof. I had to be careful as I made my way around scenery waiting in the wings: fragments of castle battlements littered my path, wizened trees grew from the boards in a thicket that caught on my clothes. An enchanter's laboratory, abandoned in one corner, gleamed with glass bottles fastened to wooden shelves and gilt-edged spell books. It rattled as I passed as if it hid a skeleton that was trying to break out of its cupboard.

"Johnny?" I called outside the prompter's room. My voice sounded frail in the yawning darkness. There was no answer. I pushed the door open. A low fire lit the room with a red glare. His office was filled with piles of scripts. A small camp bed, neatly made, stood ready in one corner. Pens, drawing equipment, and paper were bundled underneath it. But there was no Johnny. I closed the door softly.

A noise behind me like the sound of a distant door clicking to caught my ear. I spun around.

"Johnny?"

No answer.

Apart from Johnny and the night porter who manned the door, I did not expect anyone else to be in the theater. Perhaps Johnny had gone in search of me? Perhaps he had also wanted to make up? Even if he didn't, I would have welcomed a further reproof as long as I could have company.

I moved as swiftly as I could in the direction of the noise and found myself outside Mr. Sheridan's office. I paused, trying not to breathe too loudly. Yes, there was definitely someone moving stealthily about inside, but it couldn't be Johnny, not in this office. I could hear the scrape of a chair as it was dragged across the floor. Had Mr. Sheridan come in for something? That was most unusual this late on a Sunday night.

"You'll keep my jewel safe for me, won't you, Cat?"

My promise to Mr. Sheridan came back to me as I stood in the dark corridor outside his office. What if someone was in there right now? What if they had already found the diamond? I had to stop them. Looking around for inspiration, my eyes lighted upon a spear leaning against the wall: I recognized it as the one used in the pageant for "Rule, Britannia". Though blunt, it should be sufficiently menacing to scare off a would-be burglar. But what if it was Mr. Sheridan? I couldn't just go bursting in and threaten him with a spear. There was a chance that he might find it funny; on the other hand, he might decide I'd gone too far. He was very particular as to who entered his office. Taking the spear in my right hand, I gently eased the door open with my left and peeked in. I could see a dark figure, too small for Mr. Sheridan, standing on the chair, searching along the shelves opposite.

"Stop right there!" I shouted, pushing the door open with a bang. My abrupt entrance made the burglar totter on his chair in surprise, and he fell to the floor. I rushed forward, intending to capture the thief by pinning him to the ground with my weapon—he was, after all, not much bigger than me—but he was too quick. He leaped to his feet, seized the end of the spear, and pulled it sharply from my hands, sending me crashing into the table. I squealed with pain as the thief grabbed my arms and bent one up behind me.

"Be quiet!" hissed a familiar voice. "Do you want the porter to find us?"

It was Pedro! I stopped struggling.

"Let go!" I said furiously. He still had my arm bent back.

"Promise not to shout?" he asked, giving it a painful tweak.

I nodded. I couldn't believe it: Pedro was the burglar!

He released me and bent to pick up the spear.

"Thinking of sticking this in me, were you?" he said lightly, touching the blunted end of the spear before leaning it against the desk.

"What are you doing here?" I asked, rubbing my arm. He was avoiding my eyes, pretending to be busy righting the overturned chair.

"I could ask you the same thing," he replied.

"I live here, remember?" I said sarcastically. "You were looking for it, weren't you?"

"What?" he said, now tidying some papers he had pulled from the shelf in his fall.

"Pedro, don't fool with me! You were looking for the diamond."

"So what if I was?" he said with a shrug.

"But that'd be stealing. We promised to look after it!" I protested.

"*You* promised; I didn't."

"But it's still stealing!"

"So what?" said Pedro, looking up at me for the first time, his eyes full of anger. He was glaring at me, not as if he was seeing Cat, the girl he had befriended, but an English girl, a white girl from a nation grown rich on slavery. I didn't like that look. "Don't you think it was wrong that I had everything stolen from me? My family, my home, even my freedom? So what if I just want to have enough money to get away from here? To go somewhere where I can be truly free. A place where people won't see my skin first, but me."

"I see you, Pedro," I said quietly.

He shrugged. "You do perhaps—but maybe that's because you're no better off than me, Cat."

A new thought struck him and he grabbed hold of my forearms, pulling me toward him eagerly. "What about you, Cat? Don't you want to escape all this? If we found that diamond, we wouldn't have to take another beating in our lives. We could repay everyone for the insults we've suffered. When I saw that beast dangling you by your ankle, laughing at you, it reminded me . . ." He stopped and let go of me, turning his back.

"Of what?" I prompted, wondering what he had been going to say.

"Of being a slave, damn you!" he said angrily, as if it were my fault I'd made him remember. "Look, don't you realize that with that diamond you could make Billy Shepherd sorry he ever touched you?"

"No, I couldn't." I shook my head vigorously. "I'd have to run away and hide for the rest of my life if I stole. Anyway, it's different for me. You say your life was stolen from you—and it was—but Mr. Sheridan saved my life. I'd've frozen on the doorstep if he hadn't taken pity on me. I can't repay that by stealing from him."

While I spoke, I could see Pedro locking away the raw pain he had let me glimpse as he remembered his captivity.

"Your problem, Cat, is that you latch on to other people too trustingly." He shoved a ledger back on the shelf as if he were ramming a cannon-ball home. "Do you think Mr. Sheridan cares a damn about you? Of course he doesn't. You're so starved for affection that you think if someone pats you on the head, they must be your friend. Take it from me that pats all too often precede blows. You've got to learn to look after number one."

"Like you, you mean."

"Like me."

"But I do trust my friends. I owe Mr. Sheridan everything."

"It doesn't matter in any case," he said dismissively, giving the room a last inspection to check it appeared undisturbed. "It's not here. I've been through the room three times now and found nothing."

"Three times!" I protested.

"While you were out of the way, burning the

midnight oil on your stories of past adventures, Cat," he said with an ironic grin, "I was thinking of the future."

"But Pedro," I implored him, "promise me you won't risk it again! If you're caught, they'll hang you for certain."

"I promise I won't come here—but only because I'm wasting my time. He must have hidden it elsewhere."

"Pedro! I'll have to tell!" I felt like shaking some sense into him as he stood there so calm, so sure of himself.

"No, you won't." His brown eyes looked defiantly at me.

He was right. My loyalty to Mr. Sheridan did not extend to getting a boy executed. I'd have to rely on persuasion rather than threats.

"Please, Pedro!"

"Don't worry. You don't have to know anything about it. I'll be very discreet." He smiled.

"Argh!" I couldn't bear his smug face anymore. Why did he not listen? How could he hope to get away with so audacious a theft? I grabbed his jacket lapels. "Please . . . don't . . . do . . . this!" I gave him a thump on each word until he caught my fists. He was still grinning at me infuriatingly.

"Sorry, Cat, it's my chance to get out. When someone shows me the exit, I take it. And if you knew what was good for you, you'd take it too. Mr. Sheridan will tire of having you as his pet cat one day and what prospects will you have then? Unless a decent man like Syd takes pity on you and marries you, where will you be in a few years? I'll tell you: you'll be out on the street."

I released his jacket and put my hands over my ears, not wanting to hear this from him.

"You're just saying this to excuse what you're doing," I said bitterly. "But I know it's wrong. I'll be all right. I'll find some way of earning my keep— an honest way."

"You're so naive, Cat."

"At least I'm not a thief."

"I'm no thief, I'm just trying to get what I'm owed!"

"Thief!"

"Coward!"

"Thief!"

"Hey, hey," said a man's voice, "what's all this?" Johnny stepped into the room. "Why're you calling each other names? And what are you doing here in any case?"

I looked at Pedro. The pearl earring he still wore in his ear glittered in the candlelight, but he was staring at the floor, no doubt wondering if I was going to tell on him.

"It's nothing," I said. "We were just arguing about . . . about . . ."

"About today," broke in Pedro when he realized I was not going to betray him. "We were angry about what happened at the boxing."

Johnny looked dubiously at us both. "And you decided to have your argument in Mr. Sheridan's office?" He leaned down and picked up the weapon I had brought with me. "With a spear? It must be more serious than I thought."

We both said nothing. What could we say?

"Well, I'll not mention it to Mr. Sheridan this time, but I expect better from you both in future," Johnny concluded, gesturing to us to leave the room. "Especially you, Miss Royal. After all Mr. Sheridan's done for you, I didn't expect you to repay him by entering his office without his permission. Perhaps his trust in you is misplaced?"

"You don't have to worry about that," said Pedro angrily. "Miss Royal remains his loyal servant—or should I say, slave?" He turned from us both and ran off toward the stage door.

"Johnny, I . . ." I began, though I wasn't sure what I was going to say in my own defense without dropping Pedro into the mire.

"Hadn't you better get to bed?" Johnny said severely, showing no interest in hearing further excuses from me. "You've had a trying day: you need your sleep."

I nodded miserably and headed for my bed, feeling terrible that I had now disappointed him twice today. Would that mean he no longer wanted to be my friend? I could sense his eyes on my back as he watched me mount the rickety stairs to the Sparrow's Nest. When I turned at the head of the staircase to bid him good night, he was already walking to his own room. It was then that I noticed the brace of pistols stuck in his belt. Unlike my spear, they did not look like stage props. They were real.

The next morning, heartily sick of being frowned upon by Johnny, I was determined to find a friendly face. I took the opportunity of an errand to the other theater in Covent Garden to call on Syd. I had come at a bad time—for the squeamish like me, that is—for he was in the process of butchering a particularly large pig. Death had already visited, but there was still much work for the butcher to do in dividing the carcass. Syd's arms were red to the elbows in blood.

"Ah, Cat," Syd said, smiling at me over the pig's snout, his face a lattice of cuts and bruises from the match. The creature grinned affably up at us—a silent third in our tête à tête. "Ow you feelin'? "Ow's the ankle?"

"Much better, thanks, Syd," I said hovering by the door, relieved to find that he at least did not bear me a grudge for what happened.

Syd brought his cleaver down with a thwack and threw the head into a bucket, slopping the floor with blood. I hurriedly lifted my skirts out of the way.

"Sorry, Cat. Not used to 'avin' a lady watch me work."

The bloody scene before me took me back to the boxing match.

"Aren't there easier ways of earning a living?" I asked wistfully, leaning on the doorpost to take the weight off my sore leg.

Syd looked hurt. "What's wrong with butcherin'?"

"Nothing," I said quickly and truthfully. It was an honest trade of which no one should be ashamed. "I meant being battered to a pulp in the ring."

"Ah, that." Syd brought the cleaver expertly down on the pig's trotters, shearing them off. "I don't expect a girl to understand, but it's my only way to fame and fortune, Cat. Butcherin' is all right—but I want more."

"Like what?"

"To be champion, of course. Then, perhaps, one day, own a boxin' academy where fine young gents like your Lord Francis will pay me good money to teach 'em to box. Then I could afford a decent place to live, raise a family in comfort, send my sons to good schools." He gave me a quick look from under his lashes. "I'd be on the up and up." He gave two short staccato taps at the curly pig's tail and threw it onto a tray behind him.

I felt uncomfortable hearing him talk about the future; it was safer to bring him back to the here and now. "You'll be careful, won't you, Syd? Be careful about who you get involved with?"

He laughed. "Course, Cat. Don't you worry your pretty little 'ead about me." He put his cleaver down and gave me a serious look. "To tell you the truth, Cat, I'm worried about you. Word is, the Boil's after you for somethink. You stay away from the market for a bit, won't you? Until I've sorted 'im."

I swallowed. "Sorted 'im—I mean, him?"

"Yeah. We're settling it tonight. In the market. "'Is boys against mine."

"Syd!"

Syd smiled and wiped his hands on his apron, pleased to see, I think, that I was concerned for him. "Don't worry, Cat. 'E don't stand a chance. I'll walk you back now, check nothing 'appens to you."

He would not accept a refusal but escorted me like a prisoner under guard across Bow Street.

"Wait a moment," I said as we paused outside the magistrate's house. A new notice bearing a familiar name had gone up on the sign by the runners' office. A crowd had gathered around it and they were talking animatedly. I had to read it.

Syd obligingly stopped. The people at the front of the gathering respectfully made way to allow him to the best position.

"What's it say, Cat?" he asked. He had never learned to read, having contented himself with mastering a few sums, which came in handy for his trade.

"It's a reward notice," I said glumly. "They're offering a hundred pounds for information leading to the arrest of the man known as Captain Sparkler."

Syd clapped his hands. "Gawd, that'd be a nice sum for someone to pick up!"

"You're right there, mate," a bystander replied.

"I wouldn't mind an 'undred pounds—I could buy my own boxin' club for that and forget about the fightin'." He guided me away from the sign. "Won't be long before someone squeals on him, I'd say."

I nodded, while fervently praying he was wrong. One thing was certain: after last night, I would not breathe a word of what I had found out about Johnny to anyone, particularly not to Pedro. With the lure of a hundred pounds, telling Pedro would be like sending Johnny to the gallows myself.

SCENE 2—THE ROOKERIES

I didn't see either Pedro or Johnny for the remainder of that day. Signor Angelini informed me that Pedro had gone to entertain a duke's son for the afternoon. He seemed to be under the impression that this involved playing the violin; I didn't want to disabuse him, but I suspected that it meant that Lord Francis and Pedro were roaming London in disguise again. I had hoped that I could make it up with Pedro and try to persuade him not to take part in the fight planned for that night. But being warned by Syd to stay indoors, I did not think it wise to go in search of the boys.

As for Johnny, he was in the theater, but "busy." A sign had appeared on his door: "Do not disturb," it read in Johnny's elegant curling script. I pressed my ear to the door and, sure enough, I could hear him inside. From the sounds of the scratching pen, I guessed he was drawing. I could well imagine the reason he did not want any callers: seeing a half-finished drawing by Captain Sparkler on his desk would be as good a way of revealing his identity as running through the streets shouting the secret to the heavens. I waited outside for a time, sitting on a large wooden anchor used to dress the stage for the pieces with a nautical theme, but my watch was barren. Giving up, I trailed back to the Sparrow's Nest and asked Mrs. Reid if she had anything for me to do.

"Lord, girl, look at your face!" she exclaimed. "I've not seen you this miserable since Mr. Salter boxed your ears." She threw me a bundle of darning. "See what you can make of that. Small stitches, mind—none of your fishing nets!"

I picked up my needle and sucked the end of some gray wool to thread it. "Where is Mr. Salter?" I asked. "I've not seen him for ages."

"Oh, he's gone," she said, her brow creased into a worried frown. My heart leaped—at last a piece of good news! "Mr. Sheridan was kind enough to send him off to Bristol the day after his play failed. He said he had an errand for him there, but it's been over a week now and we've not heard from him. I thought the change of scene would do him good, but now I'm very worried about him." Mrs. Reid's eyes, grown short-sighted after years of close sewing, now seemed to be staring at nothing. Her glasses slipped from her bony nose and dangled from their ribbon on her chest. As a widow, it was widely known backstage that she had set her cap for Mr. Salter, the most eligible bachelor to appear in Drury Lane for many years. She had a fair bit set by for a rainy day, it was said: what with her money and his pretensions to gentility, it was an advantageous match on both sides. But I couldn't imagine it myself. Anyone marrying that dry old stick of a playwright, even if he was the second cousin to a lord over Norwich way, must need their head examined.

"Perhaps he's not coming back?" I asked hopefully. "Perhaps his cousin has decided to stop him ruining the family reputation with his plays and has offered him employment."

"Don't be silly," said Mrs. Reid waspishly, coming to herself and stabbing her velvet pincushion with a pin. "The Earl of Ranworth does not think anything of the sort. In fact, from what Mr. Salter says, it's the Earl of Ranworth's own son that causes him sleepless nights, not his cousin."

"Oh?" I said, intrigued. This sounded like good material for a story: dissension in high places, wayward sons and worried fathers. It would certainly serve to pass the tedious time of sewing.

Mrs. Reid was flattered by my interest—I knew how to coax her to be indiscreet. She loved passing on gossip and, from the sly expression on her face, I could tell that this was a piece of news she had been sworn not to relate. That made it all the more tempting, of course. She probably excused herself by the thought that I hardly counted.

"Apparently," she said, lowering her voice to a confidential whisper, "the Earl of Ranworth's son has run away. He got himself into some kind of trouble and cleared off without so much as a change of clothes." She pinched her glasses back onto her nose and picked up her needle. "Fell out with his father over plans for his future, Mr. Salter says. He'd be disinherited if it wasn't for the entail."

"The entail?"

"The Ranworth estates are legally tied to the next male heir. The poor Earl of Ranworth has no power over his son."

Lucky son, I thought. He could afford to be rebellious.

"I shouldn't be telling you this," she went on, though from her face, I could tell she was enjoying speaking so freely before me, "but Mr. Sheridan has been helping to find the young man. He sent Mr. Salter, who knows what he looks like, you see, thanks to the family connection, to search the docks at Bristol. There was a rumor that he was heading abroad from there."

I hid a smile, imagining the prim Mr. Salter poking his nose into the rough and ready dealings of Bristol docks. I could understand now why Mrs. Reid was concerned: if Mr. Salter wasn't picked up by the press gang and thrown on board one of His Majesty's ships, he could easily be worked over by a party of drunken sailors. He would stand out as rich pickings for any troublemaker.

"Oh, I'm sure Mr. Salter will be all right," I lied to comfort her. "He'll be back soon, probably bringing the young lord with him, having had a splendid adventure."

"And it might give him something worth writing about," I added under my breath.

She grumbled something in denial of my optimistic words, and we returned to our sewing. I was making a hash of mine as usual, doubly so because of my unsettled mood. I tried to hide the evidence from the eagle eye of Mrs. Reid by covering the worst with my apron. I had enough experience of her temper to know that if she was fretting about her lost beau she might take it out on me with her birch measuring rod. My hands still bore the scars of her last bad day.

It came to me as I sat there that since I had first heard about the diamond, everything had turned strange. It was as if the stone stood between me and all the usual things of my life, fracturing and distorting them from their true shape. I wasn't the only one hiding things under my apron. No one was as they seemed. Mr. Sheridan, who claimed not to have enough money to pay for candles, had a valuable diamond somewhere in the theater, probably not so very far from where I was sitting.

Then there was Johnny. At first glance he seemed an innocent young man making his own way in the world, when in truth he was branded a traitor by the government and was hiding from the law. Not only that, he continued to disguise the fact that he was still drawing his treasonous cartoons by shutting himself away from us all.

And did it bother me that we had a criminal in our midst? I must admit it didn't. I just thought that the government lacked a sense of humor if they took offense at his drawings. Some of the things he told me, like equality for men and women, for black and white, made a lot of sense. As for the "dung heap of history," you may be shocked, Reader, to know that I wasn't too concerned what happened to our monarchy hidden away in their palaces of marble and gold. ~~If the people decided to get rid of the king, good luck to them,~~* it was unlikely to make

---

* Struck through by the censor.

much difference to me stuck here at the bottom of society. But I couldn't see it happening in my lifetime, not least because we wouldn't want the Froggies to think we were copying them.

And then there was Pedro. He had been deceiving me. Since he had rescued me from the balloon, I'd taken him on trust as a friend and introduced him to my own circle, but now I thought that he'd really only ever been thinking about cheating on me. From the very first day, he had taken advantage of my indiscretion in telling him about the diamond and intended to steal from my patron. The belief that Pedro had used me hurt deeply. You see, Reader, I liked Pedro: he was talented and brave, he had a self-composure that I could never aspire to—he had the bearing of a little king. No wonder Syd and the others called him "Prince." I had wanted to be Pedro's friend and had hoped that he had begun to like me too, but it appeared I had been mistaken. I'd just been a rung on the ladder he was climbing to riches. Now I didn't know whom I could trust.

Except Syd. Yes, I thought with a smile, he was straightforward. If he didn't like something, he told you to your face and that was that. There were no surprises with him. At least, I hoped not. Recently I had begun to fear that maybe he . . . No, I didn't even want to entertain the idea that he had feelings for me. That would make them more real somehow and complicate everything horribly. Syd was Syd. I'd leave it at that.

Monday was a quiet night for the theater. After the play finished, the crowds dispersed quickly and we were ready to close up by ten thirty. I stood at the stage door with Caleb watching Mrs. Siddons, our leading actress, sign autographs for her admirers before she retired for the night. She was a stately lady with a mass of elegantly arranged hair and good taste in gowns. She shared her brother's mesmerizing dark eyes—eyes which were now bent to speak to a young admirer—but on stage she could rivet thousands to their seats by the power of her presence. Under her spell, they groaned when she groaned, wept when she wept. To see her play Lady Macbeth was to experience true horror.

"Fine lady that," muttered Caleb appreciatively. "Famed throughout the land but still remembers me by name and gives me a penny for my smokes now and then."

I murmured my agreement and thought him very lucky. Mrs. Siddons moved in circles far above mine. She rarely spoke to me—perhaps only to thank me for doing some small errand for her—but I idolized her. She was the queen of British theater and I her most loyal subject.

"Here, Caleb, can I have a word?" It was Johnny. He had waited for the crowds of Mrs. Siddons's admirers to disperse before collaring the porter. "Can you find someone to deliver this for me?"

I peered with interest at the long, thin package wrapped and sealed with red wax. It took no great brains to guess that it was the cartoon he had been working on all afternoon. Johnny saw me looking and frowned.

There was no time to dwell on this, for a ragged boy ran into the little courtyard by the stage door, his face the very picture of terror, and bounded straight up to me.

"You Cat?"

"Yes. What is it?" I didn't recognize him—his clothes were hanging on by threads and he was crusted with dirt.

"I's told I'd find you 'ere. You've gotta come wi' me. The African boy's askin' for you. It's bad."

"What? Pedro? What's bad?"

"The fight. 'E's been 'urt—mortal 'urt."

All my anger at Pedro was swept away on hearing the threat to his life. If he was asking for me at this moment, it must mean that I hadn't been completely wrong: Pedro did care for me too. What did a silly argument between us matter when he could be dead by tomorrow morning?

"Where is he?" I asked, grabbing the boy's arm.

"Foller me," he said, running back the way he had come.

"Cat! Where're you going?" called Johnny behind me.

I had no time to explain: he'd try to stop me going and every minute might count. I'd never forgive myself if I arrived too late. *Too late for what?* a voice in my head asked. I didn't want to think about that. I dashed after the boy, flakes of snow stinging my cheeks. The boy did not lead me toward Covent Garden as I had expected. Instead, he raced over Long Acre, heading northwest for the narrow streets of St. Giles, otherwise known as the Rookeries. I hesitated on the curb, but fearing to lose him, darted across the slushy street in pursuit. I knew London too well to choose to go into St. Giles of my own free will. In normal circumstances, I would have given this district a wide berth. The people who lived there, mostly vagrants, thieves, and beggars, were said to strip the possessions of any fool who wandered into their lanes, hair and teeth included. They were a law unto themselves, a patch of wild savagery, a running sore in one of the richest cities in the world.

Plunging into the maze of alleyways, I immediately felt the threatening atmosphere: the houses were so shoddily built they seemed to collapse onto each other across the street, blocking out the sky above. Whispers of smoke seeped out of the crazy chimney pots. The only lights came from the gin shops and taverns, which stank of drink, sweat, and sickness. Even the steady fall of pure white snow was sullied by the time it landed on the cesspool that passed for a roadway in these slums.

"Wait!" I called after the boy. "Where are you taking me?"

The boy paused, shifting from leg to leg nervously as I caught up with him. He too felt happier to be on the move rather than standing still waiting to attract trouble.

"Not much farther," he said, wiping his nose on the back of his hand. He had a feverish look: his cheeks were flushed and his eyes unnaturally bright. "'E's been carried into the King's 'Ead."

He set off again and darted down a side street into an even darker courtyard. The stench of overflowing drains was unbearable, and I had to force myself to follow him. I shuddered as I nearly stepped on a dead rat lying stiff in the roadway. A mangy cat with one eye and half a tail slunk past, disappearing into a crack in the wall of a boarded-up house. The boy ducked into a low doorway with a creaking sign overhead. A crude painting of Charles I, holding his severed head under one arm, swung above the entrance, snow resting like a funeral wreath on the picture. I dashed inside. Expecting to see Pedro lying in a pile of bloody rags, perhaps already dead, I found the taproom empty. There was only a small fire in the grate, a table and bench, an untended barrel of beer.

Once across the threshold, I had a very bad feeling about the place. The feverish boy had disappeared. Every instinct was screaming that, Pedro or no Pedro, it was time to run for it. I turned to leave but at that moment a customer stepped into the King's Head and shut the door firmly behind him, shaking the snow off his hat. Billy Shepherd. My heart sank to my boots. Footsteps came from the back room and Ferret-Features, Pox-Face, and Meatpie Matt lumbered in, all looking mightily pleased with themselves.

"Delighted you could make it, Cat," said Billy with menacing politeness as he gestured for me to take a seat on the bench. I remained standing, snow melting on my shawl and dripping to the floor.

"Where's Pedro?" I asked bleakly. "What've you done with him?"

"I've no idea where Blackie is, Cat," said Billy with a laugh. "'E's probably in Covent Garden waitin' for the fight—the fight they all thought was goin' to 'appen. You see, I 'ad to think up a little distraction so I could get you out of Drury Lane. It was pretty clever, don't you think? You all fell for it 'ook, line, and sinker."

I felt sick. It was a trap. There was no Pedro in his death throes, no big fight in the piazza, just stupid old me stuck with my enemy in a place where anything could happen. And I mean anything: they could murder me here and now and no one in St. Giles would turn a hair. If I wanted to live, this was no time to annoy Billy. I sat down.

"So, 'ow do you like my center of operations?" He gestured around the squalid room. "I'm thinkin' of branchin' out from the market, takin' a piece of the Rookeries under my wing. You're privileged: you're the first outsider to see my 'eadquarters. What'ya think?'

"It's very, er, very nice," I said, my voice shaking slightly.

In fact, it was cold, foul, and damp. I could see why a rat like Billy would be attracted to it.

He smiled at me, displaying his rotten teeth like gravestones in his ugly mouth. He reached forward to brush the snow from my hair. I tried not to flinch. He was testing me, looking for an excuse to hurt me as I knew he so badly wanted to do. I'd insulted him by giving him a nickname; I'd humiliated him in front of his gang; I had twice offended his "honor"; and I was to pay for it.

"Now, Cat, about our little discussion yesterday." He moved to stand behind me out of sight, but I could see Ferret-Features grinning over my head at him, anticipating what was to come. "It didn't quite end 'ow I'd like. You see, I know that you know somethink—somethink that I want to know very much."

This wasn't quite what I expected.

"Oh?" I asked. "What's that?" Perhaps I could bargain my way to safety.

"The diamond." Billy rested his hands on my

shoulders, one finger caressing my neck. "If you tell me where I can find it, I'll let you return 'ome. In fact, even better than that, I'll let you get it for me and I'll buy you a new dress for your trouble." Ferret-Features was now smirking at my street-stained woolen gown. "I can't say fairer than that, can I?"

"Diamond? What diamond?" I spluttered. How had he heard about that?

"Come now, Cat, you're not the only person to 'ang around the stage door. You were seen. We know you know."

"But I don't!" I protested.

There was a grating noise of metal on metal, and I felt a cold blade against my neck.

"Do you know what my family does for a livin', Cat?" he asked casually.

Ferret-Features stared at the knife at my neck like a dog waiting for a bone.

"No," I said, trying not to move.

"We're barbers—'andy with the razor. Now you think about that while you remember where Mr. S. put that diamond."

I was shaking with terror. I really didn't know, but if I told him that he'd probably just cut my throat and have done with me.

"Billy, please!"

"Not convinced yet, Cat? Now, 'ow'd you like it done? Cropped? Or like an Injun Mohican?" There was a sharp jerk on my head, and a lock of red hair fluttered onto the table. Billy caught it up with his left hand and pocketed it.

"A keepsake," he said calmly. "Something for me to remember your pretty curls by. Wot'ya think, Meatpie? Should fetch a decent price at the wig makers, don't ya think? Shame red's not the fashion."

Meatpie laughed dutifully, but unlike Ferret-Features he had the decency to look uncomfortable.

"Please!" I was crying now, tears rolling down my face as I sat rigid, trying not to move, though every instinct in my body was begging to make a dash for the door. "I really don't know where the diamond is. But I'll look for you—I will. I promise."

Billy gave a tug on another strand of hair.

"Sorry, that ain't good enough, Cat. You've always said you know everythink that goes on in that theater, so I bet you know where it is. Anyways, I prefer it like it is now—you 'ere with me with no backup. I think it'll 'elp you make the right decision, 'elp jog your memory. If I let you go, what's to stop you runnin' off and telling your friend Syd about our little chat, eh?"

He was right: that was just what I had been thinking of doing. What would I have given to have Syd by my side at that moment!

"No, I need an answer and I need it now. Then we're goin' to take a little stroll to the theater and you'll 'and it over to me. Agreed?"

What could I do? Make something up? That seemed my best option. At least I'd buy myself some more time.

"Agreed?" Billy said fiercely, giving a painful tug on my hair.

"I, er, I . . .

"Yeah, I'm listenin'."

The door behind us banged open and Billy spun around. As his hand was still grasping my hair, my head was pulled as he turned. Through tear-filled eyes, I saw a man standing framed in the doorway. His black cloak and hat were covered in snow. Both arms were held up in front of him, each hand holding a pistol, one trained on Billy, the other on Meatpie. Meatpie gave a whimper and dived behind the beer barrel.

"In that case, I suggest you listen to me, and listen hard. Put that razor down and move away from the girl," Johnny said. The barrels of the pistols were rock-steady in his hands, both cocked, prepared to fire.

Billy tightened his grip on my hair, dragging me from the bench so I was on my knees in front of him. He brought the blade to my throat. I could feel its sharp edge prick my skin.

"Oo the 'ell are you?" Billy growled.

Johnny gave a flick of the gun barrel, gesturing to Billy to move away from me. His eyes were fixed on my captor, blazing with anger.

"Her backup. Let her go," he said menacingly.

"Or what?" sneered Billy. "I'll cut 'er throat if you take a step nearer. 'Oo said you could come in 'ere and break up our private talk? You don't want 'im 'ere, do ya, Cat?" He used his grip on my hair to shake my head like a marionette.

"You won't find out about the diamond from her," said Johnny coldly. "She knows nothing."

Billy pulled my head back, exposing my throat to the knife.

"So why don't ya tell us then? Tell us, or I'll kill the kitten."

"You won't do that," said Johnny, not even looking at me but keeping his eyes on Billy. Pox-Face made a move on Johnny's left, trying to creep up behind to jump him. "Stay where you are!" ordered Johnny. Pox-Face stood still, eyes fixed on the second gun barrel now pointing at him.

"Oh, won't I?" jeered Billy. "Why not?"

"Because I'll shoot you first."

"You won't do that: you might 'it the girl," said Billy, pressing the blade tight against my throat.

"Take my word for it: I'm a very good shot. I won't miss. Now, what are you going to do?"

There was silence. Then a clatter as Billy dropped the razor on the floor in front of me.

"Very sensible," said Johnny. "Now let her go."

Furious, Billy released his grip on my hair and kicked me away from him, sending me sprawling onto the floor so that I landed on top of the razor. I felt it cut into my arm.

"One more trick like that and I'll blast you to hell," said Johnny fiercely. "Get up, Cat, and come over here."

I scrambled to my feet, cradling my bleeding arm, and stumbled past Johnny out of that hateful place.

"Now understand this," I heard him telling them. "I'm going to escort the young lady home. If I spot so much as a whisker of any of you following us, I'll fire without warning." With a final look at each of them, he ducked out of the room, slamming the door so violently it made the sign creak on its hinges. He then stuffed one of the pistols in his belt, seized my injured arm, and began to run.

"Come on, we must get away from here!" he urged, setting off at a smart pace.

Not needing to be told twice, I ran after him, though hampered by slipping several times on the icy cobbles. Only Johnny's firm grip on my arm stopped me falling to the ground. I was too numb to think of the pain. Pale faces appeared in dark doorways, like ghosts rising from tombs. They watched us pass in eerie silence as the snow fluttered down in frozen tears. Suddenly, a scrawny woman darted forward and made a grab for my shawl. I let it go, leaving it hanging like a tattered flag in her hands.

We turned a corner into a busy thoroughfare of smoke-filled taverns and shabby lodging houses. A drunken Irishman stumbled out of a dark alleyway and into our path.

"Gi' us that!" he shouted at Johnny, trying to pull me away.

I didn't see exactly what Johnny did, but next thing the man was doubled up, hands clenched to his stomach, and we were running out onto St. Giles High Street, and away.

"I can't breathe!" I gasped, my side pierced by a stitch.

"Forget breathing; just run!" Johnny said with an anxious look over his shoulder.

He towed me along after him, back across Long Acre and into Bow Street. Taking a side street to avoid passing the magistrate's house, he did not stop until we reached the stage door. Caleb was on the watch: he threw it open for us and we burst inside, collapsing as soon as we were across the threshold.

"What 'appened to you, sir?" asked Caleb, looking with concern at Johnny's bloodstained hand as my rescuer bent over to regain his breath.

Johnny stared down uncomprehendingly at his palm.

"But I'm not hurt!" He turned to me. I was on all fours, panting and sobbing with relief. "It must be Cat. Let's see."

I raised my left arm to him: a cut, about four inches long, was oozing bright red droplets vivid against the white skin of my inner arm.

Johnny gave a low whistle. "Nasty! An inch lower and that would have got the vein. Here, let me take you to my office and I'll clean it up."

Caleb blanched as he caught sight of the blood dripping down my wrist.

"Will she be all right?" he asked huskily.

"She'll be fine," Johnny assured him. "But keep a sharp eye out tonight, Caleb. The boys who did this might come looking for us. Bar the door and don't let anyone in unless you know them."

"Don't worry," said the old doorman, picking up a stout cudgel he had concealed behind the door curtain. "They won't get past Caleb Braithwaite in a hurry."

"Thanks, my friend," said Johnny.

He then knelt and picked me up. I was so shocked and exhausted by my adventure that I no longer cared what became of me: I just wanted to curl up, fall asleep, and forget all about it. But Johnny had other ideas. There were matters he had to attend to first. He sat me in a chair by his fireside and put a kettle on the fire to boil. Tearing up some clean strips of linen, he set about tending to my wound.

"I'm sorry about that, Catkin. I should have acted faster," he said, shaking his head over the cut.

"You're sorry!" I said in surprise. "You've nothing to be sorry about. It was all my fault: I should never have fallen for their trap."

"They set a trap, did they?" Johnny probed gently as he staunched the wound.

I nodded.

Johnny pressed my hand comfortingly. "I really must know what they said to you. I must know what they know about the diamond."

So he was in on Mr. Sheridan's secret too! It occurred to me then that he might even have been put here to help defend it. I looked up at him to see if I could read the truth in his face. His eyes were no longer cold: they had returned to their old friendly expression, and yet tonight I thought I could sense a new shadow in their depths as if he was particularly sad about something.

"And I need to know why you were with those blackguards in the first place, Cat." He turned to take the boiling kettle from the grate and poured some of the contents into a china bowl. "It wasn't you who told them about the diamond, was it?" he asked levelly as he put several teaspoons of salt into the steaming water.

"No!" I protested. "I never said nothing about the diamond—except to Pedro."

"To Pedro?" Johnny asked, his voice careful as if he was walking on thin ice.

"But it wasn't him, neither!" I added. At least, I hoped he hadn't told them. "Ouch!" Johnny had just dabbed my cut with the salted water.

"Billy Boil told me one of his gang had seen me at the stage door. It must have been the night Mr. Marchmont came."

"Who is Billy Boil?" Johnny looked puzzled.

I smiled weakly. "I mean Billy Shepherd. I'm afraid I gave him that nickname: we aren't the best of friends, as you saw. He was the one with the razor—the one you threatened with the pistols."

"Oh those," said Johnny contemptuously, taking the pistols from his belt and throwing them onto the camp bed still cocked. I ducked, half expecting them to explode. "I didn't have time to load them. If I had, I would have ended that interview much sooner, believe me. No, I was curious as to why you were running off into the night and I took it into my head to follow you."

"The messenger told me Pedro had been hurt."

"Ah. Now I see."

I suddenly realized why Johnny had taken the risk of following me into St. Giles. It hadn't been out of gallantry as I had assumed.

"You didn't trust me, did you? You thought I was going to betray you."

He tied off the bandage around my arm and sat back on his haunches.

"I must admit it did cross my mind. I was going to run for it if I saw you going to the magistrate to tip them off about the new cartoon. Whatever my motive, I am heartily thankful I did follow you. I dread to think what would have happened if I hadn't been on hand."

"I'd be dead and my hair a wig in Pollard's window. I think you can be quite certain of that," I said with a small laugh that turned into a shudder.

Johnny pressed my fingers again. "That would have been a very sad loss to Drury Lane. So, tell me, what did they know about the diamond?"

"Not much," I said with a shrug. "Just that it's hidden in the theater. They thought I could fetch it for them."

He bit his lip and looked away from me to the fire. Bright flames danced on the coals, casting an orange glow over his handsome features. I was beginning to love seeing that face about the theater. He was the only one who called me Catkin in that affectionate way of his, the only one who took the trouble to tell me things.

"I think it's become too dangerous to have the diamond here," he said. "I'll have to tell Sheridan it's got to move."

"Move where?" I asked eagerly.

"Come now, Cat. You don't really want to know that, do you?" he laughed. "Look what danger a little bit of knowledge got you into tonight."

"It was my ignorance, not what I knew, that landed me in trouble," I countered.

"So you would've handed the diamond over to them, would you, if you'd known where it was?" he asked with a strange smile.

"No, of course not. I'd've thought of something before it reached that point."

"I doubt that. Shepherd does not look the type to allow little girls to trick him out of a great prize. But in any case, you need not worry. I meant that the diamond should be put far out of anyone's reach. Sent to America, for example."

"America! So far?" I exclaimed. "What do they want with diamonds in America? I thought there was nothing but Indians and rebels in America."

"That about sums it up," said Johnny with a laugh. "Come now, to bed with you."

He helped me to my feet.

"Thank you, Johnny," I said quietly. I had to say it before I left.

"For what?"

"For saving my life."

He bent down and kissed the top of my head as a father or brother might do. Receiving this tender gesture, I felt an acute sense of loss. I had survived by not thinking too much about what I couldn't have, but tonight I suddenly missed having my own family more than ever. Being with Johnny made me realize what I might have known.

"It was the least I could do," he said, "especially as it was the diamond that put you in danger in the first place."

I was about to put him right on that and explain about the bad blood between Billy and myself, but he ushered me out.

"No more tonight, Cat. We can talk in the morning."

I turned to go but a thought snagged me like a hook.

"Johnny, don't tell anyone about this, will you?" I pleaded.

He shrugged. "I'll have to mention it to Mr. Sheridan—but no one else, I promise. But why?"

"If Pedro hears, he'll tell Syd."

"Syd?"

"The Bow Street Butcher. If he finds out what Billy did to me, it'll be war in Covent Garden. Someone might get hurt, and I wouldn't want that."

"I understand." He paused. "You know, Catkin, you are wiser than you look. Good night."

"Good night, Captain."

'Are you all right, Cat?'

Pedro found me in the auditorium, replacing the candles in one of the chandeliers. Long Tom had lowered it to be within my reach so I could assist him in the never-ending chore of keeping the theater brightly lit.

"Why do you ask?" I said, not looking at Pedro as I chipped off the drips of wax from the glass reflectors with my nail.

"Are you still cross with me? Don't you want to hear what happened last night?" He sat down on a bench and rubbed his calf muscles like an athlete limbering for a race. He was expected onstage in five minutes for his rehearsal.

I already knew, of course, that nothing had happened in Covent Garden last night, but he was not to know that. A total lack of interest on my part would look suspicious.

"So what happened?" I asked dutifully.

"Nothing. Syd thinks Billy funked it."

"Oh." I spiked a white candle on the prong in an empty bracket.

"I thought you'd be relieved," said Pedro in a disappointed voice. "This means that Billy's surrendered the market to Syd, doesn't it? You'll be able to go out again. He won't dare touch you."

When I closed my eyes, I could still feel the choking pressure of Billy's razor on my throat and touch the stub of hair where he had shaved off a fistful. Pedro's comforting words could not be more ill-founded. I swayed on my feet and reached out for the bench to sit down before I collapsed.

Pedro was alarmed. "Cat? What's the matter? You really don't look well." He now noticed my bandaged forearm. "What did you do to yourself?'

"Nothing," I said, taking a steadying breath, determined not to faint.

"But your arm!"

"It's nothing—just a cut."

Pedro gave me a dubious look but did not pursue the matter. "Well, I know something that will cheer you up. Lord Francis and Lady Elizabeth are coming to the rehearsal today."

I raised my eyebrows quizzically. "In what capacity?"

"Dressed as themselves, of course. Now that you've whetted their appetite for the stage, Mr. Sheridan invited them to bring a party of their friends. They should be here soon."

I looked around quickly, wondering if Johnny was in view: he had to be warned. He would want to keep out of sight of such an invasion in case someone recognized him.

"Come on, Cat," chided Pedro. "Aren't you the least bit pleased?"

"Sorry, Pedro," I said, turning back to him. "Of course I'm pleased." Looking into his deep brown eyes, it was hard to believe at that moment that this was the boy who had cheated on me. He did seem to care. Maybe the diamond-stealing was now all water under the bridge and we could start again?

"Good, for I told Frank that you'd show them around."

"Pedro!"

Pedro leaped to his feet and gave me a bright smile. "Well, I can't, can I? I've got to be onstage." With a final stretch, he bounded away like a gazelle, climbing over the bars to the orchestra pit and up onto the forestage.

Typical! I had just begun to like him again, and he had sprung another surprise on me, using me to entertain his guests. If it weren't for the fact that I liked Lord Francis too, I wouldn't let him get away with it!

I found Johnny in the wings, running through the cues for that night's play with Mr. Bishop. Hovering behind the stage manager, I tried to attract Johnny's attention. This couldn't wait: they could be here at any moment. Finally, my friend looked up and saw me waving at him.

"Mr. Bishop," said Johnny quickly, "I'm sorry to interrupt this, but could we finish this later?"

The rebuff annoyed Mr. Bishop. He was clearly having one of his bad days, but even he found it hard to show offense at Johnny's polite but masterful manner.

"If you must," he said grudgingly. He stuffed his dog-eared copy of the script into a deep jacket pocket. "I'll see how the enchanter's laboratory is coming along. Problem with the hidden compartment—keeps springing open."

He shuffled off, yelling to the carpenter to hurry. It appeared the poor chippie was going to bear the brunt of his anger.

"This better be good, Cat," said Johnny, steering me into the prompter's office. "I have to tread carefully around Bishop. I think he suspects something."

I hurriedly told him about the arrival of the party of young ladies and gentlemen. Striding to and fro in front of the fire, Johnny ran his fingers distractedly through his hair.

"Who do you think will come?" he asked.

I shrugged. "I met a few of their friends at the tea party. Besides Lord Francis and Lady Elizabeth, there was a young lady called Jane, a young gentleman called Charlie, and the Marchmont children."

"The Honorable Charles Hengrave, I imagine," mused Johnny. "I don't know the girl, Jane—probably some poor relation from the country. As for the Marchmonts, I know them all right: horrid little bores, the whole family. I can tolerate the father only because of his political views. As a man, I find him repugnant."

I was surprised by Johnny's intimate knowledge of Lord Francis's circle.

"The Marchmont boy's not like his father," I said quickly. Johnny looked surprised. "What I mean is, he's still horrid, but he doesn't share his father's politics. Lord Francis said he was a supporter of Mr. Pitt and dead against reformers. He certainly didn't like my manuscript—thought it revolutionary stuff, unfit for the delicate ears of his sisters, and all because I wrote about what he considers 'low' subjects."

"Hmm." Johnny fiddled with an inkwell on the mantelpiece, his shoulders in a dejected hunch. "Backstage at Drury Lane is not as safe as I thought—far too public. It's a shame. I wouldn't have minded seeing Lady Elizabeth again." He turned to me. "Is she still as pretty as ever?"

"When did you meet Lady Elizabeth?" I asked, intrigued.

"Oh, here and there," said Johnny lightly, flicking dust from a brass candlestick.

"You're not telling me everything, are you?" A suspicion was beginning to form in my mind, based on a growing awareness that my friend was not as he seemed.

"Of course not." Johnny smiled at me, his eyes twinkling. "But thanks for the warning. I'll lie low in here until the coast is clear. You'll let me know when I can come out of hiding, won't you?"

I nodded. "Of course. And yes," I added slyly before I shut the door behind me, "she still is as pretty as ever."

I met the party of visitors by the main entrance. They had come in two carriages and on horseback. In the lead was Lord Francis with his friend, the Honorable Charles Hengrave, on a pair of fine geldings, accompanied by a footman.

"Here she is!" exclaimed Lord Francis in delight as he bounded up the steps to me, shaking my hand vigorously. "You should've seen her, Charlie! She flattened that bully and saved my skin. She made a splendid boy."

I blushed as Charlie gave me a bow and a grin. It appeared that news of our recent exploits had traveled.

"I hope, Miss Royal, you'll record your adventures for us," Charlie said politely. "I am eager to hear all about it from your pen."

Lord Francis clapped his hand to his head.

"That reminds me!" he cried. "Father was very impressed by your manuscript. He told me to tell you that he'll support your first venture into print when you finish it."

"In that case, she'd better get a move on." This was from Pedro, who had ducked out of the rehearsal to greet his friend. Surrounded by the silk waistcoats and velvet jackets of the young nobles, he looked most out of place in his sailor's costume of blue jacket and white trousers. He was playing and dancing a hornpipe in the musical interlude that night.

Lady Elizabeth arrived on the arm of the young Marchmont. From the pained expression on her normally serene face, she appeared to be doing her best to humor the boy. It was a lost cause: he had come intending to despise everyone and everything. He wrinkled his nose at the tawdry gilt of the auditorium. Drury Lane was in need of renovation and it never looked its best by daylight.

"Poor Lizzie," muttered Lord Francis to Charles Hengrave, "she keeps on trying to be polite to Marzi-pain for Father's sake, failing to comprehend that he's beyond saving."

"Marzi-pain?" I whispered.

"Marzipan—Marzi-pain Marchmont—because of the hair," Lord Francis explained in a low voice.

I still looked puzzled.

"You know, marzipan, that yellowy-white almond stuff you get on cakes?"

He may get it on cakes, but I had never been so lucky. The closest I'd come to confectionery was with my nose pressed against the baker's window.

"Oh, of course," I said, trying to appear perfectly familiar with all details of the confectioner's art.

I hadn't fooled him. "I'm sorry. That was stupid of me. Next time you come to tea, I shall ensure that you sample every sort of marzipan under the sun, Miss Royal. Our French cook is a master."

Marchmont's voice now reached us. Lord Francis grimaced.

"It is not a patch on Covent Garden," he was saying loudly. "Father has a private box there, you know."

He had better pipe down or he might find himself rudely ejected by one of the crew, I thought sourly.

"But, Mr. Marchmont, I'm sure you'll agree that it is not the gaudy wrappings, but the content that counts. The acting here has no rival, with Mr. Kemble, Mrs. Siddons, and Mrs. Jordan to call on," said Lady Elizabeth as she approached us.

Bless her, I thought.

Marchmont sniffed at this statement but said nothing.

Pedro bowed to the ladies. I curtsied.

"I was just telling Miss Royal about Papa's admiration for her manuscript," said Lord Francis loudly. He had evidently not forgotten Marchmont's disapproval of my work and was happy to trump it with a duke's approbation.

Marchmont gave a thin-lipped smile. "Your father has peculiar taste, Lord Francis. I grant that she writes a fair enough hand for a girl of her class, but as for the contents . . ." he left his disapproval hanging in the air. "The drawings, however: thinking about them afterward, I was most intrigued. You surely did not do them yourself, Miss Royal? The style was very distinctive. I could almost swear it was . . . familiar." He looked hard at me, his smile as false as a stage moustache. Had he guessed too much?

Unfortunately, Pedro was oblivious to the sensitivity of the subject.

"No, she didn't. That was Johnny Smith, the prompter," he said. "Cat'll introduce you to him if you're interested. He does really wicked likenesses, really clever."

Not for the first time I could have kicked Pedro for his overeagerness to show off before prospective sponsors. The last thing Johnny needed was for Pedro to go patron-hunting for him.

"Wicked likenesses?" said Marchmont coolly. "I've no doubt of that."

"But he doesn't draw much," I added quickly, trying to warn Pedro with a look. "In fact, it was probably the first time he's put pencil to paper when he drew for me." Pedro looked surprised and was going to dispute this, but I plowed on. "And unfortunately, he's been called away suddenly to . . . to see a sick uncle. He's not here. Not in the building."

I raised my gaze to Marchmont's heavy-lidded eyes. He was now looking at me with a skeptical curl to his lips.

Guiding the young people around Drury Lane was more difficult than I anticipated. The phrase beloved of Mrs. Reid came into my head as I extricated Charles Hengrave and Lord Francis from the basket of the balloon backstage: it was like herding cats. No sooner had I headed off one group from doing something they shouldn't in one department then a new crisis would erupt elsewhere. Hardest to manage was Marchmont.

He seemed determined to open every door and every closet. I could've sworn he was looking for something, and I thought I could guess what it was.

We were approaching the greatest danger: the corridor containing the prompter's office. I had to think of a diversion before he burst in on Johnny.

"Oh, sir," I cried quickly as he approached the door, "you can't go in there."

He turned to give me a bitter smile, scenting his quarry to be nearby.

"Why not, Miss Royal? Mr. Sheridan has given us the passport to roam. He said we were to go anywhere we liked."

"Did he?" I replied, silently cursing my over-generous sponsor. "Well, I'm sure he did not intend the permission to include the ladies' powder room."

Marchmont flushed and removed his hand from the handle as if it had burned him.

"There's no sign," he said hotly.

I shrugged. "Of course not. Those who need it know what it is. If you require the privy, I could ask one of the stagehands to take you."

I enjoyed watching Marchmont's cheeks turn red. "No, no, that won't be necessary," he said, striding purposefully off down the corridor.

Just as I was about to congratulate myself on my cleverness, disaster struck. Lady Elizabeth, waiting for the young gentlemen to leave, whispered aside to me, "I'll call in here for a moment and catch you up."

"No!" I protested, trying to stop her. But it was too late. She had opened the door and stepped inside, closing it swiftly behind her.

"Miss Royal!" called Lord Francis from the scenery lot at the back of the stage. "Miss Royal, tell us again how this balloon thing works."

I stared at the door in agony, expecting Lady Elizabeth to rush out screaming at any moment.

"Leave Lizzie; she'll find us all right," Lord Francis continued.

Not daring to imagine what was happening inside that room, I tore myself away and joined Lord Francis, Miss Jane, and Mr. Charles by the deflated splendors of the balloon. I don't know what they made of my mechanical explanation: I was so distracted that I must have talked utter rubbish.

"What do you think, Charlie?" wondered Lord Francis. "Shall we test it out on old Marzi-pain and leave him up there? It would be doing the world a favor."

Charles Hengrave laughed. "Good idea. You still haven't got your own back on him for snitching to your father about that coach you drove around the Square."

"You're right! How had I forgotten that?"

"Your problem, Frank, is that you're too good-natured to bear a grudge," said his friend approvingly.

"Or too absentminded to remember anything for long," added Miss Jane, with an indulgent smile at her cousin.

Soft footsteps behind me and Lady Elizabeth appeared at my elbow. She looked a little shocked but managed to give me a small smile.

"Unusual powder room, Miss Royal," she said softly. "As I was unable to avail myself of its facilities, perhaps you would be so kind as to guide me to the appropriate chamber?"

"Of course, Lady Elizabeth," I said, feeling a wave of gratitude toward her.

Leaving the rest of the party in the Sparrow's Nest under Sarah Bowers's capable eye, I led Lady Elizabeth to the privy.

When she re-emerged, she took me to one side.

"Do you know who that is, Miss Royal? I assume you do as you were trying to prevent our paths crossing."

I nodded.

"So how did Lord Jonathan Fitzroy come to be here?" she whispered.

"So he is a lord," I said half to myself as her question confirmed my suspicion. Johnny's knowledge of the Avons and their friends had given me a hint that he had moved in higher circles than the one he was currently occupying. I should have put two and two together when I heard Mrs. Reid's story about the Earl of Ranworth and his troublesome son. The rift between Johnny and his father could be explained by the predilection of the son for treasonous cartoons. And why else had Mr. Sheridan dispatched Mr. Salter off to the other end of the country? My patron knew better than to send a fool like that to find someone. He'd been sent out of the way to stop him recognizing his cousin. But Johnny's identity as Captain Sparkler must be preserved as a secret, even from the Avons.

"I think Mr. Sheridan is helping him until a reconciliation can be arranged with his father," I explained. "You won't tell anyone, will you?"

She shook her head, her neat ringlets whispering like silk at her neck.

"No, I've given him my word. He said I could tell my brother if I wished, but no one else. He also said I could trust you." Her cheeks were now blushing. "He said that you'd pass him any messages I might care to send him and you'd bring any word from him to me."

Clearly there was much more to the history of Lord Jonathan and Lady Elizabeth than I knew. As Johnny's friend, I felt it my role to blow his trumpet for him.

"Certainly. I'd like to be of assistance to you both, especially since Johnny saved my life last night."

"He did?" Her eyes glowed with pride to hear of her sweetheart's courage.

"Yes, he saved me from certain death, armed only with a brace of unloaded pistols. I had a razor held to my neck at the time."

Lady Elizabeth frowned and took my arm in her gloved hand. "You're serious, aren't you? Someone did this to you?"

I hadn't meant her to set off on this track. I tried to shrug, but the shock in the eyes of a girl who had only ever known the comfortable life of the affluent made me realize just how far below her I was. My life was a series of buffets and blows, hers a round of tea parties and pretty dresses. I felt ashamed of myself. But, to my surprise, Lady Elizabeth said, "You are the bravest girl I've ever met, Miss Royal. I admire your courage."

I met her gaze and saw that she was not looking at me as the scruffy commoner, but as the heroine of my own tale. As her equal.

"Please call me Cat," I said. "All my friends do."

She smiled. "Yes, I'd like that. And call me Lizzie—that's what Papa and Frank call me at home."

Our friendship sealed, we returned to the Sparrow's Nest to find the rest of the party decked out in a fantastical selection of robes and crowns. Lord Francis had Pedro's turban perched drunkenly on his head, and he was making Sarah howl with laughter as he tried to imitate Pedro's spinning dance.

"Lawd love us," said Sarah. "You'd sure be a treat on the stage you would, sir."

Lord Francis stopped twirling and gave her a wobbly bow.

"Ma'am, may you be blessed a hundred times for your kind words. An actor's life for me, it is!"

"How many dukes do you know who combine their duties with clowning in front of the rabble?" asked Marchmont as he toyed contemptuously with a patched cloak.

"Not enough!" cried Lord Francis, making Miss Jane and Sarah giggle.

"I think I'd better take my brother away, Cat," said Lady Elizabeth, "before he does himself an injury. Thank you for your kind attention this morning."

Her thanks were followed by the warm farewells of the rest of the party—excepting the Marchmonts, of course. Still, I had to remove an ostrich feather that the younger Miss Marchmont had inadvertently slipped inside her reticule, much to the chagrin of her brother. I wondered if he had put it there.

"Well," said Sarah, rocking in the armchair with a pile of mending on her lap, "if all lords were like that Lord Francis, England would be a fine place."

I heartily agreed with her. Unfortunately, there were too many Marzi-pain Marchmonts to make that a reality.

SCENE 4—SNOWBALLS

"So, what's the story behind you and Lady Elizabeth?" I asked Johnny as I sat over the slate of sums he had set me. It was mid-afternoon and the sun was pouring obliquely through the grimy windows of his office, lighting his face with a pale golden glow. What a fine couple he and Lady Elizabeth would make if fortune smiled on them. No longer needing to conceal his activities from me, he was inking in a cartoon he had done about the complicated love life of one of the princes. He looked up at me and brushed a stray strand of dark hair off his face.

"A short story, I'm afraid, Cat. Not enough to satisfy your voracious appetite for information. We met in the autumn at her coming-out ball."

"Her what?"

"Her first venture into society as an adult. They call it coming out. When you see a young lady, you must ask yourself, is she in or is she out?"

"Sounds like cricket," I said glumly, remembering a tedious afternoon I had once spent with Syd's gang when they had played against a rival team from Smithfield. Johnny laughed.

"Not really. It's a kind of code, meaning is she on the marriage market or is she not?"

"And are you bidding for her?" I teased.

"I might've done—had circumstances been different. That was before I fell out with my father. He discovered all this." Johnny gestured at the cartoon lying on the table before him. "Didn't take too kindly to it, staunch royalist that he is. He failed to understand how his son could be a republican at heart."

The earl could be forgiven his confusion. How did the son of an earl end up rejecting the system that so favored him and his kind in exchange for the new ways of France and America? I wondered. Well, the only way to find out was to ask.

"Why are you?"

"Why am I what?"

"A republican."

"Ah." Johnny put his pen down and wiped the ink from his fingers with a rag. "It's all thanks to Mr. Shore, my old tutor. He taught me that all men are equal. Titles are nothing when you place man beside man in the wild. What is important then is character and intelligence. He told me how many so-called savage races around the world live noble lives, free of our corruption, greed, and envy. It's not the man's title but his qualities you should look to."

"Or the woman's."

"Quite so." He acknowledged my correction with a slight bow. "That's why I despise Billy Shepherd as much as I do the prime minister. It has nothing to do with Shepherd's lowly station in life; it's his cruelty and greed that bring him into contempt. And it's why I admire Lady Elizabeth. Her rank is nothing, but her mind and her heart are everything. She's so different from all the other young ladies I've met. When you talk to her, you know she understands you, follows your thoughts through all their fancies and wanderings."

He meant she'd put up with him rambling on about his revolutionary ideas, I thought with a smile, picturing him talking earnestly to her in some corner at her coming-out ball. But he was right: she had the air of someone intelligent and thoughtful. Not to mention her beauty. I could see how he had fallen hopelessly in love with her.

He rolled up the cartoon he had been working on and looked at me thoughtfully, tapping the end of the tube of paper on his chin. "Cat, are you happy to venture outside now? Do you think you are in any danger?"

"Not now. I'm prepared. Not during the day," I replied. I wasn't going to let a steaming pile of dung like Billy Boil stop me getting a breath of fresh air. He wasn't going to make me a prisoner in my own home.

"Then would you mind running this to Mr. Humphrey, the printer in Gerrard Street?"

"Of course." I jumped up eagerly, not least because Johnny appeared to have forgotten that I had an unfinished slate of sums to do.

"Good girl. I've used Caleb too often. What I need is a confidential messenger." He pressed a sixpence into my hand. "Keep a weather eye for danger, Catkin. Stay on the main streets."

"Yes, sir," I said with a grin. I hardly needed the warning, but it was nice to hear that someone cared.

"Oh," he said, as if an afterthought, but I could tell he had been planning to say it all along. "If you bump into Mr. Sheridan, deny all knowledge of this one."

I unrolled it and took a peek at the picture.

"I suppose he wouldn't be too pleased to see you've drawn his best friend in his underwear."

"No, he wouldn't." Johnny smiled grimly. "Sheridan may be my friend—and a good friend in times of trouble—but he hasn't bought my conscience. I serve no party but the truth."

"And," I added, "it's a good way of throwing people off the scent. Who would look for Captain Sparkler under Mr. Sheridan's wing when this is printed?"

"You are a sharp one, Cat. What are we going to do with you?"

"But mightn't he throw you out for insulting his friend?" I asked.

"He might," said Johnny with a shrug as he ushered me out of the room, "but that's a chance I am prepared to take. Hurry now. The deadline's already passed. Mr. Humphrey's waiting to let his etchers loose on it."

Pausing this time to wrap up warmly, I emerged onto Russell Street to find the world had changed. A steady fall of snow had covered the street with a purifying shroud, hiding the mud and mire that lay just beneath. London was muffled, the snow quelling the evil and violence for a few brief hours, lifting spirits for a holiday of innocence and beauty. I knew it would be all too brief an interval. The white blanket would be quickly sullied by the passage of heavy boots, hooves, and wheels. When night fell, the benign-seeming snow would become a menace to those with no roof over their heads, freezing to death the vagrants sheltering in doorways. But for the moment, I wanted to enjoy the spectacle.

Slipping my way to the market, I found Syd's boys engaged in a furious snowball fight, Pedro among them. The snow-covered houses looked like iced cakes in the confectioner's window: each sugar-frosted rooftop and window ledge good enough to eat.

"Here, catch!" Nick cried as he sent a large ball in my direction. I parried it with the tube of paper I carried, then cursed, remembering the value of the contents.

"Not fair!" I called over. "I'm on an errand. I'll get you when I come back!"

Nick laughed and Pedro sent another snowball sailing toward me. I did not duck in time and it hit the side of my cheek, leaving icy water dripping down my neck.

"You wait!" I cried, but Pedro and Nick scampered away, turning their attention to other targets.

Once out of Covent Garden, my holiday mood faded. An uneasy feeling crept over me; I felt as if I was being followed. It may have just been a shadow in my imagination cast by the events of the previous night but I could not help but look over my shoulder several times. Everyone was muffled up against the cold. It was hard to tell if I was being shadowed. I thought I saw the same gray scarf twice, but when I looked again, it had gone. The posters offering a reward for information leading to the apprehension of Captain Sparkler flapped on the brick walls of many a street corner, as if trying to snag my attention. I saw one lying in the gutter, ripped in half. Someone had scrawled on it "Down with kings!" leading doubtless to its disposal in the sewer by an angry royalist. Was Johnny really in danger of being hanged, drawn, and quartered? This was a barbaric punishment not seen in our modern enlightened times, where the felon was cut down from the noose before he was dead and disemboweled before his own living eyes. They wouldn't do it now, surely? Not to Johnny! But then, I reminded myself with a shudder, you could still see the heads of the rebels of 1745 on the spikes at the entrance to London Bridge—stuck up there like black, boiled sweetmeats for the crows. We had entered a new and fearful age: the revolution in France had made the rich fear for themselves. As for the poor, some sought the rights granted to our French cousins; others, it must be admitted, did not want the Froggies to show us how to live. Which would win out? I wondered. The rights of man or John Bull? Since meeting Johnny, I had only just woken up to understand that the answer to this would decide my future too.

Beset by dark imaginings of Johnny passing through these same streets on his way to the scaffold, I was relieved when I finally reached Gerrard Street. Set in a well-to-do area, home to a mixture of comfortable lodging houses and shops, Gerrard Street did not let my grim fantasy survive long. It was the kind of place I would like to live in one day if I had enough money, a place where I need not fear dark alleyways and thugs like Billy Shepherd, where there would be neighbors and friends looking out for you. I found Mr. Humphrey's easily: it was marked by a gaggle of onlookers outside the window ogling the latest productions of the press on display. Sharp-nosed ladies jostled with fleshy-cheeked men, all craning their necks to be up to date with the latest political gossip without having to fork out any money to do so. A ragged boy slipped between their legs, no doubt relieving them of the coins they had been so reluctant to spend.

The bell clattered above the door as I entered.

"Is Mr. Humphrey here?" I enquired of a handsome woman with rosy cheeks behind the counter.

"My brother's out, I'm afraid, miss. Can I help?"

I hesitated. Johnny had told me to put his work into the hands of William Humphrey alone.

"Will he be long?"

She shook her head and pointed me to a high stool by the counter.

"No. If you'd like to wait, you may sit there."

I sat in my corner watching Miss Humphrey deal with the steady flow of customers. It soon became apparent she did more than just serve at the counter; she was well versed in all aspects of the business and had her own firm views on what to sell to her customers.

"No, you won't like those," she said confidently to one elderly gentleman in a clerical hat. "At least,

Mrs. Buchet will disapprove, if I know her. How about this new batch by Mr. Gillray?"

"Ah, Miss Humphrey, I swear you can read my mind sometimes," said the elderly gentleman, handing over some coins. "I'll tell my wife you recommended them."

The doorbell clanged again as he left, announcing a new customer.

"Can I help you, sir?" asked Miss Humphrey affably.

"Perhaps. I'm looking for the most recent cartoon by Captain Sparkler—the one with the chamber pot."

What terrible luck! It was Marzi-pain Marchmont, the boy who had been so eager to pry into Johnny's affairs. I hid the roll of paper in my skirts and kept my head down.

"Indeed I know it, sir. But unfortunately, we've sold out and are expecting a reprint. My brother should be back soon with the new stock. Would you care to wait? This young lady is already waiting for him. I'm sure he won't be long now."

Marchmont glanced carelessly in my direction, then, seeing who it was, he stopped and turned back.

"Miss Royal! Well, this is a most unexpected pleasure," he said with a smile of suppressed triumph. He gave a shallow bow. "Quite a coincidence."

I rose to curtsy and the roll of paper clattered to the floor. I bent to pick it up but he was quicker.

"Allow me," he said, scooping it from the floor. He held it out to me. "A little something of your own or by your *friend*, I wonder?"

I took it back and shoved it out of sight.

"It's nothing," I said quickly.

"I very much doubt that," he said, meeting my eyes. His gaze was unnerving: he seemed to be staring straight through me, trying to extract the truth like a surgeon removing a gallstone. I shivered.

"So, what brings you here?" I asked to change the subject.

"I live near here—just a few doors away." I quickly abandoned my wish to live in Gerrard Street. "And you?"

Damn! He'd turned the tables again.

"I'm on an errand. For Mr. Kemble."

Miss Humphrey had innocently been listening in on our conversation.

"You're from Drury Lane, my dear? Would you mind very much taking something back for me? I've got a parcel here for the theater." She reached under the counter and pulled out a small package. I could see even upside down that it was addressed to Jonathan Smith, Esq. My hand shot out to relieve her of it before Marchmont could note it, and I tucked it away in my apron pocket.

"Of course," I said. "On second thought, I'd better run. Can you see your brother gets this?" I handed over the rolled cartoon. It seemed better to flee before Mr. Humphrey returned in case anything more incriminating was said in Marchmont's hearing.

"That I will," she said, smiling at us both. "Take care now: it's getting dark."

Marchmont and I both turned to look out of the window: indeed, it was already very gray and some of the houses had candles in their windows, making the twilight seem even gloomier by contrast.

"Miss Royal, I cannot allow you to cross half of London unescorted at this time of day. Allow me to accompany you. I'll get our man, James, to come with us. He's waiting just outside."

"Now, isn't that handsome of the young gentleman!" said Miss Humphrey, beaming at him.

"No, really, Mr. Marchmont. That's quite un-necessary," I began.

"No, no, I insist." He took my arm and propelled me to the door. "I think it is time we had a few words in private," he said in a lower tone.

James, a burly footman armed with a stout cudgel, was indeed waiting for his master outside.

"James, change of plan," said Marchmont briskly. "We're to walk this young lady back to Drury Lane."

"Right you are, sir," said the footman, not showing much interest in me or the destination. It seemed that he was used to his master's brusque ways.

"Now, Miss Royal, about those drawings," said Marchmont as we dodged our way across St. Martin's Lane, his arm firmly clamped on mine. "You do know that there is a reward promised for information leading to the capture of Captain Sparkler?"

"Really?" I said in what I hoped was an unruffled tone.

"A girl like you could do with a few guineas, I dare say."

I said nothing. He knew nothing about girls like me.

"In my opinion, it's not the reward that should tempt a person, it's the satisfaction of putting out of business one of the most wicked traitors this country has ever known."

"You won't do that by buying his cartoons," I replied, hopping over a pile of manure that I noted with pleasure Marchmont was too preoccupied to avoid.

"Dammit!" he cursed on noticing. "That purchase was research. I have a theory, but I needed a specimen of the man's work. I wouldn't touch the stuff otherwise, believe me. I'd also like another look at your manuscript, if you would be so obliging."

I knew what he suspected but he had also revealed that he didn't have the proof. No way was I going to give it to him. I said nothing.

"Miss Royal, you are no fool. You know why I'm so interested in your circle. If one of your fellows, some self-taught scribbler with pretensions to higher things, has taken it into his head to insult his betters in this low fashion, it's your duty to stop it going any further. We're living in dangerous times. Just look at France!" Marchmont's eyes were blazing with a mad enthusiasm; he thumped his fist in his other hand to give emphasis to his words. "Heads will roll if this is not stopped!"

"And what about the Englishman's right to free speech?" I asked, growing more and more alarmed at the boy's high-handed tone toward me. Who was he to talk about my friends and me in this style? He had worked himself up so much that he was scaring me with his passion on the subject. I was rather glad to have the neutral presence of James within call.

"Free speech? Pah! Englishmen who attack the very institutions that give us our freedom resign their right to claim this."

"Your father doesn't think this—or so Lord Francis said," I hurriedly covered my mistake, remembering I should claim no acquaintance with that gentleman.

"My father! I despise him." He must have seen my shocked expression—I'd never heard a son speak so ill of his father before. "I assure you the feeling is mutual. All my father cares about is his own political advancement. He sees Captain Sparkler as serving his cause."

"And you? What's your cause?"

We were approaching the market, and I was beginning to feel safer now that we were on my home turf.

"I'm amazed you have to ask, Miss Royal. King and country, of course!"

"And nothing to do with spiting your father?"

He bent toward me. "Once someone can prove where Captain Sparkler is skulking," he hissed, "expect a visit from the magistrate. It's not far from there to the lockup in Bow Street— but someone may find that that short walk is his last. And as for those protecting him, they should also expect to feel the heavy displeasure of the law."

He was right. I hadn't thought about the penalty that would be incurred by those of us who knew who Johnny really was if we were caught hiding him. Not that this changed anything of course—I knew where my loyalties lay.

"I'll bear that in mind," I said lightly.

Flump! A snowball sailed out of the twilight and hit Marchmont on the side of the face.

"What the devil!" he exclaimed.

"Come on, Cat, come and get me!" jeered Pedro. A snowball flew in my direction, but I ducked in time and it hit James squarely in the chest.

"The little beggar!" laughed James, stooping to grab a handful of snow to retaliate.

Another snowball hit Marchmont, this time full in the face so that his flat nose and watery eyes were crusted with ice. He looked at me furiously for an explanation.

I shrugged. "Just some friends, sir, having fun, if you know what that is." I dodged behind James, leaving the big footman open to two more hits. James was laughing uproariously, sending back missiles with great gusto. I aimed carefully at Pedro as he poked his head out from behind a grocer's stall and scored a hit with my first attempt. It was then that I noticed the sooty figure beside him who seemed to be sending all his throws in the direction of Marchmont. I hit Lord Francis with my second attempt.

All this while, Marchmont had been standing paralyzed with cold fury, not heeding the many snowballs that had splattered upon him.

"James, stop that!" he barked.

"Right, sir," said James, sneaking a final throw at Nick when his master's back was turned. The footman gave me a wink, but his face immediately became impassive when Marchmont next faced us.

"I bid you good night, Miss Royal," Marchmont sneered. "As you are among *friends*, I need take no further concern for your safety."

"You are very kind, sir," I said politely, though we both knew I meant exactly the opposite. He was not kind: he was insufferably interfering, bent only on bringing destruction upon one of his fellow men. I bobbed a curtsy and ran over to Syd's gang, arms held up to ward off the snowballs they were most ungallantly sending in my direction now that I had emerged from the protection of James.

"Enough!" I shouted. "Unfair!" I reached Pedro, scooped up the remnants of the last snowball to hit me, and stuffed it down the back of his neck. Pedro gave a squeal.

"Now who's unfair?" he protested.

"Do you think he recognized me?" asked Lord Francis as he watched Marchmont's small upright figure fast disappearing westward.

"Not a chance," I assured him. "Good shot!"

He grinned. "He deserved every one of them, believe me. By the by, what were you doing with him? I didn't think you two were friends."

"We're not," I said shortly.

My mind was racing as I spoke. There were too many enemies lined up to get Johnny. First, there was his father trying to find him; second, the government men were after Captain Sparkler; third, Marchmont was pursuing him because of some personal grudge to do with revenge on his father. And from the evidence of Johnny's new cartoon, he was far from being a friend to his own cause, as he seemed intent on seeking martyrdom by angering yet more people, including his current protector, almost as if he no longer cared for his own safety. He was like a man sawing off the very branch he was sitting on. Well, if Johnny had become careless about his fate, then I had to help him, but I couldn't do it on my own. I felt pretty sure of Lord Francis and Lady Elizabeth. The only problem was Pedro. Was he trustworthy or would the lure of the reward prove too much? It was best if he was left out of this.

"Lord Francis . . . ?" I began.

"Frank—it's Frank, Cat."

"Frank, would you and your sister spare me a few minutes? There's something I need your help with."

Lord Francis looked surprised. "But I already told you my father's interested in supporting your work."

"It's not that," I said, blushing that he had immediately leaped to the conclusion that I was after a handout. "No, it's about your sister's friend. It's urgent. He's in danger."

I saw that Lord Francis understood what I meant. But Pedro was naturally intrigued.

"What's going on, Cat? Which friend's this?" he asked scanning our faces.

Lord Francis did not enlighten him. "You'd better come home with me now, Cat. Our father will be out and Mother's still in the country. I should be able to smuggle you in unobserved."

"Thank you. Pedro, could you let Johnny know I delivered his parcel safely for him?"

"Absolutely not, Cat. I'm coming with you. You can't wander the streets on your own when it's getting dark," said Pedro firmly.

"I'm not on my own; I'm with Frank."

"And what good will he be in a scrape? You need someone who knows their way around." Pedro looked at me with a glint of anger in his eyes at my rebuff. I could tell that the bad feelings between us aroused by our recent confrontation in Mr. Sheridan's office were rearing their ugly head again.

"No, I don't need your help, Pedro," I repeated.

"But Cat, Pedro's right: a young lady should not wander the streets on her own, and you will need someone to escort you home," said Lord Francis, oblivious to the undercurrents passing between Pedro and me.

This was all going wrong. The last thing I wanted was for Pedro to hear about Johnny's real identity. They were both as bad as Marchmont, using the excuse of my sex to force unwanted company on me. "I'm not a parcel to be handed between you," I protested.

"Typical Cat! Too proud for her own good," said Pedro as if I wasn't there. "Of course I have to come; she knows it really."

"Good," said Lord Francis, "because I won't be able to slip out again to bring her home."

"Will you two stop it!" I snapped at them, stamping my foot in anger. "I was finding my way around London on my own before you" (I turned to the duke's son) "were breeched and when you" (I glared at Pedro) "were still baking under your hot African sun. I can look after myself."

Pedro and Lord Francis smiled in understanding at each other, driving me further into a fury.

"Stop treating me like an empty-headed fool! I can decide what's best myself!"

"Well, Cat, let us say that I have invited Pedro as my guest. If you still want to come, you will just have to put up with his company," said Lord Francis, with a wink at Pedro.

I was now sorely tempted to give up the whole idea of appealing to Lord Francis and Lady Elizabeth for help. Perhaps I should just go back to the theater and tell Johnny to make a run for it. But what was he to do for money to fund his escape? On balance, I realized that I trusted Johnny less to look after himself than I mistrusted Pedro.

"I still wish to come," I replied sullenly.

"In that case, you won't object if I ask you to accompany my friend back to the theater then, Cat?"

I shook my head. Having lost the more important battle of keeping Pedro out of the secret, I was not going to kick up a fuss about the journey home.

"Shall we go?" The chimney sweep lord offered me his arm, and we headed west for Grosvenor Square.

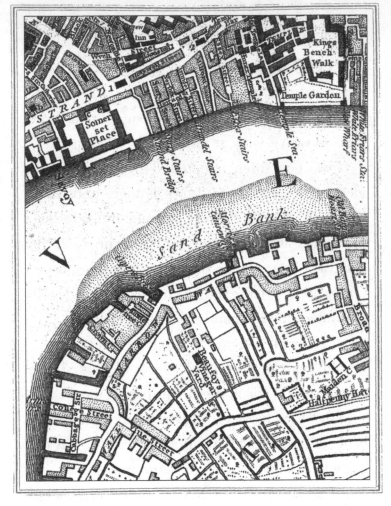

Act IV - In which Pedro is shown the ropes and reveals where his loyalties lie...

ACT IV

SCENE 1—FRIENDS

The back entrance to the Duke of Avon's London residence smelled heavily of horse. The stables in the mews were close, and from the slushy trails in the snow, it appeared that the horses were frequently employed.

"Wait a moment," said Lord Francis, disappearing into a stall. "I'll just get changed."

Pedro and I shivered by the pump in the backyard, trying to look inconspicuous. Snow still fell. Pedro's short black hair was frosted with flakes. He looked more than ever like an exotic bird out of place in cold, wintry London. He noticed me looking.

"What's the matter?" he asked. "Why are you staring at me like that?"

"I was just thinking how strange it is that you're here."

"I wasn't going to let you come on your own."

"No, not here here, I mean here in London."

He shrugged. "Is it that strange? All sorts of queer folk wash up here. London sucks us in and spits us out to sink or swim as we can."

It was time to test him out, before Lord Francis came back.

"You know what we said about the diamond?"

Pedro suddenly looked shifty. His eyes left my face to gaze at the icy pump handle. "What about it?"

"I understand you need money, Pedro, but you'd not do anything to get it, would you? There are some things you wouldn't do?"

"Many things. What do you take me for, Cat?"

"You wouldn't send a man to his death, would you?" I asked.

"Not unless he deserved it. What's this to do with the diamond?"

"Nothing. It's just that there's something other than a diamond hidden in Drury Lane at the moment."

Lord Francis reappeared from the stable dressed in his usual smart clothes, though his face and hands were still an unlordly sooty shade. He flipped a coin to the stable boy, who followed with his old garments.

"Put them away for me, Jenkins," he said.

"Right you are, sir," said Jenkins with a toothy grin.

"And now, the final step in my transformation!" Then, despite the freezing conditions, Lord Francis put his head under the spout, pumped the handle twice, and gave himself a hurried wash. He emerged dripping but returned to his normal color. "Let's get in before I catch my death of cold," he panted.

We slid our way over the cobbles to the rear entrance. Lord Francis held us back just as we reached the step. "Now understand, most of the servants can be trusted, but watch out for the French cook and my tutor. Both would see me beaten severely for being out without permission. I have to time my excursions for when they are otherwise engaged."

We nodded and crept in after him. To our right, in what I presumed was the kitchen, I could hear the sound of clattering pans and swearing.

"*Mon dieu!* Zat sauce iz not fit for a *cochon*, a pig!"

There was a loud slap and then a cry from an unfortunate maid.

"Good!" said Lord Francis in a whisper. "Monsieur Lavoisière is too busy with dinner to notice us."

Barely had he said these fateful words than an apparition in a white floppy hat and apron burst from the door on our right. With well-honed reactions, Lord Francis hauled Pedro and me into a room off the corridor on the left. From the rows of copper pans gleaming on the walls, I guessed we were in the scullery. For the first time since I had met him, Lord Francis looked scared. Heavy footsteps approached. I shrank behind a large washtub; Pedro and Lord Francis took refuge behind the door.

"Where iz zat blancmange?" shrieked the cook. "If you 'ave not finished it, Pierre, I will 'ave your guts for my garters!"

"Here it is, sir!" said another voice outside, speaking with the military precision of a lieutenant reporting to his commanding officer. Pierre appeared to be rather more fortunate than the maid: his dessert passed muster and, with only a few grumbles, Monsieur Lavoisière retreated into his den.

"Quick!" said Lord Francis. "Let's get out of here."

As quietly as we could, we ran down the corridor, mounted a flight of stone steps, and pushed through a green baize door into the hall. Once on the marble paving, Lord Francis heaved a sigh of relief.

"Safe!" he exclaimed. "Let's find Lizzie." He charged up the stairs shouting for his sister. The footman who had opened the door to us on our first visit intercepted him on the landing.

"I think you will find Lady Elizabeth in the library, sir," he said. "And Mr. Herbert said to tell you that he wanted to see you on your return."

Lord Francis grimaced. "I've not come in yet, Joseph."

"Indeed you haven't, sir. But when you do decide to come in, can I take it that my message will be delivered promptly?"

"As soon as I set foot across the threshold," he confirmed with a conspiratorial wink.

"Very good, sir."

The footman clearly had a healthy loyalty to his young master.

"Mr. Herbert is your tutor?" I asked.

Lord Francis nodded. "I've been trying to stave off going to boarding school. Mama's on my side but I rather think my days at home are numbered. Shame, just when I was beginning really to enjoy myself!" He looked at Pedro regretfully. His expeditions on the streets had evidently made a deep impression. "But I'm determined not to go until I've got your friend Syd to teach me a few moves. Should put me in good stead at school. Scare off the bullies."

"There are bullies even in schools for your sort?" I asked. I had thought that these were only to be found on the streets where my kind lived. Surely rich children were too refined for bullying? Didn't they spend all day speaking to each other in Latin and dining off china plates?

"You'd better believe it!" said Lord Francis. "Schools are a breeding ground for bullies. I could tell you a few tales of my father's old school that would make your hair curl. Not that either of you need it," he joked. "Here, Cat, what happened to you?" He'd noticed that one of my locks was missing.

"Nothing," I said quickly, feeling sick again at the reminder of my brush with Billy. I put my hand up to my forehead defensively, but that only revealed my cut arm.

Pedro had also noticed. "There's something you're not telling us, isn't there, Cat?" he asked astutely. "You've not been yourself today. You seem . . . you seem frightened."

"Is that you, Frank?" Lady Elizabeth stepped out onto the landing, a book held in one hand, her finger marking the page. "I thought I heard voices." Her face broke into a smile when she saw us all standing there. "Oh, I'm so pleased! You've brought me some visitors. Quick! In here. Mr. Herbert's on the warpath, but he'll never think to look for you in the library."

"Course not! What would I be doing in there? It's only bluestockings like you that find this a congenial place to sit before dinner," said Lord Francis.

Lady Elizabeth ushered us into the most beautiful room I had ever seen. Two high windows on one wall looked out on the darkening square. Candles flickered on the many small tables set between comfortable armchairs and sofas. A large desk, with silver inkpot, blotter, a fresh supply of paper, and wax, waited invitingly on the far side of the hearth. How I would have loved to sit at it and write! But the most impressive things about the room were the shelves upon shelves of books, all neatly arranged and lavishly bound. One could have been set loose in here and not need to emerge for years, thanks to all the fascinating reading matter on hand. I envied Lord Francis and Lady Elizabeth this privilege above the many others they enjoyed.

"Now, what is this about?" asked Lady Elizabeth, inviting me to take a seat on the silk-covered sofa. I hesitated, worrying that my grubby skirt might stain it, and I sat down on a wooden stepladder instead.

"I'm not sure," said Lord Francis, taking a final listen on the landing before closing the door. "Cat needs to talk to us. It's about Lord Jonathan Fitzroy."

Lady Elizabeth's face went red.

"Lord Jonathan Fitzroy?" asked Pedro.

"Johnny," I explained reluctantly. "He's not what he seems."

"So I see," said Pedro slowly, digesting this latest news. "A lord? He's the most unlordly lord— with the possible exception of Frank here—that I've ever met."

"You don't know the half of it," I said. "But first you must promise me, all of you, that even if you decide you cannot help Johnny and me—Lord Jonathan, I mean—what I tell you will go no further than us four. You must promise not to betray him, even if this means passing up the opportunity to earn a lot of money." I looked directly at Pedro, who was slowly beginning to understand what I had been hinting at earlier.

"Of course I won't," he said indignantly.

Still far from certain that I could take him at his word, I knew I had to proceed if I were to get the help we so urgently needed.

"Johnny has another name—a name that you all have heard before. He's also Captain Sparkler."

I was watching Pedro closely as I spoke and thought I saw a strange gleam light up in his eye. This worried me: what was Pedro thinking? He now knew that Johnny belonged to the privileged classes—he might even be from one of the many families grown rich on sugar and tobacco at the expense of thousands of slaves' lives in the West Indies. Did this weaken any personal loyalty Pedro might feel toward him? Would the temptation to sell him out prove too strong? After all, no one had cared about the feelings of Pedro and his family when they were sold. Why should he care now?

The duke's children were easier to read. From the steady expression of Lady Elizabeth I could tell Johnny's identity did not come as a shock to her; to Lord Francis the news was almost welcome.

"Fancy that! Lord Jonathan Fitzroy turning out to be the captain! I never knew he was so clever—not just a stuffed shirt then, like most of Lizzie's suitors."

"Hush!" said Lady Elizabeth as Pedro now looked at her with renewed interest. I wondered with a sinking heart what scheme he was concocting with these pieces of private information.

"But I think your friend Marchmont suspects something," I continued, trying not to let Pedro distract me from my purpose. "Not about Lord Jonathan, of course, but he suspects that the captain is hidden in Drury Lane. The net is closing in. Johnny'll have to find somewhere else to stay."

"And you need our help to find him somewhere? What does Lord Jonathan think?" asked Lady Elizabeth.

I dropped my head and examined my grubby fingers. "I have to admit he doesn't know I'm asking you. I have only just found out about Marchmont."

"He'll be cross with you," said Lady Elizabeth. "He's very proud, you know."

"But it's too much for him to handle on his own," I replied. "He's taking too many risks. He doesn't see the danger—or doesn't care. And it's not just him, it's the diamond as well."

"Diamond? You mean there really is a diamond?" asked Lord Francis excitedly. "It's not just something you made up for your story?"

I nodded, my eyes again on Pedro, who was keeping suspiciously quiet. "It's quite possible that the Shepherd gang'll try to get it, and that puts Johnny in double danger."

"What's Johnny got to do with Billy Boil?" asked Pedro shrewdly. He seemed very interested to hear that Billy had got wind of the diamond.

I was trying to think up an explanation that avoided divulging the events of last night, but Lady Elizabeth was too quick.

"Lord Jonathan saved Cat from those ruffians," she replied, remembering the praise I had given her sweetheart.

"He did what?" exclaimed Lord Francis. "This gets better and better!"

I was now compelled to tell the whole story, but only after I had again sworn them to secrecy. A stunned silence followed my brief but brutal narrative.

"So it's not only Johnny in danger. You are too," said Lord Francis, looking at me with concern.

"Maybe," I said dismissively. "But Billy's not interested in me, he's interested in the diamond and Johnny's protecting it for Mr. Sheridan—perhaps in exchange for having a place to hide. I'm not sure."

"Hmm," said Lady Elizabeth. "There's something not quite right about this. Where would Mr. Sheridan get a diamond from and why hide it?"

"The second part's easy: he's probably hiding it from his creditors," said Lord Francis. "It's well known that it's only because he's a member of Parliament that he's not arrested for debt. If they got wind that he had some money for once, they'd be down on him like a pack of crows."

"And he's best mates with the Prince of Wales, isn't he?" asked Pedro. "If anyone is dripping diamonds in this country, it'll be royalty. Maybe it was a gift."

"Maybe," said Lady Elizabeth skeptically. "I just don't see it though."

"But the long and the short of it is that Johnny's in danger," I continued. "He's got to get out and the sooner the better. He'll need help to do so. He'll need you and—" I felt embarrassed to say it "—and your resources."

He would have to leave London—go abroad even—and I had no gold to buy him a ticket out of England. If his father had disowned him, he needed rich friends to help him—friends like the children of a duke, not a pauper like me.

"Of course," agreed Lord Francis, "but it won't be easy, even for us, Cat. My pocket money hardly stretches to a passage to a safe country."

"I suppose I could pawn some of my jewels," suggested Lady Elizabeth. "That is, if someone would take them to the broker for me. Papa would be furious if he found out I'd gone."

"You are an angel, sis," said Lord Francis. "I'll take them for you."

Pedro wrinkled his nose in disdain. "Not a good idea: any self-respecting pawnbroker would fleece you and send you packing with half their value. Let me do it."

"No, I'll take them. I've an idea where to go," I said quickly. Who knew where Pedro would be this time tomorrow if entrusted with a small fortune in jewels?

Pedro frowned but did not object.

"If Cat raises the money for us, I'll find out how to get safe passage out of the country," said Lord Francis.

"Good idea. Johnny must get away as soon as possible," I said. "They might come looking for him at any moment. And when he does leave, he may be recognized, so we should prepare a disguise for him."

"Leave that to me," volunteered Lady Elizabeth. "I'll think of something so that even his own mother won't recognize him."

The clock on the mantelpiece began to strike a melodious six. Two mechanical dancers emerged from a door set in the face, approached each other, and began to twirl around. I was just thinking how pretty it was when another thought came to me.

"Pedro, aren't you supposed to be doing the hornpipe tonight?"

He looked thunderstruck. It was not like him to let a professional commitment escape his attention. "You're right! We've got to run!"

"Wait. I'll get the jewels," said Lady Elizabeth. She disappeared upstairs and returned a few minutes later with a small package wrapped in a silk handkerchief, which she thrust into my hand. "Look after them, Cat, won't you? I would like to redeem them in time. Some of them are special to me."

We arrived back at Drury Lane at half past the hour. The play had already started, but Pedro was just in time for his musical interlude. He had barely ripped off his livery and donned his costume before he was summoned onstage. I could see Johnny looking mightily relieved as Pedro bounded onto the boards.

"Safely delivered?" Johnny asked me under his breath.

I nodded, but my eye was caught by Pedro dancing in the footlights. The cartoon might now be in safe hands but I realized that Pedro had been delivered onstage far from complete.

"Violin!" I hissed under my breath to Johnny. "Pedro's forgotten his violin!" After the first dance, he was supposed to do the same steps again while playing.

"Fetch it then!" whispered Johnny urgently. "I'll think of something."

I ran to the green room and found the violin. Grabbing it, I darted back toward the wings, dodging through the press of performers, accidentally treading on Miss Stageldoir's toes, and receiving a cuff to the back of my head in retaliation.

I arrived at Johnny's side to find he had thought of something, but it was a "something" that made my heart leap into my throat.

"Here!" he said. "Put these on." He thrust an old spangled Harlequin costume at me.

"No, you!" I hissed.

"Don't be funny! I'm supposed to be in hiding, remember? But you, you can run on, do a twirl or something, and give him the violin. The crowd will think it's all part of the act. They love a clown."

"You're joking," I said hollowly as he pulled the baggy costume over my head.

"I'm not. Go! You're on!"

With that, Johnny clapped a black beaked mask over my face and gave me a firm shove in the shoulder blades. I staggered onto the stage. Pedro had just come to the end of the first fast and furious rendition of the hornpipe and was taking a bow. He had not yet realized he was missing a vital ingredient for the next part of his act. A few people in the boxes began to titter, seeing a confused Harlequin dithering by the side of the stage. I had no choice now: I had to do something other than stand here like a fool. Clutching the violin and bow under one arm, I took a short run and turned my one-handed cartwheel. I'd never performed it before others and was gratified to find it brought a wave of applause from the audience. I landed neatly at Pedro's side and presented him with the violin. Pedro looked shocked for a brief second, then recovered himself. He began to mime, making it clear to the audience that I had brought a challenge to do the dance again while playing. I nodded vigorously.

"Go on, Prince!" shouted someone in the audience.

"You can do it!" called another.

Pedro gave me a deep bow, accepting the challenge. I was about to run off, but he gestured to me to sit on the anchor that dressed the stage. I was surprised: I had thought that Pedro Hawkins was only interested in having the stage to himself. As it would have looked strange if I had refused, I sat down. All these years of living in the theater, I'd never been on the boards with a full audience in front of me. I felt heady with excitement.

Pedro composed himself to play. Signor Angelini raised his baton and signaled for his protégé to start. Pedro then began the most extraordinary dance I had ever seen. With legs stamping as in an Irish jig, upper body still, he began to play a hornpipe. Sitting so close to him, I could see the beads of sweat flying from his brow, but all the time he kept an impassive expression on his face. From a distance, it would look as if he was having to make no effort. The audience began to clap in time to the music. He went faster and faster. I thought that it must be impossible for him to carry on playing without losing step or fluffing a note, but no. It was almost as if he had found freedom in the dance and would take flight if it did not end soon. I could see him do it: he'd fly out of the theater, out of the smoke of London, into the blue sky and home to his land of hot sun and friendly faces. But before his wings had a chance to sprout, he brought the hornpipe to an end with a flourish.

The applause was immense. It rolled toward the stage like a barrage of thunder. Pedro bowed three times, perspiration dripping off the end of his nose and falling onto the boards. He then turned to me.

"How about it, Cat? Run off with a cartwheel together?"

He was testing me, I thought, paying me back for my earlier doubts about him and seeing if I could repeat my performance. I nodded, accepting the challenge.

He took my hand. "Go!"

We ran toward the wings in step.

"Now!" he shouted, dropping my hand. With perfect timing, we cartwheeled off the stage, landing neatly by Johnny's seat.

"Well, well, well!" Johnny said, laughing as he slipped the mask off my face. "Who would've guessed you could do that? If you're not careful, Mr. Kemble will give you the part. Cat the clown. Has rather a ring to it, don't you think?"

Pedro slapped me on the back. "You saved my skin out there, Cat. I owe you one."

"Don't worry, I'm not likely to let you forget," I said with a wry smile.

SCENE 2—PAWNBROKER

Early the next morning, I slipped out of the theater and headed down toward the Strand and the pawnbroker's shop that many of the actors and musicians used. I'd been there before for Peter Dodsley, the first violin. When he had been going through a particularly lean patch, he had pawned his watch on a Saturday and redeemed it after being paid on a Monday. He'd explained at the time that as he spent most of Sunday resting in bed, he did not need to know the time, but he did need a few creature comforts, such as a bottle of fine French wine. I had always thought this a poor way of managing his money, but he was by no means the only one to use the services of the broker.

As I arrived outside the shop, who should come up behind me but Jonas Miller, the hog-grubber clerk who was more usually to be seen causing trouble in the pit.

"Out of my way, girl," he said rudely, pushing me aside. He was in a fearful hurry to get into the shop. I wondered why. I probably would have followed him in to find out even if I had not had an errand myself.

Pushing the door open, I entered the darkened room. It had the secretive atmosphere of a Catholic confessional: little cubicles separated the customers from each other so they could admit their monetary failings in privacy. Behind an iron grille, Mr. Vaughan and his assistants heard their clients' troubles and offered a temporary cure. The items put up for pawn were displayed in locked cases, tempting their owners with a knowing twinkle and glitter to claim them back—if they had the money, that is, and they rarely did. Among the snuffboxes and rings, I noticed with a shudder of disgust that someone had even pawned their porcelain false teeth: it was hard to imagine what depths of despair had pushed them to that extreme. The teeth grinned back at me from their red velvet cushion in a smile like the rictus of death.

"Ah, Mr. Miller, I have your silver inkstand waiting for you," said Mr. Vaughan loudly. Perhaps he had not noticed someone else coming in, for he was speaking more openly than usual. "Have you the money?"

"That's all I have." Jonas pushed a bag of coins over to him.

Mr. Vaughan pulled the bag under the grille and carefully counted out the silver and coppers. "Hmm, not enough, sir, not enough," he said with a regretful shake of his head.

Jonas ran his fingers through his dirty hair in desperation.

"Look, I've got to have it back. There'll be hell to pay if I don't. You see, it's . . . it's not exactly mine."

Mr. Vaughan frowned. "I don't deal in stolen goods, sir," he said sharply, hand hovering over a bell to summon his assistant.

"No, no, you misunderstand me," said Jonas. "It's borrowed . . . from a friend."

A friend? All my eye! That was nonsense. I recognized that inkwell: it was the one from

Jonas's desk in the lawyer's office where he worked. I'd seen it hundreds of times when I'd passed by his window. Jonas was now fingering his pocket watch nervously.

"Perhaps we could come to some arrangement, Mr. Vaughan," he pleaded, placing his watch on the counter.

I did not see the conclusion to this transaction, for Mr. Vaughan's assistant, a pale youth with a high forehead like the dome of St. Paul's, glided out of the back room.

"Yes, miss, can I help you?" he asked, spying me waiting on the hard bench.

Jonas turned around and his eyes widened with consternation. I could tell that the presence of someone who knew him was most unwelcome. Come to think of it, I'd prefer not to be seen by anyone I knew either. I hurried over to the vacant cubicle and pushed the package of jewels under the grille.

"How much can you offer me for these?" I asked in a low voice.

With a bored expression, the assistant unfolded the handkerchief. The boredom stopped there: on to the counter fell a jumble of glittering gemstones and gold chains. His eyes lit up.

"Are these real, miss?"

"Of course."

Giving me a skeptical look, he screwed a jeweler's eyeglass into his socket and began to examine each piece. One by one he gave a little nod and put the item reverently aside. Finally, he put down the eyeglass and gave me a searching stare as if willing me to reveal where I had come by such riches.

"Mr. Vaughan, Mr. Vaughan, I need your advice on something!" he called to his employer.

Mr. Vaughan was still arguing with Jonas Miller.

"A moment, sir," he told Jonas and moved across to the patch of grille in front of me.

"All real?" he asked his assistant.

"The genuine article, sir."

Mr. Vaughan pawed the jewels lovingly. I could see he hungered to have them in his possession, if only for a short time, but he was worried how I came by them.

"I'm here on behalf of a lady," I explained as he surveyed me. "I'm her confidential agent in this transaction."

"Hmm. I can offer you five pounds for them," he said.

As an opening bid it was laughable. We both knew it.

"Fifty," I said firmly.

He smiled. "What do you take me for, miss? A charity?"

"Then I'll take my jewels elsewhere."

"Thirty," he snapped.

"Forty-five."

"Forty."

"Done." Forty was not a bad amount. Far more than any of my friends could hope to earn in a year. But the sum was still far short of the true value of the jewels: if Lady Elizabeth failed to redeem them, Mr. Vaughan would make a handsome profit.

Mr. Vaughan drew out his cashbox and counted out a weighty sack of guineas. He pushed a paper receipt under the grille.

"Tell your 'lady' that she has six months to redeem them from me. After that time, I'm at liberty to sell them."

"I understand."

I pocketed the bag of gold and receipt and turned to go. Jonas Miller was standing at the door waiting for me.

"Here, Cat, lend us some of that, will you?" he asked, with what he evidently thought was an ingratiating smile on his face. "It's all up with me if you don't help."

I shook my head. "Sorry, it's not my money. I can't lend it to you."

His smile vanished. "They weren't your jewels neither, were they, Cat? Have you been a naughty girl?" He took a step toward me. "I'll wager that you wouldn't want someone to tell the Bow Street runners about that!"

"It's none of your business," I said angrily, pushing past him. "Just because you filch from your employer doesn't mean to say everyone else does."

I slammed the door behind me and ran as fast as I could back to the theater. Jonas's threats did not bother me—I knew he was a creeper and a cheat. Lady Elizabeth could be summoned in my defense if he did go blabbing, but if Jonas was going to make trouble with the magistrate's men, it made it more important than ever to get Johnny out of Drury Lane as quickly as possible.

"You did what?"

Johnny was pounding to and fro on the hearthrug, the bag of coins glittering on the table between us. Reader, as you may guess, it wasn't going well.

"I told you. I happened to mention to Lady Elizabeth that you needed help and—"

"Do you realize what you've done?" he cut across me. "You've humiliated me, Cat. You and your friends, acting as if you can snatch me from the frying pan, but instead you're just dropping me into the fire! Did it not occur to you that I might be quite capable of making my own arrangements? I've lost everything, choosing the path I've taken— my family, my rank, even the woman I love—but I thought I had my self-respect intact!"

He wasn't going to pull the wool over my eyes with this bluster; he needed our help.

"So, Johnny, what plans had you made?" I asked coolly.

"I was going to America," he said, stopping to slump dejectedly on the mantelpiece.

"With the diamond?" I asked.

He gave a bitter smile. "That's the plan."

"And how were you to afford it? Unless Mr. Sheridan cashes in this diamond—which I doubt he'd do even for you—you'll need money for your ticket. He doesn't have any, from what I've heard."

"No," conceded Johnny, "Sheridan is short on ready money, that's true."

"And you, do you have any?"

"Only several hundred thousands—but all in my father's pocket, I'm afraid." He sighed. "I thought perhaps Marchmont might help."

"You're all abroad there, Johnny; he won't. I know their sort: penny-pinching lice hunters who wouldn't cross the road to help their grandmother. They're only happy so long as they stand to gain themselves."

"You're probably right, Cat." Johnny looked defeated, depressed by the weight of anxiety that had descended on him since he was first charged with treason. He was just beginning to find out what most of us already knew: what it was like to have no money.

"So," I said, gesturing to the guineas I had brought back with me, "why not take this?"

"Because it's hers, of course!" I must have looked puzzled, for he continued, "You're too young to understand, Cat, about . . . about love. How could I look her in the face again if I take advantage of her in this way?"

I couldn't believe the man: he was being a downright fool, too scrupulous for his own good.

"Believe me, she'd prefer to look you in the face as you wave good-bye from the deck of a ship, holding a ticket that she's paid for, than watch you go blue in the face as the noose tightens. When you die of a hempen fever, it'll be no comfort to her then to know that you owe her nothing."

He shook his head, still unconvinced. Though many years my senior, he was no better than an infant, completely oblivious to the hard truth of his situation. He made me feel so much older and wiser than him. He couldn't afford to indulge his romantic notions of honor and pride. If he did, he'd die. I tried another tack.

"You know, Johnny, I think it's you who doesn't understand love. Love is not forced; it gives without expecting anything in return. It drops like the gentle rain from heaven—"

"Upon the place beneath," said Johnny, finishing the quotation I had adapted for the occasion. "I know, I know."

"So why can't you allow her to give you this? You're denying her the right to put her love into action if you spurn it."

"But—"

"I'm certain you'd give everything in your power to help someone you love. You're not treating her as your equal if you reject her assistance."

I had finally found an argument that hit home.

"My equal?" he said.

"Yes, your equal. You mustn't treat her like some china doll that you admire but are afraid to allow off the shelf. She's a sensible person: she knows what she's doing. Anyway, it's too late: I've pawned the jewels and Lord Francis is sorting out your passage. You're outvoted on this, four to one."

Johnny laughed. "I regret I taught you about democracy, Cat. It's come back to haunt me."

"You won't regret it when you reach New York. Have you thought what you might do when you get there?"

Johnny sat down beside me, signaling that he had given in to the inevitable and would let us help him.

"I thought I'd start a community, a place where men and women can live together, dividing their time between honest physical labor and intellectual pursuits—an ideal republic."

"It sounds a load of moonshine to me. What do you know about hard work? Do you know how long it takes to scrub a floor or clean a shirt, let alone plow a field?"

Johnny looked awkward: he knew he was on dubious ground when he, the nobleman, talked to me, the commoner, about the simple life. "No, but I can dream."

"Carry on dreaming," I said briskly. Clearly, someone had to look after him, or he was heading for a fall. "But in the meantime why don't you plan for something more substantial than that? Do something you know you know well, like drawing, for example. There must be opportunities for an artist like you even in so uncivilized a place as America."

"Well, I do have a contact who has set up a newspaper in Philadelphia." He laughed. "Listen to me. Taking career advice from a—how old are you?"

I shrugged. "I don't know."

"From a young lady then," he said with a wink, pocketing the guineas.

That afternoon Mrs. Reid sent me to dust the offices. I had just finished Mr. Kemble's and had made a start on Mr. Sheridan's when the owner came in with a gentleman I did not recognize. They did not see me, for I was crouched behind the desk—if the truth be known, wondering if I could find the infamous diamond and take a peek at it before it went to America with Johnny. From Mr.

Sheridan's tone, I could tell that he was trying to get his companion away from the theater as quickly as possible.

"Look, Ranworth, why not come to the club and talk about it?"

Ranworth? I peered over the desk and saw the back of a portly, white-haired gentleman dressed in a claret-colored jacket and shiny black boots. That must be Johnny's father. Thank goodness Johnny was locked in his room for the afternoon checking over the proofs of his latest cartoon. He had better stay there. Someone had to warn him. But the men were standing between me and the door.

"Is there really no news of my son?" said the Earl of Ranworth, refusing to budge. I had the impression Mr. Sheridan had been avoiding answering his questions, and so the earl had come to the theater to corner him. "I'm ashamed of the pup, I admit, but I do have the feelings of the father. I would like to know that he is alive and well. These wanted posters everywhere make my blood run cold! Just imagine what a scandal there'd be if they knew who Captain Sparkler really was!"

"Quite so," said Mr. Sheridan, patting the old man's arm. "But they won't find out, will they? Who would suspect such a thing? I'm sure the young rascal has come to no harm."

"And Salter, you say, has drawn a blank in Bristol?"

"Completely. I've asked him to enquire at Plymouth and Portsmouth. I expect news very soon."

So Mr. Salter was safe and still on his wild goose chase, I noted.

The Earl of Ranworth took a handkerchief from his pocket and mopped his brow. With the weary movements of a man exhausted by worry, he slumped into the chair facing the desk. Seeing there was no shifting the man, Mr. Sheridan came to the far side to take a seat.

He stopped, finding me at his feet. "Cat! What on earth are you doing here?"

The earl jumped up from his seat, a look of consternation on his face.

"Dusting, sir," I said, holding up my cloth as evidence.

"Hmm," Mr. Sheridan said skeptically. "You always seem to be cropping up in the most inconvenient places, don't you?"

There was a bold knock on the open door. We all looked around. In the corridor stood a man wearing a blue coat with brass buttons and a leather hat, armed with a cutlass, pistol, and truncheon: unmistakably a Bow Street runner.

"Sorry to trouble you, sir," he said deferentially to Mr. Sheridan, "but I'm following up a report that there may be a wanted man on the premises."

The Earl of Ranworth looked up abruptly and gave Mr. Sheridan an astonished stare. He was no fool. At least for him, the penny seemed to have dropped. Mr. Sheridan gave him a quelling look.

"Indeed, Constable . . . ?" Mr. Sheridan said lightly.

"Lennox, sir."

"Constable Lennox. And what is this to me?"

"Well, sir," said the runner awkwardly, "the old man on the door said I had to ask your permission before I can carry out a thorough search."

"You have no warrant from the magistrate then?"

"No." The runner coughed. "I, er, I thought the report, an anonymous letter, was not sufficient grounds to disturb him."

I bet the letter came from the greasy paw of Marzi-pain Marchmont! I called him as many colorful names as I could think of under my breath.

Mr. Sheridan strode across the room. "But you thought it grounds enough to make havoc in my theater?"

"I intended nothing of the sort, sir! I—"

"You are already interrupting the work of my maid here. Run along, Cat; I'm sure there is something *very important* you should be doing." Mr. Sheridan shooed me out the door. As he knew I would, I sprinted as fast as I could to Johnny's office. Ignoring the sign, I burst in upon him, the surprise making him spill ink across the picture he was working on.

"For heaven's sake, Cat, look what you've done!" he exclaimed in exasperation.

"Forget that!" I said, stuffing a cap on his head and hauling him from the table. "A constable's here—so's your father."

"My father brought the runners for me?" he said incredulously, getting quite the wrong end of the stick.

"No, you fool, they came separately. But you'd better run for it."

Johnny made a grab for his drawing things.

"Leave them—I'll deal with that. You can't get caught with these on you."

"Where can I go?" he asked wildly, pulling his jacket on.

"Go to the butcher's in Bow Street. Ask for Syd. Tell him you're my friend. I'll send a message when it's all clear."

"Bow Street? But that's nearer danger!"

"Exactly—the last place they'll look for you. Now hurry!" I pushed Johnny out of the door and watched him bolt off down the corridor, colliding with Mr. Bishop halfway.

"What's got into him?" Mr. Bishop asked me in confusion.

"Urgent errand. Uncle on the point of death, asking for him," I invented.

Mr. Bishop shook his head sadly. "Reminds me of my old girl. Didn't get there in time, but she was asking for me after the baby was born. Never did see the child. . . ."

"Sorry, Mr. Bishop," I interrupted him, not having time for family reminiscences, "I've got to tidy up in here for Johnny."

"That's right, Cat, you do what you can to make him comfortable." With that, Mr. Bishop plodded away, his mind fortunately on the wife he had lost many years ago rather than on the strange behavior of the prompt.

I shut the door and began to sweep away the evidence of Johnny's employment. Roughs of his cartoons littered the floor, and I threw them higgledy-piggledy into the grate. Voices could be heard in the corridor outside.

"Why here first, constable? What's my prompter to do with this business?"

"Nothing, I hope, sir. It's just that my informant said he'd been here himself and suggested I start with Mr. Smith."

They were upon me. I grabbed the proof Johnny had been working on and stuffed it into my bodice. The door opened.

"What are you doing here, girl?" asked the runner suspiciously when he saw me kneeling by the burning grate.

I got up. "Just laying the fire, sir," I said, bobbing a curtsy.

"As I told you," said Mr. Sheridan coldly, "my staff have their jobs to do."

The runner, however, was no half-wit. He strode over to the fire and pulled out a singed piece of paper. Faintly, you could make out the bulbous nose of a cartoon head.

"And what's this?" he said severely to me. "Why were you lighting the fire with this, girl? Has someone been drawing?"

"Yes, sir," I answered nervously, twisting my apron in my hands. I could see Mr. Sheridan waving urgently behind the runner's back to stop me saying any more, but I knew what I was doing. "I'm afraid it's me, sir. I've been taking drawing lessons, you see, sir, b-but I'm not very good yet and—"

He cut through my stammered explanation with a flick of the paper. "Drawing lessons? What's a maid doing taking drawing lessons?" he exclaimed.

I turned to Mr. Sheridan. Now was the time for me to rival Mrs. Siddons with my acting ability. I had to be convincingly abject with my apology.

"I'm so sorry, sir," I said, wiping the corner of my eye with my apron. "I've been sneaking in here to practice." From my workbox over at the foot of Johnny's bed, I pulled out the drawing of Caesar I had done and held it up as proof. "Mr. Smith's half-blind, as you know, so he can't see what I'm up to. You can dock the cost of the paper from my wages, sir, if you like, but, please, please, don't turn me away for it."

Wages? Wages would be a fine thing! I never got anything but board and lodging. Mr. Sheridan eyed me closely. I could see laughter twinkling in his eyes but he was managing to look suitably stern.

"And who is this meant to be, young woman?" he asked.

"A portrait of Julius Caesar, sir." Sniff, artful wipe of the eye with my apron. "I made a mess of the nose."

"There, Constable Lennox—hardly topical political satire," said Mr. Sheridan, rounding on the runner. "Had you better not move on and look for someone whose targets are a little more up to date, by about eighteen hundred years?" Mr. Sheridan rolled up my picture and tucked it in his pocket.

"Right you are, sir," said the runner sheepishly. He could at least regain some dignity by turning on the only victim present. "As for you, miss, you keep your hands off your master's things or I'll be having words with you down at the courthouse."

I bent my head, trying to look suitably cowed.

"That's enough, man. I'll deal with my own staff, thank you," said Mr. Sheridan sharply.

He led the constable out of the room, but the Earl of Ranworth lingered. He was staring at some papers covered in Johnny's handwriting that I had not had time to burn. He gave the desk a caress with his fingertips, then came over to me.

"Thank you, my dear," he said hoarsely. "You did well." He pressed a sovereign into my hand. "And when you see my son, tell him . . . tell him the old man misses him, won't you?"

SCENE 3—ATTACK

Johnny crept back in after darkness fell and hid himself away in his office. I found him sitting on his bed, his belongings rolled up into a small bundle at his feet, all traces of his work obliterated.

"Here, I managed to save this," I said, producing the proof from my bodice.

Johnny did not even look at it but got to his feet and threw it into the glowing heart of the fire. The paper caught flame and began to curl up, writhing like a spirit in torment as the black touch of fire consumed it.

"Enough," Johnny said grimly. "Captain Sparkler is dead. Johnny Smith is bound for pastures new."

"You're really going then?" I asked, sitting in the place he had vacated. I stared down at the meager bundle—not much to show for an earl's son. "But I thought that . . . well, it seemed to me that your father was ready to have you back. He was sad. He misses you."

Johnny sighed. "And I miss him. But he has agreed with Sheridan that the best thing now is for me to go abroad for a few years, until this Captain Sparkler business dies down. He thinks the passage of time will mellow my firebrand views." Johnny gave a bark of laughter. "He thinks I'll be ready then to take up my duties and responsibilities."

"So you intend to go to America at once?"

"If I can arrange safe passage."

"Perhaps Lord Francis will have found out something useful," I said, half-hoping for a reprieve to give Johnny time to change his mind. He sounded as if he could be convinced. Though I sympathized with his principles, it still seemed madness to me for him to turn his back on the life of luxury that was his if he remained and accepted his birthright. I wasn't sure that I'd stand firm if I was facing such a choice.

"But what can Lord Francis do?" asked Johnny. He was obviously inclined to look on the gloomy side of everything tonight.

"You'd be surprised. Lord Francis knows far more about London than you'd expect, thanks to the peculiar education he has been receiving of late."

That raised a halfhearted smile. "So it would seem, Cat. You've led him far astray from the usual path of duke's sons. I doubt his father would approve if he knew, but I think it a very good thing." Johnny dug into his breast pocket and took out the money I had given him earlier. "Here, take this back. I won't be needing it. Tell her that I send my heartfelt thanks, but the Ranworth estate is covering the costs of my removal from these shores."

I took it. "Just that?" The message didn't live up to my expectations as to what was fitting between two lovers about to say farewell to each other for many years. That certainly wasn't how it was done on the stage. Clearly, Johnny needed a bit of tutoring in the sweetheart department.

"What more is there to say?"

"Shouldn't you at least ask her to wait for you? Tell her you'll gaze upon her picture every day at a certain hour so that she can do the same? Send her a token, a lock of hair perhaps, for her to wear in a locket over her heart? Assure her of your unchanging love?"

He shook his head sadly. "One of the things you'll learn as you get older is that we all change, Cat. I wouldn't ask a girl of sixteen to wait for me: it would not be fair. Who knows what we both might be feeling and thinking in a few years' time? What kind of home could I offer her?"

He was a hopeless pupil for Cupid. His spirits were too low to rise to the occasion. I couldn't blame him: he was leaving all the people he loved, setting off to live among strangers, abandoning the old certainties of his life. Added to that, he would be facing the novelty of earning his own keep for the first time. I imagined that, for all his radical, equalizing notions, this must be a fairly terrifying prospect for a gentleman raised in privilege. It was one thing to preach, another to practice. Mind you, he had a head start on most of us if only he knew it.

"You shouldn't worry too much, Johnny. You'll get on famously once you make a beginning. You possess an extraordinary talent. I'm sure you'll be able to offer Lady Elizabeth a good home when you've made a name for yourself over there." I thought he still stood in need of a little more worldly advice, so I lowered my voice. "And you know you could always pawn the diamond if things get tight. Mr. Sheridan will never know. It could set you up in your own business until you earn enough to redeem it."

"That would be more difficult than you suppose." He walked over to his desk and got out the two pistols to add to his bundle.

"Why? If Mr. Sheridan wants it back, it'll take months for the message to reach you in America. You'll have plenty of time. It wouldn't be like stealing."

That made him laugh. "No, that's not what I mean. The diamond isn't the kind of thing you can pawn." He picked up some pens, checking the nibs before slipping them inside his jacket pocket.

"Why not?"

"Well, because it's not exactly a diamond."

What did he mean? I could tell from the way he was behaving he was concealing something from me. My gaze was drawn to the pen he was examining; it glittered like a jewel in his fingers . . . Then it hit me. I had been a fool. Of course! Johnny was Captain Sparkler. *He* was the hidden jewel!

"*You're* the diamond, aren't you, Johnny? There never was a real one, when Mr. Sheridan was talking about you to Marchmont—that was the night you arrived." I shook my head in disbelief—it had taken me so long to see what appeared so obvious now. It was my imagination that had created the jewel—a fantasy that Mr. Sheridan had thought useful to continue in order to divert me from the real treasure.

Johnny sat down on the bed beside me and took my hand. "I wondered when you would guess, Catkin. There have been many times when I wanted to tell you. I realized that you needed to know the truth when it got you into trouble with the Shepherd gang, but it seemed hard to undo the lie once it had got lodged in your head."

"I've been so blind."

"Don't blame yourself. We encouraged it—Sheridan and I. We didn't know if we could trust you at first. And the price of our lack of trust in you was an injury to your arm and a very frightening night in the Rookeries. At least when I'm gone, you'll no longer be bothered by my enemies."

"But I don't want you to go, Johnny," I blurted out. "I'd prefer to spend my life defending you against all those who are after you than never see you again! Stay here. I'll look after you."

He ruffled my hair affectionately. "In your heart of hearts, you know you can't do that, Catkin. You can't keep me safe, even in Drury Lane. Anyway, I'm sure we'll see each other again, either here or in America. It may take a few years, but it will happen. Perhaps then you'll be a world-famous writer on a tour of England's former colonies and I'll have to queue for your autograph. You'll see this shabby old man in front of you holding out your best seller, and he'll remind you of someone you once knew."

I didn't like this picture very much. "No, that's not how it'll be. I'll turn up in Philadelphia and they'll be holding an exhibition in your honor: the man who changed the course of history—the man who brought the crowned heads of Europe to their knees! You'll drive past me in a coach and four and all the crowd will cheer. Next thing you'll be elected president!"

I had been intending to cheer him up, but my words had the opposite effect.

"Hardly. I don't think a renegade lord will suit the taste of Americans. They like homegrown heroes." He sighed, looking down at his ink-stained fingernails. "I don't fit in anywhere, Catkin—not in my father's house, not here, not in America."

His melancholy mood was infectious; I felt quite low when I returned to the Sparrow's Nest to hide the money under my pillow. I did not undress immediately, but sat by the window looking out at the stars and thinking of Johnny's remark about us all changing with time. Despite what he said, I didn't need to grow up to learn that there were few constants in life. Those who cared for me never stayed around for very long—my mother, my father, the old prompter who taught me so much, and now Johnny. Even this, my little refuge at the top of the theater, would not last forever. We all had to move on eventually.

A crash on the stairs below made me jump out of my skin.

"Shut up, Meatpie!" I heard someone hiss. "She'll 'ear you."

Billy's gang had broken in. They were coming for me! Quickly, I threw open the window, swearing under my breath as it rattled, and clambered out onto the roof. This was a bolt-hole I retreated to when Mrs. Reid was after me for some misdemeanor or other, but I had never used it on so cold a night, or when the leadings were so treacherously icy.

The door to the Sparrow's Nest banged open and, from my vantage point crouched beneath the window, I could hear boots thumping across the floor.

"She's not 'ere," said Meatpie, tipping up the old couch I slept on.

"But what's this?" said Pox-Face gleefully as forty pounds worth of guineas rolled across the floor. I cursed them as I heard them scrabble to collect the money. "I didn't know the pussycat was so rich."

"Ha, ha, ha! She's not now," said Meatpie with his stupid slow laugh.

They continued to upend chests of clothes and overturn racks of costumes in their hunt for me.

"'Ere, Kitty-Kitty!" crowed Pox-Face. "Come to Daddy. We've someone 'oo wants you!"

I crouched low on the ledge, shivering, praying that they would not think to look out of the window.

"It's no good. She's not 'ere," said Meatpie at last.

"But at least the pistol-man didn't get away," said Pox-Face. "Billy won't be too cross about losing the minnow now 'e's caught the fish. Let's get over there before the fun starts."

Footsteps retreated down the stairs. I paused, hardly daring to breathe. Silence. I got up slowly, taking care not to lose my footing. They'd come for the diamond. They'd got Johnny and were going to try to make him tell them where the nonexistent stone was. But what could I do? Run for help? Who to? Mr. Sheridan? He lived too far away. The law?

But the runners would arrest Johnny rather than help him. Syd's gang? Yes, Syd was my best hope.

I climbed back into the room. It looked as if a hurricane had swept through it. Mrs. Reid was not going to be pleased. I crept to the door and listened. Nothing. In stockinged feet I padded down the wooden stairs, remembering to jump over the one second from the bottom that always creaked loudly. I could hear my heart thumping, my breath hissing between my teeth, and now the murmur of distant voices. They sounded as if they were coming from Johnny's room. I had to pass his office to get to the stage door. Keeping to the shadows, I made my way past the green room and toward the hubbub. I could see several people crowded by the entrance to Johnny's office. One turned—Pox-Face—and I ducked behind the anchor propped up in the corridor. I waited a few moments and then poked my head out. They were all intent on the scene in the room. I slid along the wall, wishing I were not wearing skirts that whispered with every step I took. I was right behind Meatpie now and could smell his sweat of excitement. He leaned over to say something to Pox-Face, revealing Johnny trussed up on his back on the bed. Billy was sitting on the desk, twirling the pistols in his hands. Ferret-Features was ransacking every drawer and chest in the place. Even Johnny's little bundle had been ripped open and strewn across the floor.

"No shot?" said Billy calmly, admiring the guns. "So I could've skinned the cat then? Fortunately, it's never too late. 'Er time will come."

"Makes you feel big, does it, Shepherd, threatening a girl?" spat Johnny.

If I could've, I would've told him not to rile Billy. The consequences were felt immediately. Billy struck his prisoner across the cheek with the handle of one of the pistols. He then turned to Meatpie.

"Take 'im onto the stage. I can feel one of my greatest performances about to begin as I beat the whereabouts of that diamond out of 'im. There ain't room to swing a cat in 'ere—though perhaps we can try that later when she turns up, eh?" he sniggered.

The gang laughed sycophantically. I shuddered.

They were coming out. I had to hide. But poor Johnny—I couldn't leave him to this! First things first: I had to get myself out of sight. I would be no use to Johnny if Billy had the chance to carry out any of his threats against me. Trying not to make noise, I ran down the corridor and onto the scenery lot at the back of the stage. There, stacked against the wall, was the enchanter's laboratory Mr. Bishop's carpenter had been fixing. I clambered onto the set and groped in the dark for the catch to release the hidden compartment. There! A small hole, not much bigger than Mrs. Reid's sewing cabinet, opened before me, in the wooden fireplace to the left of the cauldron. I slid the door closed, but as I did so, one of the glass bottles fell from its shelf and smashed on the floor.

"Did you 'ear that?" said Ferret-Features, running onto the stage.

"It came from over there," said Billy. "Check it out."

"Could it be that old man from the door?" asked Pox-Face.

"Nah, 'e's out cold. I tied 'im up," said Ferret-Features.

Lanterns flared in the dark as Pox and Ferret searched for the source of the disturbance. I could hear a dragging noise and, through the crack in the compartment, saw Meatpie pulling Johnny out of the wings. Billy was standing center stage, torch raised above his head, looking up at row upon row of empty seating. Above his head the basket of the balloon from that evening's farce swung gently in the draft. He gave a deep sigh of satisfaction.

"You know, boys, I always wanted to be on stage, and now's me chance."

Footsteps approached my hiding place; the enchanter's laboratory rattled as Pox-Face jumped onto it.

"Billy, over 'ere!" he shouted, only feet from my position. "Broken glass all over the shop."

"It could've been the wind," suggested Ferret-Features feebly.

"What wind, you dung brain?" snapped Billy. "No, I smell a rat—or should I say Cat? Find 'er!"

Pox-Face began to look through the scenery leaning up against the back wall. Ferret-Features, displaying more intelligence than I had expected, started to thump on the hollow walls of the battlements and buildings. I murmured a quick prayer that the carpenter had managed to fix the fault with the compartment: the last thing I needed was for it to spring open now.

Thump, thump, thump! Ferret was right by me. Crash, smash, crash! Bottle after bottle fell from the shelf, exploding as they hit the floor. They made so much noise that he missed the strange echo as he rapped on the door of the compartment.

"Nothink, Billy," Ferret called over to his leader. "If she was 'ere, she must 'ave done a runner."

"Leave it then. Let's get on with the show."

Ferret-Features and Pox-Face moved to the front of the stage, taking their lanterns with them. Now was my chance to slip away.

"So, Pistol-Man," Billy was saying. I could see him holding Johnny by the hair. "Are you goin' to give me the pleasure of a long and painful beatin' or are you goin' to tell me now where the diamond's 'idden?"

"Diamond? What diamond?" replied Johnny fiercely. "There is no diamond."

Billy let go of Johnny's hair. He took a step back and laced his fingers together, bending them backward so they cracked like pistol shots.

"Good. I 'oped you'd say that."

I turned my eyes away but could tell by the sickening sound of knuckle on bone that the beating had begun.

I could delay no longer: I had to get help. I slipped out of my hiding place and tiptoed to the stage door without attracting the attention of any of Billy's gang. On the threshold, cudgel clutched in his hand, lay Caleb. I knelt down beside him, feeling for signs of life. He was still breathing—but out cold.

Suddenly, I heard a noise behind me. A hand clapped me on my shoulder. I twisted around and bit hard into it, giving rise to a sharp exclamation behind me.

"Dammit, Cat!" hissed Pedro, shaking his hand in agony. "Why did you do that? What's going on? Why's Caleb on the floor?"

I had too much to tell him to berate him for frightening me like that. I decided the bite would be punishment enough.

"Billy's gang's here. They've got Johnny. They're trying to make him talk—to make him tell them where the diamond is." I didn't have time to explain that the diamond had been a figment of my imagination, for an alarming thought had just struck me. I looked over Pedro's shoulder into the dark corridor. What was he doing here? He wasn't in league with Billy and his gang, was he? I moved away from him. "Why are you here? Is Syd with you, or any of the others?" I asked suspiciously.

"No, I've come from Frank. He's sorted out a passage for Johnny—if we can get him out of here."

My suspicions subsided a little, but I was left with the unpleasant truth that we were still only two against four.

"Shall we go for Syd?" I asked.

Pedro hovered indecisively. There was a shout from the stage and the snap of something breaking—I prayed it wasn't Johnny's legs.

"No time," said Pedro, his hand shaking slightly as he helped me to my feet. He looked as terrified as I felt. "Any ideas?"

I thought for a moment. Was he trying to trap me? There was a cry of pain from the stage. I couldn't afford to think like this. I had to help Johnny, and to do this I needed to trust Pedro. Surely on my home ground I should be able to beat those pea-brained thugs? At least, with Pedro's help it should be possible.

"One, but it's going to be tricky." I told him what I had in mind.

He smiled, his white teeth gleaming in the shadows of his face. "Brilliant—just show me the ropes."

After rapid instruction in backstage management, Pedro said he was ready.

"Remember, do nothing till you see them in their places. The white cross, remember," I whispered urgently as we wormed our way to the wings, keeping out of sight of the forestage. "You won't let me down, will you?"

"Of course not. Good luck!" he hissed, giving my arm a squeeze. I took a deep breath, more nervous than any actress on her debut, and walked onto the stage, my life now depending on a boy I had spent the past few days suspecting of treachery.

"Oi, Billy! I've been looking for you," I called out boldly.

My sudden appearance came as such a surprise that all five of them were momentarily arrested in their actions. Johnny, of course, had no choice: he was sagging in the ropes that bound him. Blood trickled from his nose and his left eye was puffy. He was barely conscious. Billy was poised above him, his fist raised. The three lieutenants were standing around them: Meatpie with his arms folded; Ferret hovering at his leader's shoulder for the best view; Pox feeling the edge of his knife thoughtfully— hoping no doubt for a go at the victim. Billy lowered his fist.

"Cat!" groaned Johnny in despair. I suppose his one solace had been the thought that I had escaped.

"Well, well, if it ain't my little pussycat," said Billy, pushing his sleeves up to reveal his lean, muscular forearms. "I was lookin' for you too. I knew you were about the place somewhere." He gave Meatpie a nod, and the pudding boy started forward to seize me.

I held up my arms to ward him off. "Whoa! There's no need for that between friends, surely?" I said, hoping my voice would not betray my fear. "I only wanted to tell you that I've done what I promised. I got the diamond for you."

Billy waved Meatpie off and beckoned me forward.

"Bring it here then, like a good little girl," he said with his rotten grin.

"Ah. You see, Billy, I'm no flat. This good little girl doesn't trust big bad boys like you," I said archly, hands on my hips, still keeping my distance. "How could I know you'd keep your side of the bargain? So, naturally, I put it somewhere for safekeeping."

In no mood for playing, Billy strode over and seized my elbow. In an attempt to make my movements as natural as possible, I pulled away from him, trying to lead him farther upstage to the white cross chalked on the floor. The boys formed up behind us, right on target. Why wasn't Pedro making his move?

"What bargain?" Billy asked with a dangerous edge to his voice. "You'll find that you're in no position to bargain with me."

"But what about my dress?" I asked with a petulant pout as I tried to resist turning to look into the wings where Pedro was supposed to be waiting. "You promised! You can't have one of your girls going about dressed like a scarecrow, can you?"

Billy thought he understood me now. He gave a knowing smile and eased his grip. Changing tack, he put his arm around my shoulders, which was far worse than his previous menacings.

"One of my girls, eh? You've seen the light then, Cat?" He squeezed me to him. He smelled like the Fleet ditch. "Well, if you give me the diamond, I'll let you in me gang and buy you a dress—a silk one. Anythink else?" My eyes slid to

Johnny, who was watching me in horror. He must have guessed I was up to something but he thought I had miscalculated badly. I hoped he was wrong. But what was Pedro doing?

"What about your friend 'ere?" asked Billy. He was testing me for weakness, I could tell.

"Oh, he's no friend of mine," I bluffed with a shrug. "He was planning to dump me and go to America, that one."

"Good girl," said Billy, slapping me on the back. "I'm pleased you said that 'cause it wouldn't've done to let 'im go now 'e knows we've got the stone. Come on then, give it to me."

"I can't—not yet," I added hurriedly. "I pawned it." I dug in my pocket and held out the receipt from Mr. Vaughan.

Billy squinted at it. "This says jools—gold and stuff, Cat. I can't see no diamond."

"I put it in with some other things I'd lifted," I explained. "To make it less obvious. Mr. Vaughan and I have a little understanding."

"I'm impressed, Cat! I'd 'eard 'e was straight. Well, what are we waitin' for? Let's go and get it.

I'm sure 'e won't mind openin' up for so special a customer."

"Probably not," I shrugged, "but I need my forty pounds back first." I put the receipt into my pocket.

"Forty pounds? What forty pounds?" Billy looked angry again. His grip now became painful.

"Ask Meatpie and Pox-Face," I said coolly.

Billy turned on his followers. "Is this true? 'Ave you got the money?"

"Well, Billy, it's like this," said Pox-Face digging into his pockets. "We were goin' to tell you, weren't we, Meatpie?"

"Were we?" said Meatpie dully.

"Give me that!" hissed Billy, snatching the coins from them. "I'll deal with you two later."

He began to count the gold.

"Here, Billy," I said with what I hoped was a winning smile, "let me help you."

I lifted the lantern up, moving a few paces forward as I pretended to stagger under its weight. He smiled indulgently at my girlish feebleness but moved toward me to take advantage of the light, feet now planted plumb in the center of the white chalk cross.

As Billy hit his mark, Pedro released the balloon and pulled the lever to drop the trap center stage. The floor gave way under Billy. With a curse, he made a grab for the nearest thing to hand (yours truly), pulling me over the edge with him. Flinging the lantern aside, I just managed to take hold of the edge of the trap. With a jolt, his grip on my dress gave way and he fell into the black hole, taking half my skirt. Usually put to use for Satan's sudden descents to hell, the trapdoor had sent a new devil to the underworld.

Meanwhile, the balloon had plummeted to the ground, crushing Meatpie, Pox-Face, and Ferret-Features like beetles beneath a giant's boot.

Pedro darted onto the stage and hauled me out of the hole. Below I could hear Billy cursing. He had not broken his neck then. Shame.

"Quick, we don't have long," said Pedro, hurrying to untie Johnny. Once free, Johnny slumped, limp as a rag doll, unable to get to his feet.

The boys under the basket were beginning to stir. I could see Meatpie's foot twitching. I took one side of Johnny, Pedro supporting him on the other.

"I thought you'd never pull that damned lever!" I swore as we heaved Johnny up.

"But you told me to wait until they were all lined up!" Pedro protested.

"I'd've settled for three out of four—I thought Billy was never going to move into range and I was running out of ideas."

"You? Out of ideas? I don't believe it!" said Pedro with a grin.

I smiled back into the eyes of my friend.

"Where to now?" I panted as we dragged Johnny to the door. He was so heavy, it was clear we could not keep this up for long.

"Have you got any money on you?" asked Pedro.

"Yes," I gasped. I had the Earl of Ranworth's sovereign still in my pocket.

"We'll take a cab—get him to Grosvenor Square. It's the safest place."

Pedro left us at the corner of Russell Street and ran off to find a hackney carriage. It was late and the street was quiet. The only person about was a man loitering in a doorway opposite. I did not like the look of him. Sooner than I hoped, I heard the clatter of hooves and wheels behind me.

"Let's see your money, girl," said the jarvey from his driving seat on top of the cab, skeptical that either Pedro or I could afford the luxury of a ride across town. I held up my sovereign. He gave me an appraising look. "All right," he said finally. "In you get."

Pedro and I heaved Johnny into the cab.

"What's wrong with him?" laughed the jarvey. "Too much to drink?"

Punch-drunk, I might've said, but I didn't want to share this information with the coachman.

"I'll double the fare if you get us to Grosvenor Square in ten minutes. Stop for nothing and no one," I called up.

"Right you are, miss," said the jarvey, cracking his whip. "Brownie and I'll show you the meaning of speed."

The carriage pulled away with a clatter of hooves. As it did so, I heard a yell behind us.

"Stop!" bellowed Billy after us. "Stop that cab!"

But the jarvey had his orders and with a shrill whistle urged his horse to a faster trot. I craned my head out of the window to see if Billy was gaining on us but I need not have worried: he could only manage a hobble as far as the end of Russell Street and he soon gave up. I gave him a cheery wave.

"I'll get you, Cat!" he shouted. "You're dead!"

"You forget, Billy," I called back. "Cats have nine lives!"

I sat back on the seat to give my companions a delighted smile, but I found them looking at me somberly.

"What's up?" I asked.

"Nine lives?" croaked Johnny, his hand clutching his ribs. "You seem to be running through your portion rather fast."

"He's right, Cat," said Pedro. "You shouldn't bait Billy Shepherd."

"As if I had a choice in the matter!" I exclaimed. "To hear you two, anyone would think that I enjoyed it!"

"And didn't you?" probed Johnny with a pained smile as the cab went into a pothole. "Didn't you enjoy outwitting him?"

"Just a little, a very little," I admitted, unable to keep a huge grin from my face.

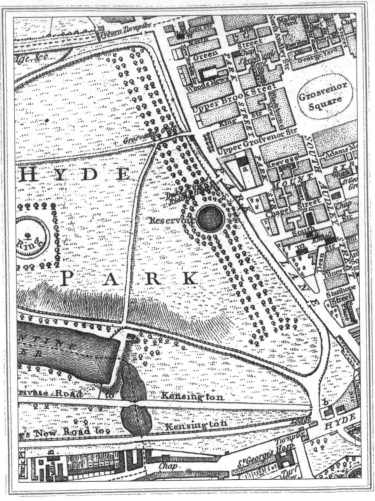

*Act V - In which our heroine
has an arresting experience...*

ACT V

SCENE 1—DRESSES

Johnny managed to walk from the cab into the mews behind Grosvenor Square without assistance. We led him into the unlocked stable Lord Francis used as a changing room and dropped him onto the straw. In the next stall, a horse stamped its feet. From the quarters above the stables came the loud voices of the grooms, punctuated by the occasional thump of a game of shove ha'penny.

"What now?" I asked Pedro, peering through a barred window at the house. It was brightly illuminated: it seemed as though the family was still awake.

"One of us needs to go in and find Frank and Lady Elizabeth," said Pedro. We looked at each other, remembering the fierce French cook and the hordes of servants we had seen on our last visit. It would be a miracle if either of us got in unseen.

Someone pulled a curtain on the third floor—a girl's hand.

"Do you think that's her bedroom?" I asked, nudging Pedro.

He nodded. "Makes sense."

"I'll go then," I said.

"No, let me," said Pedro.

"You can't. It's got to be me. Think what'll happen if they find you creeping round a lady's bedroom at this time of night! You stay and look after Johnny."

Pedro gave in, recognizing the sense of what I was saying. If he were caught, he'd be lucky if they spared his life and only packed him off to a slave plantation in the West Indies; I might escape with a thrashing.

I ran across the cobbles and slid in through the back door to the kitchens. The place was once again alive with activity: from the clatter of pans and splash of water in the scullery I guessed that the plates from some fancy dinner were being washed. No refuge there this time, then. I crept as far as the open kitchen door and peered in. The chef was sitting with his feet up on the table swilling a glass of red wine, humming to himself. I stole past and ran as quietly as I could up the stairs to the green baize door Lord Francis had taken us through.

I stopped. I could hear the confused babble of many voices and a door opening and closing. It appeared I had arrived just as the duke's guests had taken it into their heads to depart. Pushing the door open a crack, I saw a large party of gentlemen fetching their cloaks from the two footmen on duty. There was Mr. Sheridan reaching for his hat and cane and, yes, there was Marchmont senior accompanied by the Earl of Ranworth. If only Mr. Sheridan would look in my direction. How I could do with his assistance! I wished I could tell him how much danger his "diamond" was in! But to break from my hiding place would be to reveal my unauthorized presence in the house and attract far too many questions from the host. I watched despondently as Mr. Sheridan resolutely looked the other way, bade the duke goodnight, and left.

So, no way up those stairs while the duke was still about. I backed down the steps to the corridor and paused for thought. Where were the back stairs? I wondered. There had to be some for the servants to pass unseen about the house. As if in answer to my question, a maid emerged from the scullery carrying a jug of steaming water. I hid behind a row of aprons hanging from pegs along a wall. The maid walked straight past me and took a passageway on the left. I crept after her. She then took a sharp right and disappeared. I followed, discovering that she had indeed led me to the stairs. I had to be quick: this narrow flight offered no hiding places. I'd have to be up and off them before she headed back down.

She carried her burden up three flights, pausing only to straighten her cap when she reached a landing. She then knocked on the door of the room closest to the stair and entered.

"Put it over there, please, Mary." It was Lady Elizabeth! Feeling a wave of relief, I remembered to dart behind a linen chest just in time.

Mary's feet could be heard getting farther away as she went down the stairs. I had a final look up and down the corridor—all clear.

Tap, tap! I knocked softly on Lady Elizabeth's door.

"Come!" she called.

I opened the door and saw her reflection in the dressing-table mirror. She looked beautiful, like a mermaid rising out of a silver pool: her hair was strewn with pearls and her silk dress was the color of bluebells.

"Cat!" she exclaimed, dropping her brush onto the table with a clatter. "Whatever has happened to you?"

I caught a glimpse of myself in the glass. My hair was in a hopeless tumble, and half my skirt was missing, displaying grubby white petticoats beneath.

"Ah," I said gesturing to my dress ruefully. "I had a merry meeting with my friend Billy Boil."

She got up, moved swiftly across the thick rose-colored carpet, and pulled me inside the room. She took a quick look at the silent corridor before she closed the door and turned the key.

"Oh, Cat, are you all right?" she said. "Have a seat. Tell me what happened."

"Forget about that, Lady Elizabeth—"

She held her finger to my lips. "Lizzie, Cat. Remember!"

"Lizzie, then. What I've come to tell you, Lizzie, is that Johnny's here. He didn't come off quite so well in his encounter with our friend, so we've brought him here. He's in the stable with Pedro."

Lady Elizabeth now ran to the window and peered out into the yard.

"Is he all right?" she asked anxiously.

I nodded.

"He'll be safe there for the moment," she told me. "It's quiet now. It is very fortunate you did not arrive half an hour earlier: we had all the carriages lined up in the yard. They've only just gone around to the front of the house."

"Will you help us?" I asked anxiously.

"Of course. Stay where you are. Don't answer the door unless you hear four taps. I'll fetch Frank." She picked up a candle from her dressing table. "Father sent him to bed an hour ago, but if I know him he'll be spying on the guests as they leave, giving their carriages marks out of ten or some such fancy of his."

She slipped out and I locked the door behind her. It would not do for a maid to find me in here alone. I sat at the dressing table and stared at myself in the mirror. I did not have the luxury of my own glass at home, though there were plenty in the dressing rooms for the actors. A solemn face looked back out at me. My red curls were matted with dirt. My freckled nose was smudged, my bodice torn where the skirt had parted from it at the waist, my hands red raw with marks of hard work and blows. Compared with the vision with white skin and chestnut locks that had just sat there, I was a complete troll. It was a depressing comparison.

Four taps on the door. I quickly opened it to find myself almost knocked down by the arrival of Lord Francis.

"Cat!" he exclaimed, giving me a relieved hug before remembering himself and giving me a formal bow at arm's length. "Lizzie's told me what happened. I'm so pleased to see you in one piece. When our gang gets to hear about this, Shepherd'll wish he had never been born!"

Our gang? Since when had Lord Francis been enrolled among Syd's followers? But I had forgotten—he was a boy, wasn't he? That was sufficient to earn Syd's approbation.

"Now, you sit down and let Lizzie look after you. I'll fetch the others," he said, taking charge.

To be honest, it was a relief to relinquish responsibility for seeing Johnny to safety. This was Lord Francis's home: it was right that he should deal with the ticklish matter of smuggling a wanted man inside it. He led me back to the dressing table, gave me a pat on the arm, and left.

Minutes later Lady Elizabeth returned. She slopped some hot water into a porcelain bowl decorated with pink roses and carried it over to me.

"Here, you can clean yourself up with this," she said, passing me a linen towel.

It was worse somehow with her standing there watching me. I went hot with embarrassment, feeling common and dirty. A girl like me should not be sullying her bedchamber with my presence. I was distressed to find a tear had trickled out of the corner of my eye and dripped in the bowl in front of me.

"What's the matter, Cat?" Lady Elizabeth asked, coming to kneel beside me.

"I'm not fit to be here," I said despairingly, dropping the linen cloth into the now gray water. "I should go."

"Nonsense," she said, getting up and going to a closet on the far side of the room. "You won't feel like that when you've put this on tomorrow. I've grown out of it but it should fit you." On the bed she laid the loveliest emerald silk dress that I had ever seen. "Green never was my color, but it will suit you.'

"I can't take it," I protested.

"Of course you can," she said, smiling. "Now, you get yourself into bed. You must be exhausted."

"Bed?"

I looked around the room. The only bed I could see was Lady Elizabeth's four-poster, hung with muslin curtains and covered with a white satin counterpane.

"My bed, of course," said Lady Elizabeth. "There's plenty of room for both of us. You get in; I'll just go and check on the boys to see they have arrived safely."

She left, closing the door softly behind her. I stood irresolute for a moment in the middle of the carpet and then made my decision. I was used to sleeping on the unyielding surface of the old couch in the Sparrow's Nest. I had no need of the luxuries Lady Elizabeth had so kindly offered me. Finding a spare blanket in the chest under the window, I curled up on the floor behind the screen and, despite my determination to stay awake to hear her news when she returned, I must have dropped off to sleep.

I was woken the next morning by hushed voices at the door to the chamber.

"No, Mary, I really do not require your assistance to dress this morning, but I would like you to prepare a bath for me next door."

The door clicked to, and a bare foot appeared around the corner of the screen.

"I am sorry to have woken you, Cat. I had to send her away or she would have discovered you. Did you sleep well?"

I nodded, noticing for the first time that my cheek was cushioned on a feather pillow. I sat up and stretched.

"I thought you had gone when I came back," laughed Lady Elizabeth. "You did give me a fright."

"Johnny and Pedro—are they safe?" I asked anxiously, throwing off my blanket.

"Yes, quite safe. Pedro went back to his master's house once Johnny was smuggled into Francis's room. He wanted to find out how it all ended at the theater last night. He said he'd come back and tell us this morning."

That was good. There would be an uproar when Caleb was discovered and Johnny and I were found to be gone. I hoped the old man was all right, but I dreaded to think what construction would be put on the whole affair. Would they be worried for me or blame me? Probably the latter if Mrs. Reid had anything to do with it.

"I did wonder if you would like a bath," Lady Elizabeth asked delicately. "I've arranged for one to be put in the dressing room next door and will propose that Lord Jonathan take a dip, but I thought I'd give you first refusal."

A bath? What a luxury! I could not remember the last time I had had one, as normally I had to make do with a basin of hot water once a day.

"That would be wonderful."

"Good. Then would you be so kind as to help me into my clothes and I will go and tell Francis what I've planned."

Dressing a lady was a far more complicated affair than I had imagined. I did my job as lady's maid very inexpertly, buttoning garments and lacing stays. Not surprisingly, Lady Elizabeth would not let me near her hair but dressed it herself in the mirror. She took a final look, straightening her rumpled skirt.

"That'll have to do. When you're ready, go through there." She pointed to a door in the corner of the room. "The bath should be waiting for you. I'll make sure Mary is out of the way, but remember to lock yourself in."

I gave her a few minutes to fulfill her promise about the maid, then quietly opened the door into the dressing room. The window was veiled with a curtain, filtering the morning light. In the center of the wooden floor stood the very same bath I had seen down in the scullery only a few days ago. It was now filled to the brim with steaming water. A pile of linen towels stood waiting on an ebony rack. To me, so unused to such an excess of comforts, it was like stepping into the heart of a temple dedicated to cleanliness, the steam rising like incense to the gods of soap and water. I locked both doors as instructed and stripped to my skin. I knew it was immodest of me to take a bath without keeping on my shift but I had only one and besides, who was there to note my behavior? Then the wonderful moment of truth came: I stepped in and submerged myself completely under the water.

I allowed myself some fifteen minutes of indulgence and then toweled off quickly. The bath water looked far less enticing now that it was filled with soap bubbles, but Johnny would just have to put up with it. I assumed that as a lord, he had the frequent pleasure of taking a plunge, so today it was just his hard luck that I got there first.

Lady Elizabeth was waiting for me when I came back into her bedroom wrapped in a large white towel, clutching my pitiful bundle of clothes.

"I'll go and tell Lord Jonathan he can go in now. I've put some clothes for you behind the screen," she informed me.

She had laid out a complete change of clothes: a bright white shift, petticoats, and the emerald green dress I had refused the night before. This morning my rejection of her bounty evaporated like mist under the newly risen sun, and to honor my scrubbed state, I succumbed to temptation, putting on each garment with due reverence. But the greatest wonder were the silk stockings: they slid up my legs so that I hardly knew they were there, so different from the scratchy woolen stockings I normally wore.

"Shall I help you do up the back of your dress?" Lady Elizabeth had returned.

"Please." I emerged from behind the screen and displayed my new finery for her approval, arms held wide.

"I told you it would suit you," she said, guiding me to the dressing table. "As I have forced you to be my maid this morning, it is now my turn to do you the same service."

I definitely got the better part of the bargain. Lady Elizabeth brushed and fastened up my damp hair to look like something from a fashion plate. I had never seen myself so smart. I looked almost like a highborn lady.

"Now I will need your help with Lord Jonathan," she said, giving my curls a final tweak. "He will be here in a moment."

"Help? What kind of help?" My playtime was over, and I was businesslike once more, remembering we were far from safe.

"With the disguise." Lady Elizabeth moved to the closet on the far side of the room and pulled out a pile of clothes she had prepared. "Frank has secured a berth for Lord Jonathan on a ship leaving for America. It will sail as soon as the wind is favorable. He's arranging to bring around the carriage so that we can take Lord Jonathan to the docks this morning. He can hide on board until the packet sails. All that remains is to ensure that he is not recognized on the way there."

She threw the clothes onto the bed. I could now see that they consisted of a large red velvet gown, stays, a shift, and other items of female apparel. A black wig crouched among them like a cat curled up before the fire.

"You're going to dress him as a woman?" I asked, wondering if I was allowed to giggle.

"Of course," she said with a smile. "What better disguise could there be? I did promise to dress him so that even his own mother would not recognize him. Though my mother might, for it is one of her gowns I've borrowed."

"Does Johnny know yet?"

She shook her head.

At that moment, there was a tap on the dressing room door.

"Come!" said Lady Elizabeth.

Johnny stepped into the room wrapped in a dressing gown, admittedly looking far better than he had last night, but nothing surely could disguise that puffy black eye and cut lip?

"What are you smiling at?" he asked, looking from one of us to the other.

"Nothing," Lady Elizabeth said brightly. "Now, go behind the screen and put on the things I give you."

Obediently, he did as he was bidden. I had never heard Johnny swear before a lady, but that changed when the shift was handed over the top of the screen.

"Dammit, what's all this?" he spluttered in outrage.

"Your disguise," said Lady Elizabeth calmly. "Now stop making a fuss and get yourself dressed."

"I can't wear this!" he exclaimed, jiggling the stays over the top of the screen. "It's bad enough that I've been beaten black and blue around my ribs without squeezing into this infernal contraption."

"Stop complaining," she told him in a firm, no-nonsense voice. "Half the population wears them all the time: I'm only asking you to put it on for a few hours."

The grumbles ceased and Johnny finally emerged wearing the dress. In my opinion, the disguise was not convincing: he looked like a man in a gown. Anyone would see at a glance that he was an impostor.

Lady Elizabeth, however, was not down-hearted. She hadn't finished with him yet.

"Sit by the glass here," she ordered.

Johnny shuffled over, tripping on his skirts.

"Pull the strings tighter, Cat," she said, gesturing to the laces dangling from the back of his dress. "Then do up the buttons."

As instructed I began to pull.

"Wait a moment," she said. Diving into a drawer in the tallboy by the screen, she pulled out a pair of woolen stockings.

"I think you can guess where to put these," she said, blushing scarlet as she handed them to Johnny. With a few furtive gropes down the front of his dress, he suddenly began to take on a much more womanly form.

"Ow!" Johnny cried as I resumed pulling on the strings. "I don't know how you ladies stand for all this."

"Neither do I," agreed Lady Elizabeth, now approaching his face with a large powder puff. "Pure madness."

As I buttoned Johnny's dress up at the back, Lady Elizabeth placed the wig on his head, adorning it with a lace cap and bonnet.

"There!" She stepped back, hands on hips.

The transformation was uncanny. Gone was handsome Johnny; in his place was an ugly matron with her face plastered in white powder.

"As long as he doesn't move or speak, we might get away with this," I mused.

"I'll ring for some breakfast," said Lady Elizabeth enthusiastically. "We'll try it out on one of the servants. I'll tell them you are my dressmaker come for a fitting."

In response to the summons, a maid appeared at the door.

"Jenny, is Papa in the breakfast room?"

Jenny nodded.

"Can you tell him that I can't come down as the dressmaker has arrived? I'll take my breakfast up here."

Jenny's eyes slid to Johnny, who was busying himself with a sewing bag Lady Elizabeth had thrust in his hands a moment before. Lady Elizabeth took her to the door and said in an undertone, "I would be most obliged if you would not stare at the lady's eye, Jenny. Her husband is a nasty piece of work—he beats her. She has been in floods of tears this morning telling me about it."

Jenny's face now registered pity for the unfortunate seamstress.

"Of course, your ladyship."

"In fact, would you bring up some tea for us all—to help settle her nerves?"

Jenny bobbed a curtsy and left.

"What do you think?" asked Johnny anxiously. It was most unnerving to hear his deep voice issuing from the bonnet. "Was she fooled?"

"I think so," said Lady Elizabeth, taking a seat by the window. "Women are always the hardest to deceive, but if she had thought you were a man, she would have run from the room screaming."

After breakfast, Lord Francis came to announce the arrival of the carriage. He could not resist

smirking at Johnny and was cuffed by the seamstress for his rudeness.

"Sorry, ma'am," he said, giving Johnny a deep
bow. "I won't do it again."

"And I won't give you the opportunity again,"
growled Johnny, picking up his skirts and following
Lady Elizabeth down the corridor with a sturdy
stride.

"We had better be quick!" warned Lord
Francis. "Papa was still reading the newspaper when
I left the table, but he could be out at any moment."

We descended to the foyer without incident and
were almost at the front entrance when a door to
our left opened and the Duke of Avon strode out,
newspaper tucked under his arm. "CAPTAIN
SPARKLER STILL AT LARGE!" read the headline.

"Morning, Lizzie!" he said, kissing his daughter
on the cheek. "Off out so early?"

"Yes, Papa. I have to return some calls.
Frightful bore, but there you are."

The duke's eyes turned to Johnny.

"Ah, this is my seamstress, Papa," she filled
in quickly.

"Not the one that keeps sending in such scandalously high bills, I hope? Madame what's-her-name?"

"Madame Martine," said Lady Elizabeth as the duke gave the seamstress a hard stare.

"Is she good?" he asked turning back to his daughter.

"The best."

"Well, in that case, I suppose she's worth the money. *Enchanté, madame,*" he said gallantly, bowing and kissing Johnny's gloved hand.

"*Merci, monsieur,*" said "Madame Martine" in flawless, if somewhat gruff, French.

The duke now looked at me.

"Miss Royal, isn't it? What are you doing here? I didn't know you were in the house."

"Cat—I mean Miss Royal—came early on my request. We are paying calls together. All my friends want to meet her," said Lady Elizabeth.

The duke now took in my new finery and a small frown appeared on his brow. My cheeks reddened.

"Hmm," he said disapprovingly. "I'd like to have a word with you when you return, Lizzie. There's something we must discuss."

The duke dismissed us with a nod and retreated into the breakfast room. I could guess what he wanted to talk to his daughter about: he was going to warn her against introducing girls like me into her intimate circle. I had a very dubious position in society, and my company would do nothing to enhance her reputation.

Lady Elizabeth led the way down the steps to the carriage. Hanging on the back, next to the stable boy Jenkins, was Pedro. He jumped down and opened the door for us. Lord Francis handed each of us in and climbed in last.

The coachman had already raised his whip to lick the horses into a trot when there was a respectful cough at the streetside door.

"Your lordship, might I have a word?"

All of us turned to look at the speaker. I saw to my horror that it was Constable Lennox, the Bow Street runner who had checked in at Drury Lane yesterday. He was now standing by the side of the carriage watching us closely. I lowered my head to hunt for something in my reticule. Johnny put a handkerchief to his eye as if wiping away a tear.

"Yes, Constable?" said Lord Francis in a surprisingly crisp tone. I had never heard him sound so lordly before. "Call back later and I will see you then. I have an engagement this morning that I must not break."

"I understand, sir, but I wonder if I might be so bold as to have a look at your carriage? I received a report from one of our informants that two fugitives fled to your house last night in the company of a third person. That person was followed back here this morning. I've already searched the stables but found nothing. That leaves me to conclude that they might be secreted somewhere in this carriage."

"Are you serious, sir?" said Lady Elizabeth, sounding suitably concerned. "How terrible! Lady Catherine, can you imagine it?" She turned to me, her eyes wide. Though surprised to find myself so rapidly ennobled, I gave a shudder by way of agreement. "Of course you must look, Constable. Shall we alight so that you can examine the carriage thoroughly? Countess, would you mind?" This latter remark was directed to Johnny, who was now applying smelling salts to his nose, as if overcome by fright.

"I'd be much obliged, my lady," said the runner.

Johnny, Lady Elizabeth, and I dismounted from the carriage and waited on the pavement while Lord Francis supervised the officer, who began checking under the seats.

"Nothing," the runner said at length when he had exhausted all possibilities. "Though, if you don't mind, my lord, I'd like to question your black servant."

"My servant? What has he to do with it?" said Lord Francis imperiously. "Haven't you wasted enough of our time today, my man?"

The runner looked awkward. "It's just that my informant saw a black boy here last night and followed the same boy here this morning."

"Are you sure it is the same boy? Gustavus did indeed go on an errand for me but I can swear that he was with me last night. Your informant must be wrong."

"True, he might," said the runner, scratching his chin. "And you say this boy, Gustavus, was with you last night?"

"Yes, wasn't that so, Jenkins?" Lord Francis called over to the stable boy.

"Yes, my lord," lied Jenkins cheerfully.

"In that case, I must apologize for intruding. Ladies." The runner gave us a bow and held the carriage door open.

"Not at all, sir," said Lady Elizabeth graciously. "You were just doing your duty." Constable Lennox glowed with pride and bowed again.

As I got in, I felt the runner's gaze fix on me. I could tell he found something about me familiar.

"We'd better get out of here," I whispered urgently to Lord Francis, "before he remembers where he saw me."

Lord Francis nodded and thumped the roof of the carriage.

"Drive on!" he called.

The carriage surged into motion, throwing us back into our well-padded seats. Looking out of the window as we turned out of Grosvenor Square,

I saw the runner suddenly clap his hand to his forehead and start off in pursuit. But even Bow Street runners could not outstrip a carriage pulled by four stallions. He was soon left behind.

"That was close," I said slumping back with relief. "He remembered me—but too late."

"And as for the countess here—he didn't have a clue," said Lord Francis, turning to Johnny. "But may I say, Countess, you do look quite ravishing this morning."

The countess gave the young lord a hearty thump for his impertinence as Lady Elizabeth and I dissolved into laughter.

SCENE 2—THE THAMES

The carriage took us through the narrow streets of the city to the docks beyond the Tower of London. The sky was iron gray behind the white turrets of the fortress, a sign that more snow was on its way. As I watched, a raven launched itself from the battlements of the White Tower and circled over the roofs of red brick buildings crowded up against the outer walls. Disturbed by some unseen menace, a flock of gulls abandoned their scavenging on the muddy shoreline, spiraled up, and then headed eastward over Traitor's Gate. After the brief pleasure at our escape, a grim mood stole over me: even the birds sensed the threat that hung over us like an executioner's ax.

As we left the Tower behind and rattled through Wapping, Lord Francis leaned over his sister to point out Johnny's ship moored in the stretch of water known as the Pool.

"There she is: the fastest little merchant vessel in the business!" Lord Francis said cheerfully. "Or so Jenkins's second cousin swears. He's a customs man so he should know."

The ship was hard to spot, being but three masts amid a forest. Like the most intricate Brussels lace, the rigging stretched from stem to stern on each boat. From this distance it looked as if some gigantic kitten had got in the yarn bag and made a hopeless tangle. It was hard to imagine how any vessel could escape that knot.

"But even the fastest ship needs a favorable wind," said Johnny, looking anxiously up at the weather vane on top of St. Katherine's Church. It was stuck resolutely pointing east. "Pursuit has been too hot on my heels of late. I'd appreciate a cool west wind to blow me out to the estuary and put some sea miles between me and my enemies."

"I may have many gifts, Lord Jonathan," said Lord Francis, punching his friend in his bodice, "but controling the wind is not one of them." Johnny cuffed him back and laughed. I wondered how they could both be so lighthearted in view of the dangers that surrounded us. My stomach was sick with anxiety.

"I've spoken to the captain," continued Lord Francis. "He's an American, a friend of liberty— you can trust him not to give you up to Mr. Pitt's bloodhounds. We'll put you in a lighter and have you on board the *Potomac* in a jiffy."

The carriage jolted through an icy puddle and turned toward the riverside. Having never been to this part of London before, I craned my head out of the window. The buildings—every other one a tavern, as far as I could tell—were crowded together in a heap as if all London's leftovers had been dumped here higgledy-piggledy. Even stranger were the faces of the people. Among the sailors, I spotted a group of pigtailed Chinese in a tavern window intent on a game played with small white tiles; a curly-haired African dressed in rags shivered by a coil of rope; on a street corner, a turbaned Indian used sinuous hand gestures to negotiate with a fur-hatted Russian who chopped at the air like a woodcutter with an ax. Three smart girls trotted by, their cheeks rouged scarlet, dressed in brand-new red woolen shawls. They held their heads high as they showed off the gifts given them by their sailor sweethearts. The African shuffled out of their way but they paid him no attention.

"Here's the landing place," said Lord Francis as the carriage slowed. He opened the door and jumped down onto the muddy ground. "Wait there, ladies, Pedro and I will look for a boat to carry our cargo."

Johnny made to get up but I grabbed on to the back of his skirts and pulled him down.

"Sit still. People are watching," I whispered. "What'll the coachman think if he sees you striding off after the boys?"

Reluctantly, Johnny returned to his seat but he could not keep from the window, anxiously watching for any signs of trouble.

"That's not very ladylike," Lady Elizabeth warned him as she set him the example of how to sit demurely in a carriage, her hands folded in her lap, her back straight.

"Francis is only a boy!" muttered Johnny. "I feel responsible. What if something happens to him and Pedro?"

"He'll be fine," I reassured him. "He's far less likely to run into difficulties if we do as we're told and stay here."

Lord Francis and Pedro returned a few minutes later with a burly waterman at their elbow. Even in this frosty weather the boatman's arms were bare, displaying his muscled limbs honed by many hours of rowing on the tricky tides of the Thames. His gray-flecked hair straggled like limp seaweed down his back.

"As the lady any luggage?" growled the waterman as Lord Francis handed us out of the carriage.

"No," said Lord Francis curtly. Then, realizing how strange this sounded, he added, "It's being sent on later."

The waterman, however, was not interested in us or our concerns. He spat on the pavement, turned on his heel, and led the way down to the landing stage. Suddenly, after the confines of the maze of alleyways, there it was: the Thames, stretched out before us, free of the buildings that had obscured its full extent from our sight. The tide was rising, the brown waters swallowing up the mudflats, erasing the bird prints and footmarks of the scavengers. The river was buzzing with life: along its banks small boats were coming and going from all directions, crowded with people. Now I had a clear view of the ships anchored out in the Pool, and I was intrigued by the variety of shapes and sizes before me. The sharp prows and sleek lines of the smaller ships promised speed. The blunter prows of the big-bellied merchant vessels, the ones that carried priceless cargoes from the Indies of porcelain and gold, silks and spices, suggested a stately rise and fall, coupled with stubborn resistance to the storms that blew them around the Cape. Even as we watched, another Indiaman, its wooden sides painted in bold, battered colors of gilt and red, sailed in on the tide and glided to a berth on the southern bank, its white sails furling like a butterfly closing its wings after flight. I wondered what treasures it contained— perhaps some real diamonds or silks like that of my new dress?

A splash to our left—out of one of the buildings overhanging the river someone had thrown the contents of a chamber pot. The riverside smelled rank, but now I perceived that the tide bore with it a fresher smell—the smell of the windswept spaces of the estuary and the open sea. The stones of the landing stage glittered with fish scales in the weak morning light. A flake of snow drifted in the air like a dandelion seed before melting on contact with the ground.

The waterman jumped down into his boat and held up a hand to assist "the countess."

"Well," said Johnny in a low voice as he turned to us, "this is it then. This is good-bye. How can I ever thank you all enough?"

"You can't, my friend," said Pedro with a grin. "You are eternally in our debt."

Johnny seized Pedro's hand and shook it. "I can't think of four people to whom I would rather owe so much. I hope to see you again, Pedro—perhaps when you come to America with your own show."

"Perhaps," said Pedro with a pleased shrug.

"And you, Lord Francis, take a bit of advice from an old woman and stay out of trouble!" Johnny clasped the boy's arm in his firm grip.

"Old woman, you worry too much," said Lord Francis, twisting Johnny's hand up to his lips and kissing it. Johnny shook him off with a laugh

"Lady Elizabeth." Johnny turned hesitantly to his sweetheart. "Lizzie . . ."

She said nothing, keeping her gaze steady on his face. I saw a tear glisten at the corner of her eye, but she managed a brave smile.

"What can I say?" he murmured. "You know my wishes, my hopes. . . ."

She nodded. "I know. Good-bye. Write very soon."

"I will. Look after my heart for me, won't you? I'm leaving it in your keeping."

"And you take care of mine too, Johnny."

He squeezed her hand and with great reluctance let it go.

"And now my Catkin." He turned to me, free of the shyness that had hampered his farewell to Lady Elizabeth, and folded me in a brotherly hug. "I worry about you, Catkin. I won't be happy unless you write frequently to let me know how you are. Remember, if ever you need a friend—a home even—there'll be one for you in Philadelphia."

I returned the hug.

"Thank you. I will remember."

Johnny released me and jumped nimbly down into the boat, much to the surprise of the waterman, who had patiently been waiting to assist "the lady."

"To the *Potomac*!" called Lord Francis, flicking the man a coin.

The boatman touched his cap and picked up the oars. The four of us stood shoulder to shoulder, waving at the bonneted figure of Johnny, until the boat dipped out of sight behind the first of the moored vessels.

Lord Francis and Lady Elizabeth set us down in Bow Street to avoid the spectacle of arriving at the stage door in a carriage. As my foot touched the ground, what was waiting for me at Drury Lane came back like the rush of an incoming tide.

"What did everyone make of the break-in?" I asked Pedro. "And how's Caleb?"

"He's recovering—though he's complaining of a thumping headache," said Pedro, scanning the street with quick, furtive movements to be sure we were unobserved. "When they heard about the attack by Billy's boys, they were worried for you, of course," he added, taking my arm as we slid down Russell Street. "Mrs. Reid was relieved when I told her you'd fled to a friend's house for the night. But cheer up, Cat: I've got some good news for you."

"Yes?" A chill breeze cut through my new finery, reminding me of the virtues of woolen stockings.

"They caught Billy. The night patrol got him soon after we made our exit. You won't have to worry about him anymore."

"Really?"

"Yes, really."

"But that's wonderful." A great weight lifted from my shoulders, and I felt as if I had actually grown an inch or two: not only had we got Johnny safely away, but my enemy was no longer able to reach me. With any luck he'd be for the drop—or at the very least transportation to the other side of the world.

We turned into the little courtyard by the stage door. Seeing my home ahead, I broke into an eager run.

"Come on!" I called to Pedro. "Let's celebrate with a hot drink in the Sparrow's Nest."

"Not so fast, miss."

A hand landed on my shoulder, pulling me to a sudden stop.

"Let go of her!" protested Pedro, rushing to my assistance, but the man pushed him away.

"If you don't want me to arrest you too, Blackie, I suggest you keep away."

"Arrest me?" I turned to stare up at my captor in astonishment. It was Constable Lennox, the Bow Street runner who had come to Grosvenor Square—the same one who had searched Johnny's office. "But what've I done?"

"You know best, miss. I'm arresting you on suspicion of theft."

"Theft? What theft?"

"Oh, don't come over the innocent with me, young woman. We know you are the leader of a gang of thieves preying on the theatergoers. I have my informant—your accomplice—already under lock and key. He's told us all about it. He's been very cooperative."

"But I haven't . . . I'm not . . ." I spluttered helplessly, looking to Pedro for some way out of this nightmarish turn of events.

"You can explain all that down at the station, miss," said the runner pompously, increasing his grip and beginning to march me away.

"Pedro!" I shouted over my shoulder. "Fetch Lizzie!"

"Don't worry, Cat, I will!" Pedro called back, overtaking us as he ran off to Grosvenor Square.

"You've been having a rare old time, haven't you, young woman?" said the constable, giving me a shake as he nodded down at my fine clothes. "First you pop up as a maid, then as a lady going about in a fine carriage. That's what I can't abide: little vicious tricksters who take the softhearted for a ride, rob them, and run off laughing. Well, my girl, it's just as well we caught you young and can put an end to your criminal activities. Nip evil in the bud is my motto."

I let him ramble on. My mind was in a whirl. It was not hard to guess his informant. Billy Boil would be singing like a blackbird to get himself let off. But surely the mistake would all be cleared up once Lady Elizabeth vouched for me? I comforted myself with the thought that I was certain to be allowed back home before the day was out. As long as Johnny was kept out of it, all would be well. I was mindful that, with the wind in the east, he would not yet have sailed and was still within reach of the law.

The runner took me through a side door of Bow Street Magistrate's Court into the sparsely furnished office used by the patrol.

"Sit there," he said, pointing to a wooden bench. "Don't try nothing clever or it'll be the worse for you. We don't normally put nippers like you in irons, but that can change. The clerk will take down your particulars." He nodded over to an old man who was hunched over a writing desk. "Real little vixen this one, Amos. Head of a gang of thieves at her age, would you believe it!"

Amos peered at me shortsightedly over the top of the desk, quill in hand. His thin white hair shone like a halo around his balding crown.

"Ah, a little Moll Flanders in the making, eh what!" he said. "Hard to credit it when you see them so young. They look so innocent."

"Maybe, but this one's heart is as rotten as a six-month-old egg," said the runner, straightening his uniform in the glass-paneled door leading into the court.

"No, it's not!" I could no longer contain my indignation. To hear him speak I was the most hardened of criminals.

"Name?" said Amos, cutting across my protest.

"Catherine Royal," I muttered, blushing despite myself as two runners marched through the office and gave me a curious look. I must appear very out of place, dressed like a lady but being treated like the lowest of the low.

"Residence?"

"Theater Royal, Drury Lane."

Amos raised his eyebrows. "Really?"

I nodded.

"Parents' names?"

"Don't know."

"You're an orphan?"

"I suppose so."

"Guardian then?"

"No one." I was feeling increasingly desperate, as his questions drove home the fact that I had no close family to defend me.

"No parents, no guardian. So, to whom do you belong, child? I suppose I could put down 'abandoned' or 'vagrant' maybe," he mused, sucking the end of his quill.

"I'm no vagrant," I said hotly. "I belong to Mr. Sheridan's household." That's if he did not disown me for ending up in so disgraceful a situation.

Amos gave me another of his bleary looks and scratched Mr. Sheridan's name down on my record.

"Charge?"

"Theft," interjected the runner.

"With a value of how much?"

"Jewels with a value in excess of forty pounds."

"Ah! A capital crime then," said the clerk with a weary shake of his head. "Another one for the hangman."

I thought I was going to be sick. This was like some nightmare! Surely I would wake up any moment and find it was all a dream?

The runner came over to me. "Turn out your pockets, miss."

I got up unsteadily and emptied every last penny and scrap of paper I had in my possession on the counter. The runner poked the pile with distaste and fished out the crumpled pawnbroker's ticket.

"I thought as much. I was told you'd have the proof upon you."

"But I never pawned anything stolen!" I exclaimed staring at my signature on the piece of paper he was waving before me.

"No? I've been watching you since yesterday, my girl. Not long after our first meeting in Drury Lane, I had a witness here who had come to answer questions about a missing inkwell. He was very eager to be obliging and volunteered the information that he saw *you* giving a very large amount of jewelry to a broker two days ago—jewelry that you admitted to him was not yours," the runner said triumphantly. "So how did you come by it if you did not steal it? Did it drop from the sky into your lap or did you find it lying in the road? No, no, miss; your best hope now is to admit everything and pray that the magistrate is in a merciful mood. If you talk, he might think a spell in the new penal colony in Botany Bay punishment enough. If he's not feeling so lenient and you refuse to admit your wrongdoing, it'll be the noose for you or my name's King George."

Amos began to laugh like a pair of wheezy bellows at his colleague's wit. "That it certainly is not, Constable."

Constable Lennox gave him a tolerant smile. "Have you finished, Amos? Can I lock her up now?"

"All done," confirmed Amos, tucking the quill behind his ear.

"Follow me, miss," said the runner, taking a key from a chain at his belt and going over to a heavy iron door behind the clerk's counter.

I had no choice. I followed him and for the first time in my life found myself in jail. Never in my darkest dreams had I imagined I would end up here.

SCENE 3—JAIL

The constable led me down a narrow flight of stairs to the brick-lined basement of the magistrate's house. Once used for storing fine wines, the cellars had been converted into holding cells for unfortunates like me. The only daylight came in through gratings set in the pavement above. You could see the flicker of shadows of the people passing by, oblivious to the captives below their feet. My resolve to keep a brave front in face of adversity was crumbling and I wished I had someone whose shoulder I could weep on and be comforted. I wished I had a mother. I felt very young and very alone.

Before I had a chance to break down, the constable opened the door to the cell. There, sitting against the wall on the far side, was Billy Boil. No way was I going to let him see me cry.

"'Ello, Cat! I thought I'd be seeing you sooner or later," said Billy. "Welcome to my mansion." He threw out a grubby arm to point out the delights of his new abode.

The cell, about ten feet square, smelled worse than the foulest privy. Moldering straw covered the brick floor. A single bucket for the use of the prisoners stood in one corner—I did not look too closely, but it appeared to be full. Gray cobwebs festooned the flaking mortar, home to some disturbingly large spiders, and four rough-hewn benches flanked the walls. Billy was the only occupant for the present, except for the rat that had just scuttled out of sight.

"Glad to see you've found somewhere to your taste, Billy," I said, making light of the horror.

He laughed and stretched out on the bench, taking a bite from a wrinkled apple he held in his fist.

"You can jest, Cat," he mumbled through a mouthful of pulp, "but don't forget: you're in 'ere too. What does that say for your taste?"

"It says that it was tragically bad taste ever to have anything to do with you, you lying ball of cat sick. It's your lies that've brought me here."

"Now, now, that's enough," said the runner, pushing me into the cell. "I'd advise you, miss, to keep a civil tongue in your head, or it'll be the worse for you."

"You're not leaving me in here alone with him?" I asked desperately, grabbing hold of the runner's jacket.

He shook me off. "Naturally. There's only one holding cell and you're looking at it. If you're lucky, you won't be in here long—just a day or two."

"A day or two!"

"Until the magistrate can spare the time to hear your case. Then you'll be moved to a proper prison, of course."

"But if you leave me here with him, he'll kill me!"

"Ha!" barked Constable Lennox. "Serves you right, don't it? You should've thought of that before you got mixed up in this game."

With that, he shut the door behind him and turned the key. I moved to the bench on the opposite side of the room from Billy and sat down, head bowed, hands in my lap, wondering when my enemy would make his move. There was silence for a few moments, punctuated only by the sound of him chewing on his apple. Finally, he spoke.

"May I say, Pussycat, that you're looking remarkably swell today. I'd almost take you for a fine lady. Pity there's only me and the rats to appreciate it."

I said nothing but stared at my hands resting in the green silk of my lap.

"It's good to 'ave some company. Shame your pistol friend couldn't make it. Run off with the diamond and left you in the lurch, 'as 'e? You should've stuck with me, girl. None of this would've 'appened if you'd done that. But don't you fret, Kitten: if we blame the 'ole thing on 'im, we might just squeak out of this one. You tell the beak where 'e is and we're laughin'."

He took another bite of apple and crunched it loudly.

"Want some?"

He held out the half-eaten apple to me. I shook my head. I'd let nothing he had touched pass my lips.

"Fine. Suit yourself. But you'll find them a bit short on the old commons 'ere, Cat—not like those flash 'ouses in Grosvenor Square I 'ear you've been frequentin'. Is that where you got those togs?"

I said nothing.

"Gawd, Cat! It's gonna be a long night if you don't keep me company. We're both in the same boat now, both facing the drop. Can't you at least talk to me?" He took a final bite of the apple and threw the core into the corner, where vermin could be heard fighting over it. "I've been 'ere since the early 'ours, and I can tell you that it's not nice—no, not nice at all. Won't you need someone to run to when the rats start nibbling at your lace, eh?"

I looked up at him. He was grinning at me, enjoying every moment of my distress.

"You'd be the last person I'd run to, Billy. I'd go to the rats for help first."

His grimace broadened.

"That's what I like about you, Cat: your sense of 'umor. We'd've made a great team. Perhaps there's still time: if we stand by each other, we might get out of this mess. And when we do that, where'd you go? The respectable folk at the theater won't want you back. You could come with me and 'elp me set up my little business in the Rookeries. I've got some ideas—big ideas."

"I'm surprised you have any ideas at all."

He let this pass. "Ah, that's where you're wrong. That place is ripe for the pickin'. I'll start with askin' the innkeepers for a small consideration for protectin' their establishments. Move on to ownin' a few places myself. I'd give a fair price for goods people might come by 'inadvertently' like. 'Ave some boys and girls—workin' for me. You'd be a real 'elp, Cat, knowin' what you do about the 'igh end of the thievin' line. You'd make a capital fence. You could run the girls, if you like, if you give me a percentage of your take."

His picture of our "future" together was laughable. I had to say something.

"Billy, you've got me all wrong: I've never stolen anything in my life."

He gave me a wink. "'Course you ain't, Cat. Nor've I. We're as innocent as a pair of newborn babes, ain't we? Or that'll be our story."

I almost smiled: he was like some persistent suitor, not taking "no" for an answer. He didn't know that I had Lady Elizabeth rushing across town to come to my defense even as we spoke.

"Forget it, Billy. When your heels are swinging in the wind, I'll be free as a bird. You can forget the Rookeries: you're going to pay for what you did last night and I'll be in the front row cheering the executioner on."

"Pay, will I?" said Billy menacingly. He sat up, his boots thumping on the ground with a dull thud. "You may pretend to be Miss Goody Two Shoes, but don't forget, I know you and your game. If I'm for the nipping-jig, you'll be swinging up there with me. I'll make sure I take you."

"Dream on, Boil!" I replied, though I had felt a shiver down my spine as he spoke. "I've got powerful friends. I'll be out of here."

"Not before I've knocked some sense into you!" He sprang to his feet, kicking a mug of beer over as he did so. The sour liquid seeped into the straw. "Face it, Cat, no respectable friend is goin' to 'elp you now you're in 'ere. We're beyond the reach of all that's nice and polite. You've got to rely on yourself now." He ground his fist into his palm in frustration at my obstinacy. "Look, if we stick together, tell the same story, we're both free; if you split, I'm dead meat—and I'm not 'avin' that!" He made a lurch toward me. I cowered on my bench, face screwed up, having all too good a reason to fear his fists. But no blows fell. I opened my eyes and saw that he couldn't reach me: like a guard dog on a chain, his ankle had been manacled to a bolt in the floor. The ridiculous sight of an irate Billy trying to make a grab for me set me off into a peal of hysterical laughter.

The laughter quickly turned into hiccupping sobs. Billy glowered at me and retreated to his side of the room. He slipped a knife from his boot and began to pick at the bolt on the crumbling brick floor. My hysterical fit stopped as suddenly as it had come when the cold realization dawned that he would—given time—be able to work himself free.

Scrape, scrape, rattle went the knife on the manacle.

Neither of us spoke.

"Catherine Royal?"

The runner had returned and was standing by the door, a lantern in his hand. I sat up with a start, having dropped off into an uneasy slumber.

"Yes?" I said blearily.

"You're to come with me."

I got to my feet eagerly. Billy's eyes were on me, the knife concealed in the sleeve of his jacket. So had Lady Elizabeth finally arrived? I wondered. I had expected her to be here much sooner, and terrible doubts had begun to undermine my confidence in her, but at least she'd arrived before Billy had had a chance to work himself free of his bonds.

The runner led me back up the narrow stairs and into the office above. But we were not stopping there: he took my arm and led me through a pair of glass-paneled doors and down a corridor carpeted in a rich dark woolen cloth. We were clearly getting closer to the inner sanctum of the magistrate. The runner paused before a door with a polished brass handle and knocked.

"Come!" came a man's deep voice.

Constable Lennox opened the door to reveal a study lit by two high windows overlooking a pleasant garden at the rear of the house. The walls were lined with books; papers lay scattered in comfortable confusion on the desk and every available surface. In contrast to the chilly cellar the room was very warm, thanks to a fire roaring high in the grate, and in other circumstances it would have struck me as pleasant.

Though I took in all these details, my attention was mainly occupied by the people in the room, who had all turned to watch me enter. An unfamiliar bewigged elderly gentleman dressed in black with a snowy white stock at his neck sat behind a desk, fingers laced together as he surveyed me. On the edge of a chair in front of him perched Lady Elizabeth. Her face was drained of color and tear-stained. She looked quite wretched to see me in this state. By her side stood Lord Francis. His face was pale also, but it was the paleness brought on by the effort of suppressing great anger. On the far side of the room, looking out of the window at the garden, stood Marzi-pain Marchmont. He turned on my entry and gave me a triumphant smile. I now began to have some inkling of what was happening. Next to Marchmont stood the duke. His eyes were directed at me with blazing anger, and I felt their force almost as if he had actually lashed out at me. Marchmont whispered something to the duke, who then nodded as if his worst fears had been confirmed.

"Here's the prisoner, sir," said the constable, standing behind me with his arms folded as if I was some dangerous beast that he was here to guard.

The magistrate cleared his throat. "You are Catherine Royal, also known to the criminal fraternity as 'The Cat'?"

"It's just Cat—and that's to friends, not to criminals," I said quickly.

The magistrate surveyed me with disapproval. "Answer my questions with yes or no, girl. I don't want to hear any long speeches from you. Is that understood?"

"Yes, sir," I said meekly, my eyes straying to Lady Elizabeth for some clue as to what was happening here. I had half hoped for profuse apologies and instant release. This did not now appear to be in the cards.

The magistrate turned to the duke and Marchmont.

"Is this the girl—the impostor—you saw this morning in your house, your grace?"

The duke gave a curt nod. "Yes. I took careful note as the boy here—" he nodded to Marchmont "—had warned me only yesterday of the undue influence she seemed to have over my children. And I will swear that those are my daughter's clothes she is wearing—I recognize them. She must have stolen those as well as the jewels."

"She didn't steal them!" burst out Lord Francis, unable to restrain himself any longer. "Father, you are a fool to listen to the poison that that toad's been whispering in your ear! Lizzie gave them to her, as we've told you already ten thousand times, sir!"

"Silence!" barked the duke, glaring at his son. "I will not have anyone, least of all my own son, call me a fool!"

"Then stop acting like one!" snapped Lord Francis unwisely.

"I warned you," said the duke, his voice menacing, "before we came here, that you are to say no more on this subject. I am shocked—shocked and grieved to find out that a son of mine has allowed his sister to fall into the clutches of so artful a creature. I expected better from you. This means school, sir, school!"

"I don't care if you send me to school, Father, as long as you listen to the truth for once!"

"Insolent boy!" cried the duke, raising his hand as if to box Lord Francis's ears but at the last moment letting it drop.

Marchmont was grinning, enjoying Lord Francis's discomfort. I wished I were close enough to slap him.

"But, Papa," said Lady Elizabeth, laying a gentle hand on her father's sleeve, "it is true—I did give her those things."

The duke patted his daughter's arm tenderly.

"I know you're just saying this in a misguided attempt to help the girl, Lizzie. You would not willingly have pawned the jewels your mother and I gave you on your coming out—I know how dear they are to you. What earthly reason could you have to do this? You want for nothing, need nothing. I've always seen to that."

Lady Elizabeth turned agonized eyes to me. I could guess what she was thinking: if she mentioned Johnny now, before the magistrate, then he would be joining me in the holding cells with little or no chance of escape. Who knows what the law would make of our attempt to help a wanted man? We were all bound to silence until his ship sailed.

"Papa, you've always been very generous to me, but I didn't want to tell you that . . . that . . ." Lady Elizabeth floundered.

"That she needed money to pay my gambling debts," said Lord Francis quickly.

The duke wheeled around to his son.

"Gambling debts? This is the first I've heard of debts! When did this happen?"

"At the boxing last Sunday—the match between the Bow Street Butcher and the Camden

Crusher," he said, the details rolling fluently from his tongue.

The duke flushed red, realizing that his son's illness had been feigned. He had escaped a morally improving dose of church for a surfeit of pleasure at the ring.

"And how did you get to a boxing match, sir? Who took you?" he asked coldly.

"Pedro, the African violinist, took me. Cat was against it and didn't want me with them."

"This girl went to a boxing match?" said the duke, looking at me incredulously. I suppose it did seem very unlikely, dressed as I was in lace and silk with my hair in ribbons. "Did you, girl? Is my son telling the truth?"

I nodded as it seemed I must if the gambling story were to be corroborated.

"She was dressed as a boy, of course," said Lord Francis, wrongly thinking that this would make it more excusable in his father's eyes.

"Dressed as a boy?" The duke's blue eyes blazed beneath his beetling white brows.

I nodded again.

"And I suppose she trapped you into gambling, didn't she?" said the duke to his son.

"No, no, that was entirely my fault. She was against that as well. Later, Lizzie offered to help me out by pawning the jewels. Cat volunteered to take them to the broker."

"Hmm." The duke looked from his son to me. "It would be just like Lizzie to let you impose on her, Francis. You should be heartily ashamed of yourself for abusing your sister's trust."

Lord Francis hung his head, hoping this reprimand was a sign that his father was swallowing the story.

"But you didn't see a penny of it, did you, you young fool?" Lord Francis opened his mouth to protest, but the duke silenced him with a warning finger. "Admit it: you were let down. You chose your agent badly, didn't you? The girl went off with the money and gave it to that Shepherd boy."

"A very bad character, that," interjected the magistrate. "He was caught with the whole forty pounds on him, your grace. The girl had the pawnbroker's ticket in her pocket when we picked her up. It seems an open and shut case of theft by deception—possibly extortion as well when we add in the clothes." He peered down his nose at me as if I was something unsavory the dog had dug up. "That dress must be worth ten pounds at least, I'd say. Faced with such a breathtakingly audacious crime, I don't think I can even take into account the tender age of the offender. I doubt I'll recommend mercy when she comes for sentencing."

Marchmont appeared delighted by the news.

"And, sir, if I may add," he said, driving a further nail into my coffin, "I have cause to think she has been consorting with criminals of an even worse kind—traitors, no less—protecting them, no doubt in exchange for money."

We had to get him off the subject of Johnny. I could find no words to speak in my own defense as the realization hit me that neither the duke nor the magistrate believed in my good character, and both were determined to see me punished for sins I had not committed. I was going nowhere but back to the holding cell; from there to the dock; from the dock to . . . I did not even want to think about that.

"But, Papa, she's not like that! Mr. Marchmont is wrong. You don't understand," pleaded Lady Elizabeth.

"Ah, Lizzie, Lizzie!" said the duke with a sad shake of his head. "Perhaps this whole experience will be a good lesson for you. You've been brought up so narrowly by your mother and me that you were not prepared when you came across your first experience of the depravity of men's hearts. You saw an innocent-looking girl needing your help; I see a bloodsucking leech who has latched on to you and has taken advantage of your unsuspecting nature. If young Marchmont here had not alerted me to the danger, who knows what other liberties she would have taken?"

His insults were too much.

"I'm not a leech!" I protested. "You can have the dress back—I don't care. I never stole that money. It was taken from me before I could give it back to Lady Elizabeth."

"I warned you, young woman," said the magistrate portentously, "save your speeches for the trial. I only allowed you up here on the request of the duke so that he could confront his children with your crimes. I think we've heard quite enough. You can take her back down."

The runner put a heavy hand on my shoulder.

"Cat!" exclaimed Lady Elizabeth, breaking free of her father and dashing across to me to grab my wrist. "I swear it'll be all right. I'll make sure it is."

"Don't touch her!" barked the duke. "You don't know what kind of pests and diseases she might be harboring. I don't want to lose my precious rose to a jail fever." He stepped between Lady Elizabeth and me so that my head butted against his embroidered waistcoat.

Lord Francis scrambled roughly past Marchmont and around the desk to intercept me at the door.

"Is there anything you need, Cat? Other than to get out of here, of course?" he asked with an attempt at a brave smile.

My voice broke into a sob as the runner began to drag me away. I tried to school my lips to respond in kind, but my heart was breaking.

"Ask Pedro to bring some of my things from the theater—if they'll let him," I said in a strangled voice. "But get me out of here quickly, please! I'm in a cell with Billy Shepherd, and I don't think . . . I don't think I'm going to last long."

"Dammit, Cat, we'll get you out—I promise you! Even if it's the last thing I do!" called out Lord Francis as I was led away to my cell.

SCENE 4—CHAMPAGNE

R eader, I can safely say that my first night in jail was the worst experience of my life so far. The green silk dress no longer felt luxuriously soft against my skin; it had become a torment, eating into me with the acid touch of shame. I wanted to rip it off and even would have if I had had something else to put on. I did not dare sleep a wink, for though Billy gave up on working on his chains around midnight and was snoring loudly stretched out on his bench, I was afraid that if I dropped off to sleep, I would wake to find his knife at my throat—or not wake at all. Added to this, I was cold, hungry, and just plain uncomfortable. I sat for many hours hugging my knees, willing myself to stay alert, listening to the sound of the carriages and wagons rumbling past outside, the scratch of tiny clawed feet rooting in the straw. Somewhere in the darkness a steady drip, drip, drip marked the passing moments.

I found myself wondering if I would ever see the light of day again. Just how firmly set against me was the duke? Would his children be believed once Johnny sailed and they could tell the whole truth, or would he think this just another invention to save my neck? And even if by some happy chance I was freed, what then? As Billy said, unless I was released without a stain on my character, no respectable place would want me back. Mr. Sheridan would perhaps believe my story, but even he might be persuaded to doubt me. After all, my conduct over the past few days, eavesdropping and popping up where he least wanted me to be, would hardly endear me to him. Mr. Sheridan had not felt able to trust me with the secret of the diamond. I would understand if he now preferred to see the back of me.

My dark thoughts were interrupted in the small hours of the morning by a soft metallic tapping noise. I started, wondering for a disconcerted moment if Billy had begun work on his fetters again, but then realized that the sound came from the grating in the ceiling—the only entry for light and air to the cellar beneath.

"Cat!" came a soft hiss. "Cat!"

I leaped to my feet and moved as quietly across the room as I could so as not to wake my cellmate. Rats scattered from my path, squeaking in alarm. Billy gave a murmur. I stopped. He then rolled over onto his back and resumed snoring even louder than before.

"Cat!" came the voice again, now more urgent.

I reached the grating and stood directly below it, looking up into the darkness.

"Who is it?" I whispered.

"It's me, Pedro!" said my friend, rather too loudly.

I could have wept to hear his voice.

"Ssh!" I cautioned. "Billy's here—asleep for the moment, but he could wake up."

Pedro lowered his voice. "I've got Syd and Frank with me—they're keeping watch. We couldn't get to you before now. The night patrol's just gone in for some refreshment. We've only got a few minutes, I'd guess."

"I'm so pleased you came." I didn't need to tell him how awful it was. Pedro had been on the lower decks of a slave ship. He'd know only too well and would have seen worse.

"I've got some food. Frank took it from home. I'll slip it between the bars. I've got something to drink too, but I can't get the bottle through," Pedro said.

"Wait!" I said. "I've got a mug." I ran to fetch the cup of water I'd been given with my crust for supper. I tipped the remains into the slop bucket and held it up. Pedro uncorked a bottle and carefully began to pour the contents between the bars. I had to stretch on my tiptoes to reach up and I wobbled slightly at one point. The liquid splashed on the side of the cup and cascaded down onto my upturned face.

"What is it? I gasped as the sweet mixture splashed into my eyes and mouth. I wiped it away.

"Champagne," said Pedro.

"Champagne!"

"It's all Frank could steal from home, Cat."

"I must be the first prisoner at His Majesty's Pleasure to sup on champagne!" I said, managing my first smile since I had arrived down here.

"Cat, you're a marvel." In the faint moonlight, I could see Pedro's eyes twinkling. "Here's the food." He pushed a flat parcel between the bars.

"What's this?" I joked, stuffing it into my pocket for later consumption. "Smoked salmon and syllabub?"

"No," answered Pedro with perfect seriousness. "Game pie, roast beef, and apple and almond tart. Leftovers from some fancy dinner party, Frank says. It might be a bit jumbled up—sorry about that—but I had to squash it to get it through."

We were both silent for a moment, Pedro staring down, me looking up.

"Oh, Cat . . ." he began. I could tell he was going to commiserate with me but I couldn't bear that. It was all I could do to keep from breaking down as it was.

"How's the wind? Has Johnny sailed?" I asked quickly.

"No." Pedro looked nervously over his shoulder, presumably to where the others were waiting. Our time was running out. "And we've agreed that tomorrow we'll let Johnny know what's happened and tell the duke the whole story."

"You can't do that!" I said, aghast. "They'll catch him."

"But we all know that Johnny wouldn't want us to leave you down here on his account. The only way the duke can be brought to believe his children is if Johnny can be produced. The duke's already packing Frank off to school tomorrow—our chances to change his mind are fast running out."

"But the duke will tell the magistrate, then Johnny'll be down here charged with treason!"

"We know," said Pedro grimly, "but in case you haven't noticed you're facing a capital charge too. We think that there's more chance of a rich man with powerful friends, like Johnny, being let off by an English jury for insulting the king, than for an orphan like you, charged with theft by a peer of the realm. Let's face it, Cat, you're as good as dead if this goes any further."

"But— !"

"There are no buts. You're outvoted on this—four to one. Five to one if Johnny were here."

"Four? Who's the fourth?"

"Syd. We've told him the whole story. He said that if they don't let you go he'll break you out himself and finish Billy off while he's at it, but we've persuaded him to hold off for the moment."

"Tell him thanks, but he's not to get into any trouble for me," I said, though heartened to find I still had friends on my side.

Pedro looked over his shoulder. I too heard a sharp whistle.

"That's it. I've got to go. But you're all right, aren't you, Cat? Billy's not giving you any trouble?"

"I'm fine," I lied. What was the point in telling the truth? It would only upset them. "But Pedro, don't tell Johnny just yet. Let's see if we can think of something else. I don't want his death on my conscience."

Pedro gave my outstretched fingers a gentle squeeze. "And we don't want yours on ours! No promises, Cat. Good-bye!"

And with that he sprang to his feet and dashed off into the darkness.

His departure was rapidly followed by the tramp, tramp, tramp of the night patrol resuming their duties.

I returned to my bench and set my mug carefully down beside me. With great care I opened the package of food and spread it on my lap. So there I sat on a hard seat with my back against the slimy wall of the cell, staring down on a terrible irony. On my skirt was the finest supper I had ever seen, even though, as Pedro had warned, it was somewhat mangled in its journey across town. And I had champagne to wash it down—a drink I had never tasted before. Well, it was either look at the food until the rats stole it from under my nose, or eat and have done with ironies. I ate—and enjoyed it. But there was one unanticipated side effect: the wine sent me into an overpowering sleep. Murderous cellmate or no, the bubbles of champagne could not be resisted.

"Morning, Cat."

I was rudely woken by an apple core bouncing on my forehead. I sat up with a start.

"Still 'ere then with poor old Billy, I see. Might be thinking my offer weren't so bad after all, eh?"

I looked across the cell and saw Billy grinning like an evil goblin in a fairy tale.

"You don't look so fine this morning, girl. You'd better get out of 'ere before you ruin that there new dress of yours."

I looked down. The silk was now dirty and stained with the champagne that had spilled on it last night. My once-white silk stockings were gray and had a large hole on one knee. My hair straggled over my shoulders, the once-neat ringlets ruined by a night on the bench.

"So where are your fine friends? Forgotten about their pussycat, 'ave they?"

No they haven't, I thought to myself, determined not to let Billy wear me down with his jibes. After all, I had supped on fine meats and sparkling wine.

"Good morning, Mr. Shepherd," I said, stretching and yawning as if just waking from a deep sleep on a goose feather mattress. I was feeling strangely light-headed, as if buoyed up still on the bubbles of the champagne. "I see the weather is set fair today."

Billy half-turned to look up at the grating but then caught himself.

"You've cracked, ain't you, Cat? Poor girl: one night behind bars, and you've lost it."

"No, *au contraire, mon ami*, I have never been more in my right mind. I was just reflecting on the pleasure a good supper can give an empty belly."

"A good supper? You call a crust of bread and a mug of scummy water a good supper? They must 'ave been meaner at the theater than I thought."

I picked up my mug, which still had an inch of pale golden liquid at its bottom, and raised it to my companion.

"Your good health, sir," I toasted him and downed it with a gulp, then gave a small, contented burp.

"Mad! Quite mad!" exclaimed Billy, rubbing his hand across his forehead, half in admiration, half in doubt.

The rattle of keys at the door made us both look up. Constable Lennox appeared in the entrance.

"Miss Royal. Come with me."

My heart leaped into my throat as I wondered what this summons signified. Surely it was too early for the magistrate to be sitting? I would have thought he would be sipping hot chocolate in his powdering gown, not choosing to deal with the London riffraff like me. Or—I swallowed hard—had they caught Johnny? But I had no choice in the matter: I had to follow.

Billy must have been wondering the same thing. My premature departure did not suit him at all: he'd not yet had time to persuade me to lie to save us both.

"Where's she goin'?" he asked the runner urgently, again rushing to the length of his chain like a zealous guard dog.

The runner did not deign to give an answer, but shut the door on him.

"This way, miss."

He did not place his hand on my shoulder as he had done on my last outing from the cell but walked ahead, shining a lantern so that we would not miss our step. Anxious but intrigued, I followed him up the stairs and into an office. There, standing in front of the desk occupied by the clerk Amos, was a gentleman in a claret-colored jacket and black boots. He turned to face me: it was the Earl of Ranworth, Johnny's father.

"Is this the child, my lord?" asked the runner respectfully, ushering me forward.

"Indeed it is," said the earl. He was staring as if stunned to see me there, though apparently he had asked for me to be brought to him.

"And you say you know for a fact that she gave forty pounds to your son on behalf of the duke's daughter, which he returned to this child on the evening of the day before yesterday, after receiving money from you?"

"That is exactly right. So, you see, Constable, the girl would not have had time to return the money to its original owner as no doubt she intended to do."

"So how did it end up in the hands of Billy Shepherd?" the runner asked, looking at me doubtfully.

"I suggest you ask her. Has anyone thought to listen to what she has to say about the whole matter?"

Constable Lennox coughed uncomfortably. "Well, sir, I can't say that . . ."

"Ask her then, man!"

The runner turned to me. "You heard the gentleman," he said roughly. "What's your story?"

"Billy's boys broke in to steal . . . to steal something they thought was in the theater," I began quickly. "Two of them—I don't know their real names—found the money under my pillow and took it. I told Billy and he took it off them later to count it."

"So he wasn't one of the thieves who stole it from you?"

I reluctantly shook my head, but the truth was I couldn't incriminate Billy without explaining more about Johnny and the beating.

"There you are, Constable," said the earl loudly, putting an arm around my shoulders. "You've got the wrong people. It's those two boys you should be after, not this little girl. Tell the man what they were like, child, and I'm sure that'll be the end of the whole business."

"Now wait a minute, my lord," stuttered the runner. "I can't just let her go. I need proof. Where's this son of yours? What's he to do with it? I'll need to speak to him."

"You can't, sir. He sailed this morning on the tide."

"Where to? When will he be back?"

The Earl of Ranworth drew himself up to his full patrician height and glared at the runner. He reminded me forcibly of Johnny in one of his more frightening moods, such as when he had confronted Billy's gang with empty pistols.

"I don't know, man," he said irritably. "He's gone and that's that. You can't keep an innocent child in prison just because my son's not here. My word not do then?"

"But the duke!" said the runner feebly.

"Heavens, man! I'll deal with that. Look, here's fifty pounds bail for the girl." The earl drew a large paper banker's draft from his pocketbook and let it flutter down onto the desk. "You let her go now and I'll swear that the duke will have dropped all charges by mid-morning, or call me an ass!"

As the unfortunate runner did not want to be accused of calling a lord an ass, he reluctantly picked up the banker's order and nodded to Amos.

"Start to make the necessary arrangements, Amos," he said. "I'll clear this with the magistrate."

"Sir John Solmes, isn't it?" said the earl.

Constable Lennox nodded.

"In that case, I'll come along and help you. We're old friends—went to the same school. You sit there, child. I won't be long."

The earl led me to a chair by the fireside and handed me into it as if I were a fine lady.

"Thank you," I said hoarsely, bemused by this unexpected turn of events. How had he known I was here? And would he really be able to get me out?

In the interval that followed, all that could be heard in the office was the scratching of Amos's quill and the crackle of the fire. For the first time since yesterday afternoon I did not feel cold.

"Ready to go, my dear?"

In my exhausted state I must have fallen into a doze, for the earl was at my elbow before I knew it.

"Go?"

"Yes, child. You are free to go."

"She's on bail, sir," corrected Constable Lennox, looking at me with distrust. He clearly still suspected me of as yet unspecified crimes. After all, he had me down as the mastermind behind one of London's most fearsome gangs.

The earl ignored him.

"My carriage waits outside. We have a call we must make before I can return you home, I'm afraid, Catherine." The earl helped me to my feet. "Good morning." He tipped his hat to Amos and the constable and led me out into the sunlight.

"How did you know?" I asked once we were settled in his carriage. The earl tucked a large blanket around me and handed me a flask of warm tea.

"Sheridan. Last night he sent an urgent message explaining how you'd ended up in jail thanks to my miscreant of a son. I came as soon as I could, but I had to check that Jonathan had gone."

"So it's true—he has left."

"Yes, sailed this morning with a stiff breeze to fill his sails. You need not worry about him anymore, Catherine."

"It's Cat. Johnny calls me Cat."

"Does he indeed?" The earl smiled and ruffled my hair in the exact same gesture used by his son. "Well, here is one father who is mighty pleased that his offspring had the sense to choose you for his friend. That African boy—Pedro, isn't it?—told me all about your exploits this morning when he took me to the docks. We were just in time to see the *Potomac* heading out to sea."

I snuggled back into the blanket. "So where are we going now?"

"To get that fool of a duke to drop his ridiculous charges, of course!" said the Earl of Ranworth.

We arrived at the front door of Grosvenor Square just as the big house began to wake up for the day. Footmen were opening the shutters. A maid was scrubbing the doorstep as we made our entrance. She bobbed a curtsy as we passed.

Joseph, the footman, opened the door to us.

"My lord," he said with a bow, recognizing the caller. His eyes slid to the shabby urchin bundled up in a blanket and I saw a look of alarm flicker in his eyes, but when he spoke his voice remained calmly professional. "His grace is at breakfast. Shall I tell him you are here?"

"That won't be necessary," said the earl, striding past him. I hovered on the doorstep, uncertain as to my welcome across this threshold, until the earl turned back. "Come on, Catherine. You have to come too."

Joseph stepped forward. I thought for a moment that he was going to throw me out, but instead he said, perfectly politely:

"Would miss like me to take her . . . her cloak?"

"If it's all the same to you," I said in an embarrassed whisper, "I think I'll keep it on." Underneath I was hardly fit to be seen in these halls.

Joseph bowed. "Of course, miss."

I stepped into the foyer and saw a chest waiting at the bottom of the stairs.

"His lordship's," said Joseph in a low voice. "Off to school after breakfast, I'm afraid, miss." The footman gave me a significant look as if to say he was fully aware of the circumstances that saw me arrive there smelling of the sewer and that would drive his master off the premises.

"Avon!" The Earl of Ranworth strode on while Joseph and I hung back to have our brief conversation. He was opening door after door, looking for the duke. "Dammit, man, where are you?"

Joseph hurried to overtake him and opened a door on the far side of the foyer.

"The duke is in the breakfast room, my lord," he said, ushering us through. "Good luck!" he muttered as I passed.

The Duke of Avon was indeed at his breakfast, sitting at the far end of a long table draped in a snowy linen cloth. He had a newspaper propped up on the salt cellar in front of him and was tucking into a hearty meal of eggs and bacon. On his right sat a disconsolate Lady Elizabeth, who was toying with a piece of dry toast. Standing by the sideboard with his back to his father was Lord Francis. He was in the act of slipping a muffin into his pocket, and I guessed he was hoping to supply me with my own breakfast later that morning as his parting gesture.

"What the devil!" blurted the duke on seeing the Earl of Ranworth burst into the room with so little ceremony. He then spotted me and dropped his fork with a clatter. "What's she doing here? Joseph! Joseph!"

But Joseph did not come. I suspected that he had become conveniently deaf and was preventing any other servants answering the summons from his post outside the door.

"Cut that out, Avon!" barked the Earl of Ranworth. "You are not turning anyone—least of all this child—out of your house until you've heard me through. You've been a complete fool and thrown an innocent girl into prison. You would have murdered her too if I hadn't come to hear of it."

"What the . . .!" said the duke, unable to find the words to express his astonishment.

"She had that money to pay for my wretched boy's ticket to America. Your daughter—as kind and lovely a girl as a father could wish for—was ready to help Jonathan, for she cared more for him than those bits of glitter and gold that she had in her jewelry box—and you should be proud of her. As for your son, his only crime was to help a friend in trouble and find a safe passage for him. He is completely blameless."

"But, but . . ." The duke was looking from son to daughter, who both were staring at the Earl of Ranworth, openmouthed. They had been as unprepared for his entrance as their father. "But what has Lord Jonathan got to do with all this?"

The Earl of Ranworth gave a great groan as if it cost him much to admit his family's shame.

"The foolish boy only got himself charged with treason."

"Treason!" exclaimed the duke in astonishment.

"Yes, man. He is Captain Sparkler, of course. Stupid boy! Well, he is paying the price for it now. Some years in exile should knock that nonsense out of him."

"Captain Sparkler?" The duke was having difficulty keep pace with developments. He turned to Lady Elizabeth. "You knew this?"

"Yes, Papa," she said meekly.

"And is all this true?"

She nodded.

"My God!" exclaimed the duke, throwing his napkin onto the table and striding to the window. He looked out on the Square, trying to find counsel in the trees and grass.

"So you see, Avon, you've been a fool," continued the Earl of Ranworth. "You should go on bended knee to ask this child's pardon. Think what you would have felt if someone had put one of your own children into that hell pit, eh? But *you* did that, paying no heed to the pleas of your family. An innocent child, Avon! Look at her! And thanks to you she's passed the night in a cell with one of London's most hard-bitten criminals."

The duke turned his eyes to me. I must have made a sorry sight in my blanket. Was he finally convinced or not?

"Well, Miss Royal . . ." the duke began. He stopped and cleared his throat. "It does appear that I owe you an apology."

Despite myself, I let out a sob and crumpled into the nearest chair, tears of relief now streaming down my face. The Earl of Ranworth patted my shoulder comfortingly.

Lady Elizabeth leaped to her feet and clapped her hands. "Oh, Papa! You believe us now?"

He nodded. "I believe you. But why on earth didn't you tell me the truth—the whole truth, mind? All this rubbish about boxing matches and betting—what was I to think?"

"Well, sir . . . you see, sir . . .," said Lord Francis, pulling on his collar as if it were choking him.

Lady Elizabeth saved the day. "But, Papa, look at poor Miss Royal! She's in a frightful state. The least we can do is make sure she is bathed and rested. Then you must take her back to the theater yourself and make sure everyone understands that she is blameless in this whole affair."

"You are right, as usual, Lizzie," said the duke, patting his daughter on the arm. "Miss Royal, I hope you will accept my apology and my daughter's offer to assist you now."

"Thank you," I said, struggling to control my tears. "I would be most grateful." I took a calming breath and smiled at Lady Elizabeth and Lord Francis, feeling the trails of salty tears on my cheeks.

I was free at last!

EPILOGUE

DIAMOND

I shall never forget my return home. The duke refused to let me skulk in by the side entrance but escorted me into the auditorium, followed by Lady Elizabeth on her brother's arm. There, to my astonishment, was gathered the entire theater company—and more besides! As my foot crossed the threshold, Peter Dodsley led the orchestra in a fanfare and everyone broke into applause.

Before I knew it, I was back among them all. Syd pulled me firmly away from the duke and into the middle of a scrum of his boys. I had my hand shaken, my hair ruffled, and my back slapped by so many that I lost count. Pedro elbowed his way to the front, and we gave each other a hug, needing no words to express our relief that we were together again.

"Order! Order, gentlemen!" laughed Mr. Sheridan as he extricated me from the Butcher's Boys. "I need this young lady for a moment. You'll get her back, I promise."

He led me up onto the stage, where the Avons were waiting by the grounded balloon.

"In you go, Cat," said Lord Francis mischievously.

"What?" I protested as he hoisted me over the side of the basket. Mr. Sheridan hopped in after me and gave a wave to Mr. Bishop. The ropes began to creak and I grabbed onto the rim.

"Are you sure this can take two?" I asked anxiously.

Mr. Sheridan laughed, showing no sign of concern as we were heaved over the heads of the crowd. "I thought you liked living dangerously, Cat."

"Now what gave you that idea?"

He grinned and turned to address his audience.

"My lords, ladies and gentlemen, now that we have our returning heroine center stage, the Duke of Avon would like to make an announcement!"

A hush fell in the theater. The duke stepped onto the forestage.

"I am sure you are all relieved to have your friend back among you after the distress of the last few days." He paused and coughed. "I would like every one of you to know that not a single cloud shades this young lady's reputation. It was all a stupid mistake on my part, for which I am most heartily ashamed and sorry.

"You should be proud of her. She will always have a welcome at my house and, I hope, here at yours."

"Hear! Hear!" shouted Peter Dodsley. Applause erupted again from all sides. Syd and his boys whistled. My cheeks were burning and I didn't know where to look. The upturned faces suddenly became very blurry.

Mr. Sheridan handed me a handkerchief.

"So, Cat, you did look after my diamond after all," he said softly as he gave me a moment to compose myself.

"Look after the diamond?" I blew my nose. "No, I did a hopeless job. I didn't even know what

I was looking after until it was too late. Shepherd's gang was convinced there was a real diamond by then and came looking for it. I had no time to let them know that there was nothing here."

"Oh, but there was."

"You mean the reward for Johnny? I suppose they would have accepted that gladly enough."

"No, I didn't mean that. They didn't realize that under my nose I had a real treasure that I had ignored all these years. You see, Cat, even with Captain Sparkler gone, I still have one treasure left in Drury Lane. I have my Cat— useful in a tight spot. I'll certainly bear you in mind next time I or any of my friends land themselves in trouble."

His words warmed me, thawing the last remnants of fear that lingered from my night among the disreputable and disgraced. I blushed at his kind words. No one at the theater had ever before said that I was of any value.

"So, are you ready to return to the party?" he asked.

"Party?"

"Yes, to welcome home Cat: the diamond of Drury Lane."

Balloon descends. Curtain falls.

ALL ABROAD—wide of the mark

ALL MY EYE—a load of rubbish

ALL UP WITH—doomed, finished

ANNE'S FAN—a rude gesture with thumb to nose and hand spread (don't do this at a Bow Street runner unless you want your ears boxed)

ARSY-VARSY—preposterous; it can also mean "head-over-heels," bum upwards

BARTHOLOMEW FAIR—fair held in August at Smithfield; the entertainments are spectacular—rope-dancers, acrobats, wrestling . . . what more could you want!

BEAK—magistrate

BEAU—sweetheart (and whatever that Billy says, I don't have one)

BOW STREET MAGISTRATE'S COURT—a place you definitely don't want to end up

BOW STREET RUNNERS—the magistrate's men who police the streets around Westminster (not my favorite people)

CARRIER—horse and cart that carries people and parcels, usually very slowly

COVENT GARDEN—fruit and vegetable market; there's also a theater of that name but we don't talk about it

CREEPER—louse, toady

DAGGLE-TAIL—slatternly woman

DONE A MIDNIGHT FLIT—run off

THE DROP—the gallows; a hanging

FLASH—showy

FLAT—someone easily fooled

THE FLIES—area above the stage where scenery and lighting is suspended

FOGRUM—senile old man

FROGGIES—a rude nickname for French people

FUNK—to back out, to fight shy

GERRARD STREET—a favorite street of writers, artists, and print sellers

GIMCRACK—showy but worthless

GOB-FULL OF CLARET—a bloody mouth

THE GODS—balcony seats

GREEN ROOM—place where actors wait to go on stage, so called because of the color of its walls

GROSVENOR SQUARE—high-class part of the West End of London

HEMPEN FEVER—death by hanging (the rope is made of hemp)

HOG-GRUBBER—mean, nasty, sneaking person

HOYDEN—boisterous girl

ISLINGTON—country village, north of London

JARVEY—driver of a hackney cab

JOHN BULL—the British nation; the government

LAID UP IN LAVENDER—pawned

MARYLEBONE FIELDS—open land just north of Oxford Street

MOONSHINE (a load of . . .)— insubstantial rubbish

NIPPING-JIG—dance of death on the gallows

NOSEGAY—little bouquet to hide bad odors (and there are plenty of them around my neighborhood)

NOT WORTH A FART—you don't really need me to explain this, do you?

THE PENNY SEEMED TO HAVE DROPPED—to suddenly realize or understand something

THE PIT—lowest level in the theater, frequented by gentlemen and those aspiring to be counted in that class

THE POOL—moorings in the Thames

PORTER—a dark beer

PRIG—self-righteous know-it-all (as well as lots of other meanings I won't repeat)

RETICULE—a small, drawstring purse

THE ROOKERIES—also known as St. Giles, a dangerous district you should avoid if you want to emerge with your possessions, teeth, and hair intact

SCARPERED—run away

THE SERPENTINE—a lake in Hyde Park

THEATER ROYAL, DRURY LANE—the best theater in the world. And my home, just off Covent Garden

TOGS—clothes

TOWER OF LONDON—fortress and prison

WAPPING—the docks (keep an eye on your valuables)

WITH KNOBS ON—even more; that goes double!

THE WRONG END OF THE STICK—misunderstanding; being confused

questions for the author

JULIA GOLDING

What did you want to be when you grew up?

When I was eight I knew I was going to be an author— then talked myself out of it in my teens thinking I would need a proper job! Fortunately, sanity returned a decade later and here I am.

When did you realize you wanted to be a writer?

When I wrote my first story and got positive feedback from my victims, I mean, audience.

What's your first childhood memory?

Going around a French supermarket in a pushchair asking for "flat" bread and complaining about the cheese smell.

What's your most embarrassing childhood memory?

Performing a two-hander version of *My Fair Lady* for my Brownie guide drama badge and thinking I was good at it . . .

As a young person, who did you look up to most?

My dad—he was a lot taller than me. . . .

What was your worst subject in school?
Swimming.

What was your first job?
First full-time job was as a British diplomat working in the embassy in Poland.

How did you celebrate publishing your first book?
I had a big party where everyone dressed up as eighteenth-century characters. We had a quiz and lots of fun.

Where do you write your books?
In a café.

Where do you find inspiration for your writing?
It comes from everywhere. Cat Royal came from a love of theatre.

Which of your characters is most like you?
Lizzie maybe—but they are all me in a way.

When you finish a book, who reads it first?
I read it to my family as I write it, chapter by chapter.

Are you a morning person or a night owl?
Definitely morning.

What's your idea of the best meal ever?
A really well-cooked baked potato with yummy topping whilst watching a fireworks display.

Which do you like better: cats or dogs?
Cats.

SQUARE FISH

What do you value most in your friends?
Being there when you need them.

Where do you go for peace and quiet?
My bedroom—or if I can travel, Iona, a Scottish island.

What makes you laugh out loud?
My friend, Clare. We are capable of getting hysterical over the stupidest things.

What's your favorite song?
"Land of the Silver Birch"—a traditional Canadian song that I sang to all my children as a lullaby.

Who is your favorite fictional character?
Lizzie Bennet from *Pride and Prejudice* (though I also have a soft spot for Mr. Darcy).

What are you most afraid of?
Something bad happening to my family.

What time of the year do you like best?
May.

What is your favorite TV show?
A British sci-fi series called *Doctor Who* about a time traveler.

If you were stranded on a desert island, who would you want for company?
Ray Mears—well-known in England as a survival expert. He'd build the shelter, get the food, cook the meal in no time at all.

SQUARE FISH

If you could travel in time, where would you go?
Georgian London, of course.

What's the best advice you have ever received about writing?
Don't get pigeonholed in one genre.

What do you want readers to remember about your books?
That Cat's life is fun and exciting—history doesn't have to be dull.

What would you do if you ever stopped writing?
Return to working for Oxfam, an international aid agency.

What do you like best about yourself?
That I'm creative.

What is your worst habit?
Reading when I should be doing other stuff.

What do you consider to be your greatest accomplishment?
Having my children.

What do you wish you could do better?
Swim!

What would your readers be most surprised to learn about you?
That I don't like ice cream (this is true).

SQUARE FISH

*K*eep reading for an excerpt from
Julia Golding's **Cat Among the Pigeons**,
available now in hardcover from Roaring Brook Press.

EXCERPT

I still can't believe it happened—not here, not in my theater.

Forgive my scrawl: my hands are shaking even as I write this. I find it hard to put pen to paper when I want to scream at the unfairness of the world and throw the inkpot across the room. Oh yes, we Londoners pretend to be all civilized and cultured, a beacon to the world, but it's all lies. We're rotten—and will remain so as long as a man is able to walk into the Theater Royal, Drury Lane, and claim a fellow human being as his property.

I must calm myself.

Part of it is my fault, for I told Pedro that we would have the place to ourselves this early in the morning; I thought we'd have plenty of time to practice away from hostile eyes. How wrong I was.

You see, Reader, Pedro has just been cast in his first speaking role: that of Ariel, the sprite who serves the magician Prospero in Shakespeare's *The Tempest*. I am so proud of him—and of Mr. Kemble, who has taken a gamble in giving the role to Pedro over the heads of many more experienced actors. There had been quite a rumpus backstage when the news leaked out to the cast that one of the choice roles had gone to my African friend. It wasn't enough for some of the disappointed actors that he had proved himself a skilled musician and a dancer—to them he is still an outsider and he's black-skinned: that damns him in their eyes. With the lingering jealousy and prejudice backstage, Pedro wanted to prove his detractors wrong and be word perfect for the dress rehearsal today.

"Come on, Pedro, give me a hand here!" I put my lantern on the floor and struggled with the winch that raises the curtains. Pedro was standing motionless on the forestage, staring into the darkness of the empty auditorium. Doubtless he was imagining a variety of receptions for his debut. Would it be orange peel and turnips or flowers and applause?

"Stop thinking about it," I cautioned him. "What will happen will happen. Nobody, not even Mr. Sheridan himself, can guess how an audience will behave on the night."

Pedro turned to me and flashed a brilliant smile. The light of his candle lit him alone, leaving the rest of the theater in darkness. "They're going to be amazed." He threw his arms wide and bowed. "I'll make sure they love me!"

"Hmm, we'll see." I'd forgotten that Pedro was never one to underestimate his own abilities. "If you're going to be so astonishing, we'd better practice some more. Give a lady a hand, will you?"

Pedro took the other side of the winch and we turned it together, lifting the heavy red drapes as if we were furling a sail.

"Blow the man down, bully,

Blow the man down."

Pedro began to sing. I joined in.

"With a way, hey,

Blow the man down."

By the end of the verse the curtains were stowed and we had the whole stage to play on.

"We'll need some more light, or one of us is going to end up in the orchestra with a broken neck," I said, crouching over the footlights to coax them into life with a taper.

"Not me. I think I could act on this stage blindfold," boasted Pedro. He lit a second taper and began at the other end. Exchanging a glance, we raced to see who could reach the middle first. I won. At least I was still better at some things than my accomplished friend.

"There, that's done." I stood up. "Let's start from your entrance." I hitched up my skirts and strode into the center like a man.

"Approach, my Ariel... Come!"

I was in my element, aping Mr. Kemble's deep voice as I swept my hand commandingly to my servant, imagining the ranks upon ranks of empty seats before me filled with invisible creatures waiting on my magic. Unlit, the theater was like a vast echoing cavern, a fitting backdrop to my wizard powers. I could call storms from the ornate ceiling, spirits from under the benches in the Pit, strange music from the silent orchestra.

"Is there more toil?" said Pedro sorrowfully from behind a silver mask. He'd stripped off his street clothes to reveal his costume—vivid blue silk breeches and shirt, topped off with a white cloak fixed to his wrists like a pair of wings. Mrs. Reid, the wardrobe mistress, had copied it from pictures of the Venetian Carnival and was very proud of the result. His favorite pearl earring, trophy of his first performance in Drury Lane, hung from his lobe, shining dully in the half-light.

"Since thou dost give me pains..."

"Louder!" I interrupted, having heard Mr. Kemble say it often enough in rehearsals. "Pretend you're speaking to a hard-of-hearing dwarf in the gods."

Pedro gave a snort and hitched his voice up a peg for the rest of the speech. Listening to him, I realized that he was showing real promise. I'd seen many actors come and go at Drury Lane, but none had his grace and feeling tone. Not that I was going to tell him, of course: he already had too keen a sense of his own greatness. I wasn't about to sharpen it further.

And now for Ariel's acrobatic exit. Pedro was to tumble off-stage in a series of cartwheels, backflips and somersaults. Giving me a cheeky wink, he took a run up and –

Clap, clap, clap.

Pedro crashed to the floor at the side of the stage as a slow round of applause rang out from the shadows of the Pit, startling us both.

"Oh, well done, Pedro, well done." From the auditorium came a man's voice. He had a strange accent–American or West Indian, I guessed.

Pedro froze. Sprawled in the dust, his dark eyes looked up at me through the slits of his mask, wide with terror. It was his expression that made me feel afraid. I moved to the edge of the forestage and shaded my eyes from the guttering footlights, my heart beating unsteadily in my chest. Few things could stop Pedro in his tracks, but this person had succeeded with no more than the sound of his voice.

"And my, little gal, you ain't bad neither—not that Kemble need worry for his position any time yet."

A broad-shouldered man in a brown jacket and black breeches was making his way down the central aisle, an iron-tipped cane in his hand. As he approached, he seemed at first glance a handsome man, bronzed by the sun. But when he stepped into the pool of light by the orchestra, I saw that his eyes were hard, the lines around his mouth cruel. Black hair shot with gray straggled from beneath his hat. He walked as if he owned the place—it annoyed me intensely.

I bobbed a curtsy. "I'm sorry, sir, but the theater's closed until six," I said tartly, clearly signaling that he was not wanted here, whoever he was.

He waved me away with his cane like a bothersome fly.

"I ain't here for no play. I'm here to reclaim my property."

Thinking he had probably dropped something in the scrum to get out the night before, I asked more politely than he deserved: "What have you lost, sir? Perhaps I can fetch it for you?"

He gave a belly laugh. "Maybe you can, missy. I've come for my slave—Pedro Hawkins."

I heard a whimper as Pedro scrambled to his feet. Clasping

my hands behind me I made rapid "get going" gestures, giving him the chance to back slang it out of the theater.

"Your slave? I think you must've made a mistake."

"I don't make mistakes," said Hawkins, moving closer. "He's my boy and I'm coming to get him."

"Is that so, sir? Well, I'm sorry, but you can't have him," I replied airily.

"Oh, can't I?" With unexpected agility for one so large, the man bounded across the orchestra pit and clambered onto the stage. I retreated a step to prevent him following Pedro into the wings. "A bantling like you won't stop me getting what's mine," he added, swiping the cane at me. I tried not to flinch.

"Of course not, sir," I replied, my tone studiously polite. "What I'm trying to tell you, sir, is that the Ariel you just saw isn't your boy Pedro."

"No?" the man said sarcastically. We were now doing a strange sort of Barnaby dance: shuffling to and fro as I blocked his attempts to set off in pursuit.

"No. Sadly, Pedro Hawkins died of a fever last Monday. That was the understudy you saw."

"Balderdash!"

"It's God's honest truth, sir," (said with fingers crossed behind back). "I can understand your confusion—what with the costume and the mask. But black boys are ten a penny around here. We keep a few in stock in case they up and die in this cold climate as they so often do."

He wasn't fooled. "Let me at him then—I'll soon tell you if it's him or no."

"I can't, sir. I'm not allowed to let anyone backstage. I'll be fined five shillings if I do."

He felt in his waistcoat pocket and pulled out a handful of coins. "Here, this'll more than make up for any fine. Now let me by, or I'll stop being so reasonable."

I ignored the coins. "I can't do that."

"Out of my way!" His bloodshot eyes glaring, he raised the cane.

"No!" I stared back at him, my chin thrust forward. I wasn't going to let a big bully like him lay hands on Pedro! The man then lunged, grabbing me by the scruff of the neck. His sudden resort to violence caught me unprepared. I was dangling in his grip like a puppet with broken strings and could do nothing but curse him. How dare he lay hands on me!

"You know what we do with pert gals like you back where I come from?" he hissed, thrusting his cane under my chin. "We teach 'em a lesson with this." He jabbed me hard on the jaw. "That'll stop your mouth."

"What, sir, are you doing to that child?" a voice roared from offstage. Mr. Kemble strode onto the boards decked out in the crimson robe of the magician, his face made up a startling white with dark eyebrows over flashing black eyes. Power seemed to radiate from him.

"Teaching her some manners," said the man. He shook me like a terrier with a rat in its mouth.

"He's trying to get backstage, sir! He's trying to steal Ariel!" I squeaked.

"Put her down this instant!" boomed the actor-manager.

"Bring me the boy first."

"You're talking rubbish, man. Put her down."

"I told him Pedro died last week but he won't believe me," I added, half suffocating under his grip on my neck.

Mr. Kemble raised an eyebrow but said nothing to refute the lie.

"Hold your tongue," snarled the man. "Don't think for one moment that you can bamboozle Kingston Hawkins, you little witch. The boy is mine by law. You're keeping him here against my will."

Mr. Kemble took a step closer. "The boy you are talking about is...was an apprentice bound to my musical director, Signor Angelini."

"Your Angelini's a macaroni-eating fool. He wouldn't know a genuine agreement if it bit him on the ass. The man who sold Pedro to him had no darn right to do so. The boy's mine, I tell you, dead or alive, and no jumped-up player can tell me otherwise!"

Jumped-up player! I kicked hard at his shins in my outrage—he had insulted the most admired actor in the land! But in doing so I only earned myself another shake.

"Well, sir, unfortunately for you," Mr. Kemble returned icily, "you are in the theater of this 'jumped-up player'—" I heard footsteps: Mr. Bishop, the irascible stage manager, ran up brandishing a hammer, his one good eye fixed on my persecutor, the other hidden by his black eye patch. Behind him, Long Tom appeared out of the shadows slapping a chain threateningly into his palm. "– And you are surrounded by his cast and crew. I suggest you take up your claim with the proper authorities and stop manhandling our Cat as if she were some stray you had a mind to drown."

My captor let out a hissing breath. Caliban, otherwise known as Mr. Baddeley, now stumped into sight, his mass of wild whiskers and mud-splattered sackcloth making an appalling apparition. He was wielding a log with evident intention to apply it to any offending body he could reach. Six extras dressed as sailors followed and formed a semicircle behind Mr. Kemble, pushing up their sleeves in eager anticipation of a brawl.

"You have 'til the count of three. One..."

Kingston Hawkins looked around him, counting his opposition.

"Two..."

He looked down on my bedraggled head, wondering if I was worth the fuss.

"Three."

I was dropped to the floor.

"I will be back!" he shouted as he leapt down into the Pit. "In force. You'd better have my slave or his coffin waiting. And understand this: if he's dead I own even the maggots eating his corpse. You can't keep him from me."

The door to the Pit slammed. There was complete silence onstage. Mr. Kemble extended his hand to help me to my feet.

"Now," he said lightly as if nothing untoward had happened, "where were we? Ah, yes: our Ariel has flown off. Hadn't you better bring him back from the dead, Cat?"